POLLUTION SCIENCE, TECHNOLOGY AND ABATEMENT

NON-CONVENTIONAL TEXTILE WASTE WATER TREATMENT

POLLUTION SCIENCE, TECHNOLOGY AND ABATEMENT

Additional books in this series can be found on Nova's website under the Series tab.

Additional e-books in this series can be found on Nova's website under the e-book tab.

ENVIRONMENTAL HEALTH - PHYSICAL, CHEMICAL AND BIOLOGICAL FACTORS

Additional books in this series can be found on Nova's website under the Series tab.

Additional e-books in this series can be found on Nova's website under the e-book tab.

POLLUTION SCIENCE, TECHNOLOGY AND ABATEMENT

NON-CONVENTIONAL TEXTILE WASTE WATER TREATMENT

AHMED EL NEMR

EDITOR

Nova Science Publishers, Inc.

New York

LIBRARY OF CONGRESS CATALOGING-IN-PUBLICATION DATA

Non-conventional textile waste water treatment / [edited by] Ahmed El Nemr.
    p. cm.
  Includes index.
  ISBN 978-1-62100-079-2 (hardcover)
  1. Textile waste. 2. Dyes and dyeing--Textile fibers. 3. Dyes and dyeing--Waste disposal. 4. Water--Purification. I. El-Nemr, Ahmed, 1962-
  TD899.T4N66 2011
  677.0028'6--dc23
                                    2011031635

Published by Nova Science Publishers, Inc. † New York

CONTENTS

PREFACE

Environmental pollution is known as any deterioration in the physical, chemical, and biological quality of the environment. The pollutants fall under the broad category of xenobiotic compounds and are released into the environment by the action of human and occur at concentrations higher than "natural levels". Environmental pollution can be implied by any alternation in the surroundings. All types of environmental pollution may affect directly or indirectly the living organisms and particularly human health.

Textile industry is amongst the major contributors to the environmental pollution but it is very important for nation's economy because clothes are the basic needs of human beings. The dye is the key material used in textile industry and many other industries to give color such as leather, paints, cosmetic, and food industries. We just have to open our eyes and look around us to observe how important a part of color in our life. Colors are obtaining from a wide variety of natural and synthetic sources. Natural colors are all around us in the earth, for example, the trees flowers, leaves, grass, animals and birds. The textile materials were colored exclusively with the use of natural color until mid 19th century. Since, the most of the natural dyes are rather unstable, and we need large and stable amounts of dyes, synthetic dyes were the most important alternative. The problem raised from synthetic dyes was the environmental pollution due to the large amounts of wastewater that produced from dyeing process. With the increased demand for textile products, the textile industry and its wastewaters have been increasing proportionally, making it one of the main sources of severe pollution problems worldwide. In particular, the release of colored effluents into the environment is undesirable, not only because of their color, but also because many dyes in textile wastewater and their breakdown products are toxic and/or mutagenic to life

Although the concentration of dyes in wastewater is usually lower than the other chemicals present, they are highly visible even at very low concentrations, therefore causing serious aesthetic and pollution problems in wastewater disposal such as water transparency and gas solubility. The removal of this color from wastewater is often more important than the removal of soluble colorless organic substances, which usually contribute the major fraction of biochemical oxygen demand (BOD). Conventional biological wastewater treatment systems are inefficient in treating synthetic dyes wastewater due to the chemical stability and low biodegradability of these dyes. Dyes wastewater is usually treated by physical- or chemical-treatment processes, which include chemical coagulation/flocculation, ozonation, oxidation, ion exchange, irradiation, precipitation and adsorption.

The purpose of this review book is to provide the latest research to find out a non-conventional method effective in treatment of textile wastewater. As reported in chapter 1, textiles processing wastewaters, typically contains dyes in the range 10-200 mg l^{-1}. Hence, textile wastewaters are usually highly colored and when discharged into open water it presents an aesthetic problem. Various physical, chemical and biological treatments have been reported to remove the colors from dye containing wastewater. Biological treatment offers distinct advantages over commonly used chemical and physicochemical methods, for the dye removal from effluents. In recent years number of studies has been focused on the use of microorganisms for the biodegradation as well as biosorption of dyes in the wastewaters. Variety of microorganisms involved in the dye decolorization includes, some bacteria, yeast, fungi and algal species. Dyes are the chemical compounds that exert severe effect on the surrounding environment. Hence nowadays many of the researchers are focusing their attention on the dye related toxicological studies. Cytotoxicity, genotoxicity and phytotoxicity of the dyes are amongst the key toxicity studies. Many of the researchers have studied the toxicity of dye molecules using various plant bioassays. Chapter 1 is intended to summarize the general information of the textile dyes and its environmental aspects in the present scenario.

Chapter 2 reports that the release of xenobiotic dyes to the environment and their harmful effects. Textile dyeing effluents containing recalcitrant dyes are polluting waters by their color and formation of toxic or carcinogenic intermediates such as aromatic amines that formed from azo dyes degradation.

The expanding uses of synthetic dyes such as triphenyl-methane, azo, and anthraquinone are alarming, given that the release of colored compounds into the environment may cause substantial ecological damage, not only due to their color, which may have an impact on photosynthesis in aquatic plants, but also because many dyes and their breakdown products may be toxic and/or mutagenic to living organisms. Biological decolorization and degradation is an environmentally friendly, cost-competitive alternative to chemical decomposition and do not produce large quantities of sludge. Chapter 3 reports how several marine microorganisms have the ability to bio-decolorize and treat wastewater containing textile dyes.

Chapter 4 shows while conventional chemical and physical decolorizing techniques were used for a long time, yet biological treatment or "bioremediation" has recently gained an interest due to its cheap and effective decolorization of a wide range of dyes. The process of bioremediation in general could be either a spontaneous process or a controlled process in which the microorganism could act to remove a specific contaminant. Fungi and their enzymes are thought to be one of the preferred tools in bioremediation. Biosorption by fungal cell wall is also an evolving attractive option as it presents an inexpensive biosorbent. The biosorptive capacity of fungi may be manipulated through pre-treatment with alkalis or acids to increase the available surface area for biosorption. The introduction of genetic engineering in environmental biotechnology may provide an insight to methods for up scaling the textile wastewater treatment. The study of the fate of the degraded dyes is also required to ensure the safety of their direct disposal to sewer systems after decolorization. Chapter 4 reports the recent research elucidate fungal applications in bioremediation that have deeper implications to fungal cell-dye interaction than just color removal of dye molecules. On the other hand, chapter 5 shows the literatures examine of a wide variety of micro- and macro-algae species, which are capable of decolorizing textile wastewaters; discusses the effects of various parameters such as pH, temperature, concentrations of dye and biomass in solution, pretreatment method, etc., on the dyes removal process. Also, it discusses the equilibrium and kinetic models used in batch and continuous biosorption systems, which are important to determine the biosorption capacity of the sorbent and to design of treatment units.

Presently, enzyme based procedures have attracted attention of the researchers for targeting aromatic pollutants as a new, simple, cost effective, potential and viable eco-friendly alternative to conventional methods which are associated with harsh side effects. The inhibition by toxic substances in enzymatic treatment is low and the process can be operated over a broad range of aromatic concentrations with low retention time. Majority of dyes are recalcitrant to the action of enzymes, however, the presence of redox mediators facilitates decolorization of such dyes to a great extent. These redox mediators enhance the range of substrates and efficiency of degradation of the recalcitrant dyes by several folds. Chapter 6 reviews the enzymes whose potential has been exploited for this purpose such as laccases, lignin peroxidase, manganese peroxidase, horseradish peroxidase, turnip peroxidase, tomato peroxidase, bitter gourd peroxidases, white radish peroxidase, bilirubin oxidase, tyrosinase, quinone reductase and others. Also chapter 6 reports that among several redox mediators reported in the literature, only very few are frequently used, for example, 1-hydroxybenzotriazole, veratryl alcohol, violuric acid, 2-methoxyphenothiazone, 3-hydroxyanthranilic acid, anthraquinone 2,6-disulfonic acid, 2,2-azino-bis(3-ethylbenzothiazoline-6-sulfonic acid), N-hydroxyacetanilide, phenol, phenol red, 3,3',5,5'-tetramethyl benzidine; dichlorophenol red, 2,2',6,6'-tetramethylpiperidine-N-oxyl radical, syringaldehyde, acetosyringone, acetovanillone, p-coumaric acid, ferulic acid, sinapic acid, vanillin, lawsone, menadione, phloroglucinol and thymol. Chapter 6 shows that the enzyme-redox mediator system seems to be a promising tool to enhance the chances of remediation of a wide spectrum of textile dyes present in various industrial effluents/wastewaters.

The electrocoagulation (EC) process was developed to overcome the drawbacks of conventional wastewater treatment technologies. This process is very effective in removing organic pollutants including dyestuff wastewater and allows for the reduction of sludge generation. The word ''electrocoagulation'' sometimes used with the word ''electroflotation'' (EF) and hence the technique can be considered as the electrocoagulation/flotation (ECF) process. Through the process of electrolysis, coagulating agents such as aluminum or iron hydroxides are produced. When aluminum electrodes are used, the aluminum dissolves at the anode and hydrogen gas is released at the cathode and the coagulating agent combines with the pollutants to form large size flocs. As the gas bubbles rise to the top of the tank they adhere to particles suspended in the water and float them to the surface. A conceptual framework of the overall ECF process is linked to coagulant generation, contaminant aggregation, and contaminant removal by flotation and settling, when it has been applied efficiently to various water and wastewater treatment processes. Chapter 7 has attempted to demystify electrocoagulation by showing that it is possible to classify a wide diversity of reactor systems on a simple basis, to obtain and interpret detailed dynamic data from a batch reactor system, and to show that the complexity of electrocoagulation is a natural (and understandable) consequence of the interactions between a number of processes occurring in parallel. It made to bring the chemistry and physical processes involved into perspective and to focus attention on those areas critically needing research. Chapter 7 also reports the effects of the operating parameters, such as pH, initial concentration, duration of treatment, current density, interelectrode distance and conductivity on the removal of a synthetic textile dyes wastewater in the batch electrocoagulation (EC)–electroflotation (EF) process. A significant number of common applications of EC process, which have been used for textile dye removal are also considers in this chapter. It is hoped that this evaluation will play its part in focusing attention on electrocoagulation as a viable localized water treatment technology in the near future.

The wet-processing operations, namely preparation, dyeing and finishing of textile products which are used to give the desired characteristics to the yarn or fabric, require the use of several chemical baths. They consume vast amount of energy, chemicals and water. Emissions of volatile organic compounds (VOCs) mainly arise from textiles finishing, drying processes, and solvent use. VOC concentrations vary from 10 mg m^{-3} for the thermosol process to 350 mg carbon m^{-3} for drying and condensation process. Process wastewater is a major source of pollutants. It is typically alkaline and has high BOD and chemical oxygen demand (COD) (approximately 2 to 5 times the biochemical oxygen demand (BOD) level), solids, oil and possibly toxic organics, including phenols (from dyeing and finishing) and halogenated organics (from processes such as bleaching). Dye wastewaters are frequently highly colored and may contain heavy metals such as copper and chromium. Wool processing may release bacteria and other pathogens. Pesticides are sometimes used for the preservation of natural fibers and these are transferred to wastewaters during washing and scouring operations. Pesticides are also used for moth proofing, brominated flame retardants for synthetic fabrics, and isocyanates for lamination wastewaters may also contain heavy metals such as mercury, arsenic, and copper. Air emissions include dust, oil mists, acid vapors, odors, and boiler exhausts. Towards the search for sustainable industrial enterprises, recent studies indicated that there are many cleaner (sustainable) production opportunities which lead to waste reduction as well as increased raw material use efficiency in textile wet processing industry. The relevant reduction/conservation strategies, process modifications, chemical substitutions and reclamation/reuse techniques which reduce the wastes (air, water and solid/hazardous) originating from preparation, dyeing, printing, finishing, and other sources in textile mills were reported. The objective of chapter 8 is to: (a) provide an environmental profile of the wet textile industry, (b) review cleaner (sustainable) production opportunities in textile wet processing industry, and (c) report the progress obtained in the textile demonstration project in the context of the UNIDO Eco-efficiency (cleaner production) project which has been implemented in Turkey since 2008.

There is an increasing interest in the textile industry for eco-friendly textile processing, in which the use of naturally occurring materials such as phospholipids becomes important. The non-uniformity that occurs in the dyeing process of polyamide, caused by the irregularities in the surface properties of the fiber, is reduced by the use of leveling agents. The leveling agents can promote both levelness and coverage of fiber irregularities, blocking the accessible sites in the fiber. The use of natural products such as soybean lecithin, as auxiliary in the dyeing of polyamide and cotton, instead of chemical products can improve the effluent characteristics and also reduce the initial rate of dye uptake. The last chapter in this book shows the different affinities of phosphatidylcholine with the polyamide fibers and cotton and also compares the retarding effect of the Acid Blue 62 release on polyamide fibers dyeing by encapsulation of the dye in mixed cationic liposomes of dioctadecyldimethylammonium bromide (DODAB)/soybean lecithin with pure soybean lecithin liposomes or synthetic auxiliaries. The retarding effect of liposomes on the dye release was analyzed through changes in the absorption and fluorescence spectra of the acid dye at different conditions. The effect of temperature on the spectroscopic behavior of the dye in the absence and in presence of polyamide was also investigated, in order to simulate the dyeing conditions.

Ahmed El Nemr
National Institute of Oceanography and Fisheries
Alexandria, Egypt

In: Non-Conventional Textile Waste Water Treatment   ISBN: 978-1-62100-079-2
Editor: Ahmed El Nemr   © 2012 Nova Science Publishers, Inc.

Chapter 1

TEXTILE DYES: GENERAL INFORMATION AND ENVIRONMENTAL ASPECTS

Jyoti P. Jadhav[*1] *and Swapnil S. Phugare*[2]

[1]Department of Biotechnology, Shivaji University, Kolhapur- 416 004, India
[2]Department of Biochemistry, Shivaji University, Kolhapur- 416 004, India

ABSTRACT

The dyes, more accurately known as colorants, are highly colored substances and can be used to import color to infinite variety of materials described technically as a substrate. Until the end of 19th century, all the coloring matters were obtained from natural sources. William Perkin discovered first synthetic dye *"Mauveine"*. Perkin named his dye after the French name of non-fast color which was made of natural dyes. So *"Mauve"* was the first synthetic dye stuff. Dyes contain chromophores (delocalized electron systems with conjugated double bonds) and auxochromes (electron-withdrawing or electron donating substituents). The chromophore imparts the color to the dye molecule and auxochrome intensifies the color of the chromophore by altering overall energy of electron system. Usual chromophores are C=C, C=N, C=O, N=N, NO_2 and quinoid rings. The auxochromes are NH_3, COOH, SO_3H and OH. A dye may have multiple chemical groups. Hence, dye belongs to more than one chemical class. The chemical classes are unlimited as dyes with new chemical classes are being constantly developed. Textiles processing wastewaters, typically contains dyes in the range 10-200 mg l^{-1}. Hence, textile wastewaters are usually highly colored and when discharged into open water it presents an aesthetic problem. Various physical, chemical and biological treatments have been reported to remove the colors from dye containing wastewater. Biological treatment offers distinct advantages over commonly used chemical and physicochemical methods, for the dye removal from effluents. In recent years number of studies has been focused on the use of microorganisms for the biodegradation as well as biosorption of dyes in the wastewaters. Variety of microorganisms involved in the dye decolorization includes, some bacteria, yeast, fungi and algal species. Dyes are the chemical compounds that exert severe effect on the surrounding environment. Hence nowadays many of the researchers are focusing their attention on the dye related

---

* E-mail: jpjbiochem@gmail.com; Phone: +91-231-2609153.

toxicological studies. Cytotoxicity, genotoxicity and phytotoxicity of the dyes are amongst the key toxicity studies. Many of the researchers have studied the toxicity of dye molecules using various plant bioassays. This chapter is intended to summarize the general information of the textile dyes and its environmental aspects in the present scenario.

1. Introduction

Food and clothes are the basic needs of human beings. Hence, the textile industry is amongst the major contributors to the nation's economy. The dye is the key material used in textile industry for dyeing purpose. We have to open our eyes and look around to observe how important a part of color in our life. Color emanates from a rich diversity of sources, both natural and synthetic. Natural color is all around us in the earth, the sky, the sea, in vegetation (trees flowers, leaves and grass), animals and birds. The textile materials were colored exclusively with the use of natural color until mid 19th century. Since, the most of the natural dyes are rather unstable, they were applied together with mordant. In the beginning of the 20th century, synthetic dyes had almost completely replaced natural dyes [1]. Synthetic textile dyes are exclusively organic compound, their origin is much more recent. Synthetic colors are used in the cloths, paints, plastic articles, photographs, cosmetics, pharmaceutical, food, and ceramics, on television, film and in a wide range of multicolored printed materials such as posters, magazines and news papers.

Dyes and dyestuffs find use in a wide range of industries but are of primary importance to textile manufacturing. The picric acid was the first synthetic dye, which was first prepared in lab by treating indigo with picric acid; much later picric acid from phenol was developed as a starting material. Picric acid was found to silk dye but it did not attain any real significance as practical dye (use). Synthetic dye manufacturing started in 1856, when the English chemist W.H. Perkin discovered purple dye to which he originally gave the name Aniline purple, but which was later to become known as Mauveine or Tyrian purple [1]. Chemist was discovering a wide range of structurally related dyes, which could be produced synthetically and which had excellent color properties and technical performance. This is the beginning of a chemical industry producing approximately 700,000 tons of colorants on yearly basis 131 years later [2]. Perkin initially discovered around 90% of textile dyes was synthetic rather than natural and aromatic dyes had emerged as the dominant chemical type. Among the initial discoveries, the triphenylmethane dye, the first important Magenta was introduced in 1859. Majority chemists concentrated on aniline as the starting material for colored compound and discovered several other synthetic textile dyes with commercial potential. Dyes are compounds that absorb light with wavelengths in the visible range, i.e., 400 to 700 nm [3]. Normal daylight, or white light, is a mixture of all the wavelengths to which we can respond and some to which we cannot, in particular the infra-red and ultra-violet rays. We respond to wavelengths between about 400-700 nm. When light absorption taking place in visible range, the compounds attain a color that is complementary to the light absorbed, this is roughly represented by the wavelength of maximum absorption. The relation between the light absorbed and color perceived is as shown in the Table 1.

Table 1. The relation between light absorbed and color perceived of an object

Wavelength of absorption (nm)	Light absorbed	Color perceived
400-500	Blue	Yellow
400-440	Violet	Greenish yellow
460-500	Greenish blue	Orange
400-620	Bluish green	Red
480-520	Green	Magenta
560-700	Orange	Cyan
600-700	Red	Bluish green

The ability of a compound to absorb light depends on the presence of certain kinds of structural features called chromophores. A chromophore is a moiety of the compound responsible for its color. Usual chromophores are C=C, C=N, C=O, N=N, NO_2 and quinoid rings. In many cases dyes contain additional groups called auxochromes. The most important auxochrome groups are: hydroxyl and derivates, OH, OR; amino and derivates, NH_2, NHR, NHR_2; sulphonic, SO_3H; carboxylic, COOH; and sulphide, SR [3]. Also the potential of various attractive forces viz, Van der Waals, hydrogen, ionic or covalent binding dyes to fibers, [4, 5] and often more than one type of chemical bonding.

2. DYES

A dye can generally be described as a colored substance that has an affinity to the substrate to which it is being applied. Archaeological evidence shows that, particularly in India and the Middle East, dyeing has been carried out for over 5000 years.

William Henry Perkin (1838-1907). Mauveine was the first man made organic dye, discovered by William Henry Perkin in 1856.

Figure 1. Photograph of William Henry Perkin [6].

Many thousands of dyes have since been prepared and because of vastly improved properties imparted upon the dyed materials quickly replaced the traditional natural dyes. Dyes are now classified according to how they are used in the dyeing process.

2.1. Classification of Dyes

Dyes are classified usually by two separate ways, either according to dye structure or according to how they are used in the dyeing process. Classification according to chemical structure: a number of chemical classes of dyes reported in color index. The Color Index (CI) number, developed by the Society of Dyers and Colorists, is used for dye classification. Once the chemical structure of a dye is known, a five digit C.I. number is assigned to it. Each different dye is given a C.I. generic name determined by its application characteristics and its color. The dyes are also classified according to how they are used in the dyeing process in textile industries. Various classes of the dyes include reactive, acid, basic, direct, disperse, mordant, sulfur, azoic, and vat dyes.

2.1.1. Reactive Dyes

The use of reactive dyes has increased ever since their introduction in 1956, especially in industrialized countries. In the Color Index, the reactive dyes form the second largest dye class with respect to the amount of active entries: about 600 of the 1050 different reactive dyes listed are in current production. Reactive dyes are also highly water-soluble anionic dyes, but have excellent wet fastness with binding to the textile fibers via covalent bonds. During dying with reactive dyes 10 to 50% will not react with the fabric and remain .hydrolyzed in the water phase. The problem of colored effluents is therefore mainly identified with the use of reactive dyes. Most (80%) reactive dyes are azo or metal complex azo compounds but also anthraquinone and phthalocyanine reactive dyes are applied, especially for green and blue.

2.1.2. Acid Dyes

Acid dyes are water soluble anionic dyes with different chromophore (color-bearing) groups substituted with acidic functional groups such as nitro-, carboxyl, and sulfonic acid. By adding a sulfonic group, the water-insoluble dye becomes soluble. Acid dyes are anionic compounds that are mainly used for dyeing nitrogen-containing fabrics like wool, polyamide, silk and modified acryl. The largest class of dyes in the color index is referred to as acid dyes (2300 different acid dyes listed, 40% of them are in current production). Most acid dyes are azo (yellow to red, or a broader range colors in case of metal complex azo dyes), anthraquinone or triarylmethane (blue and green) compounds.

2.1.3. Basic Dyes

Basic dyes are cationic types with chromophores typically having amino groups and for dyeing acid-group containing fibers, like modified polyacryl. They bind to the acid groups of the fibers. Basic dyes represent 5% of all dyes listed in the Color Index. Most basic dyes are diarylmethane, triarylmethane, anthraquinone or azo compounds.

2.1.4. Disperse Dyes

Disperse dyes are barely soluble, nonionic dyes for the application to the hydrophobic fibers from aqueous dispersion. This diffusion requires swelling of the fiber, either due to high temperatures (>120°C) or with the help of chemical softeners. The charge and hydrophobicity characteristics of these polycyclic dyes and the solution pH may explain the environmental fate of these dyes in dyeing processes and subsequent treatment processes. Disperse dyes form the third largest group of dyes in the Color Index about 1400 different compounds are listed, of which 40% is currently produced.

2.1.5. Vat Dyes

Vat dyes are water-insoluble dyes that are particularly and widely used for dyeing cellulose fibers. The dyeing method is based on the solubility of vat dyes in their reduced (leuco) form and reduced with sodium dithionite then impregnate the fabric. Next, oxidation is applied to bring back the dye in its insoluble form. Almost all vat dyes are anthraquinones or indigoids. Indigo is a very old example of a vat dye, with about 5000 years of application history.

2.1.6. Sulphur Dyes

Sulphur dyes are complex polymeric aromatics with heterocyclic S-containing rings. Though representing about 15% of the global dye production and mainly used for dyeing cellulose fibers. Dyeing with sulphur dyes involves reduction and oxidation comparable to vat dyeing.

2.1.7. Mordant Dyes

Mordant dyes are fixed to fabric by the addition of a mordant, a chemical that combines with the dye and the fiber. They are used with wool, leather, silk, paper and modified cellulose fibers. Most mordant dyes are azo, oxazine or triarylmethane compounds. The mordants are usually dichromates or chromium complexes. The use of mordant dyes is gradually decreasing: only 23% of the 600 different mordant dyes listed in the Color Index are in current production.

2.1.8. Direct Dyes

Direct dyes are used for dyeing especially cellulose fibers and make Van der Waals forces for binding fiber. Direct dyes are mostly azo dyes with more than one azo bond or phthalocyanine, stilbene or oxazine compounds. In the Color Index, the direct dyes form the second largest dye class with respect to the amount of different dyes: About 1600 direct dyes are listed but only 30% of them are in current production.

2.1.9. Ingrain Dyes (Naphthol Dyes)

The name ingrain used to describe small group of dyes. The all dyes formed *in situ*, in or on the substrate by the development, or coupling, of one or more intermediate compounds and a diazotized aromatic amine. All naphthol dyes are azo compounds.

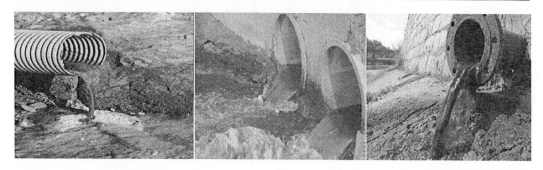

Figure 2. Colored wastewater from different industries [18].

2.1.10. Solvent Dyes (Lysochromes)

Solvent dyes are non-ionic dyes that are used for dyeing substrates. They are not often used for textile-processing but their use is increasing. Most solvent dyes are diazo compounds that underwent some molecular rearrangement. Also triarylmethane, anthraquinone and phthalocyanine solvent dyes are applied.

2.1.11. Pigment Dyes (Organic Pigments)

Pigment dyes represent a small but increasing fraction of the pigments, the most widely applied group of colorants. These insoluble, non-ionic compounds or insoluble salts retain their crystalline or particulate structure throughout their application. Pigments are usually used together with thickeners in print pastes for printing diverse fabrics. Most pigment dyes are azo compounds or metal complex phthalocyanines. Also anthraquinone and quinacridone pigment dyes are applied. About 25% of all commercial dye names listed in the Color Index are pigment dyes but these 6900 product names stand for less than 800 different dyes.

2.1.12. Other Dye Classes

Apart from the dye classes mentioned above, the Color Index also lists *Food dyes* and *Natural dyes*. Food dyes are not used as textile dyes and the use of natural dyes (mainly anthraquinone, indigoid, flavenol, flavone or chroman compounds that can be used as mordant, vat, direct, acid or solvent dyes) in textile-processing operations is very limited.

A dye may have multiple chemical groups it belongs to more than one chemical class. Based on chemical structure or chromophore, 20-30 different groups of dyes can be discerned. Azo (monoazo, disazo, triazo, polyazo), anthraquinone, phthalocyanine and triarylmethane dyes are quantitatively the most important groups. Other groups are diarylmethane, indigoid, azine, oxazine, thiazine, xanthene, nitro, nitroso, methine, thiazole, indamine, indophenol, lactone, aminoketone and hydroxyketone dyes and dyes of undetermined structure (stilbene and sulphur dyes).

Azo dyes, aromatic moieties linked together by azo (-N=N-) chromophores, represent the largest class of dyes used in textile-processing and other industries. The majority of the important azo colorant contains a single azo group and therefore referred to as monoazo dyes, but there are many which contain two (diazo), three (triazo) or more such groups. Azo dyes are the largest and most important group of dyes mainly due to the simple synthesis. So it has a continual demand to develop longer lasting, more applicable dyes. Azo dyes must be continually updated to produce colors that reflect the trends dictated by changing social ideas and styles. The fundament of the production of azo dyes was laid in 1858 when P. Gries discovered the reaction mechanism, diazotization, for the production of azo compounds [2]. Presently, azo dyes are used for coloring many different materials such as textile, leather, plastics, food, pharmaceuticals, for manufacturing paints, lacquers and for printings purposes as well.

2.2. Environmental Aspects of the Textile Dyes

The dyes are usually heavily used irrespective of actual need of the process, hence eventually unbound dye molecules releases as the waste product. Many dyes are visible in water at very low (1 mg l^{-1}) concentrations. About 100,000 commercially available dyes are known and nearly 1 million tons of dyes are produced throughout the year, whereas, out of the total usage, 10% of dyes are released in environment as dyestuff waste [7-9]. The extensive use of the textile dyes has put forth two major problems: one stemming from carcinogenic, mutagenic, allergic and toxic nature of these dyes and other from environmental pollution, like accumulation of sludge which creates disposal problem; the latter is of much concern [10, 11]. It is very difficult to treat the effluent from the textile and dyeing industries because of its high BOD (biological oxygen demand), COD, color, pH and presence of metals [12, 13]. The treatment of such dye containing effluent was initially carried by using physical and chemical treatment processes including adsorption, concentration, chemical transformation, but with time, potential hazards and disadvantages of these methods were noted as, formation of toxic sludge and even more toxic metabolites [9, 14-16]. Sometimes, physico-chemical treatments are unable to remove the recalcitrant azo dyes and/or their organic metabolites completely, eventually generating a significant amount of sludge that may cause secondary pollution problems [16].

2.3. Dyes Containing Industrial Wastewaters

Colors gives delightful pleasure to eyesight but at the same time they may act as serious pollutants when their origin is dyes and dyestuffs. The routine use of dyes in day-to-day life is increasing because of rapid industrialization, most widely in textile, rubber, enamel, plastic, cosmetic and many other industries [17]. Increasing demand of overgrowing population enforced the industries to utilize the available resources as much as possible to meet the requirement. Such industrialization resulted into the server environmental pollution and water is the prime factor affected, amongst these. Recently, many of the South Asian countries are experiencing the severe environmental pollution problems because of their rapid industrialization. This phenomenon is common where the polluting industries like textile dying, leather tanning, paper and pulp mills and sugarcane industries thrives as a cluster. The effluent discharge from these industries leads to serious pollution of surface water, groundwater, soil and other natural resources ultimately affecting the livelihood of poor. The wastewater from the textile and paper pulp industries is a major problem of water pollution as they not only contain harmful chemicals but also the color, which severely affect the aquatic life by reducing the light penetration.

2.4. Textile Industries

In almost every developing nation, textile manufacturing is among the first industries to be established. The textile industry is energy, water, and chemical-intensive. Within the industry, the majority of energy, water, and chemicals consumed are for wet processing. Most wet processing involves treatment with chemical baths, which often require washing, rinsing, and drying steps between key treatment steps. Consequently, wastewater is generated, having a very diverse range of contaminants that must be treated prior to disposal. The textile industry has been condemned as being one of the world's worst offenders in terms of pollution because it requires a great amount of two components:

1. *Chemicals:* as many as 2,000 different chemicals are used in the textile industry, from dyes to transfer agents; and
2. *Water:* a finite resource that is quickly becoming scarce, and is used at every step of the process both to convey the chemicals used during that step and to wash them out before beginning the next step. The water becomes full of chemical additives and is then expelled as wastewater; which in turn pollutes the environment: by the effluent's heat; by its increased pH; and because it's saturated with dyes, de-foamers, bleaches, detergents, optical brighteners, equalizers and many other chemicals used during the process.

Mills discharge millions of gallons of effluent each year, full of chemicals such as formaldehyde (HCHO), chlorine, heavy metals (such as lead and mercury) and others, which are significant causes of environmental degradation and human illnesses. The mill effluent is also often of a high temperature and pH, both of which are extremely damaging.

3. EXISTING APPROACHES FOR TREATMENT OF INDUSTRY WASTEWATER

Several methods have been attempted for the removal of color from the industrial effluents. These can be classified into physical, chemical and biological methods. Physical and chemical processes are quite expensive and remove high molecular weight chlorinated lignins, color, toxicants, suspended solids and chemical oxygen demand. The biological color removal process is particularly attractive since in addition to color and COD it also reduces BOD and low molecular weight chlorolignins [19, 20].

3.1. Physicochemical Techniques

Physicochemical techniques include membrane filtration, coagulation/flocculation, precipitation, flotation, adsorption, ion exchange, ion pair extraction, ultrasonic mineralisation, electrolysis, advanced oxidation (chlorination, bleaching, ozonation, Fenton oxidation and photocatalytic oxidation) and chemical reduction (Table 1).

Table 1. Different physicochemical techniques used for the dye decolorization

Technique	Methodology	Application mode
Membrane filtration[a]	Nanofiltration and reverse osmosis using membranes with a molecular weight cut-off below 10,000 Dalton	A quick method with low spatial requirement. Advantage of this method is reuse of dyes. The disadvantages of this method were flux decline and membrane fouling, necessitating frequent cleaning and regular replacement of the modules.
Coagulation/ flocculation[b]	Use of coagulants viz. lime, magnesium iron, aluminum salts and organic polymer for flocculation and coagulation of dyes	This method was used to partly remove COD and color from raw wastewater.
Adsorption[c]	Adsorption of dyes using various adsorbent viz., activated carbon, non-modified cellulose (plant) biomass, modified cellulose biomass, bacterial biomass, yeast biomass, fungal biomass, chitin, soil material, activated bauxite or alumina, pulp mill waste.	Equilibrium capacity varies with dyes and adsorbents, correlated well with mesophore and large micropore volume.
Photocatalytic (TiO_2)[d]	TiO_2 catalysts supported on three different absorbents	Over 95% color removal; TiO_2 supported on absorbents is more efficient than that of bare TiO_2. It generates the harmful reactive radicals.
Ozonation and ultrasound enhanced ozonation[e]	Varying ozone, ultrasound and ultrasound enhanced ozone operational conditions	First-order rate constant increased to 200% using ultrasonic power inputs compared to ozonation alone. The disadvantage of this technique was generation of highly oxidizing reactive radicals.
Sonication[f]	Use of varying frequency of ultrasound waves.	Complete decolorization and increase in rate of decolorization under spent dye bath conditions. Decolorization efficiency decreased with an increased dye concentration.
Electrolysis[g]	Applying an electric current to the wastewater using electrodes.	Dyes were decolorized using combined electrochemical oxidation and reduction, electro-coagulation and electro-flotation reaction. It requires the high amount of energy.

[a] Yun *et al*. [21]; [b] Joo *et al*. [22]; [c] Crini, [23]; [d] Bizani *et al*. [24]; [e] Gultekin and Ince, [25]; [f] Okitsu *et al*. [26]; [g] Daneshvar *et al*. [27].

3.2. Biological Techniques

Alternatively, approach is shifting towards the use of conventional biological methods to treat such effluents and wastewater containing dyes and toxic chemicals [28]. These methods are gaining more importance nowadays because of their lesser cost, effectiveness and eco-friendly nature. The metabolites produced after biodegradation are mostly non toxic or comparatively less toxic in nature [9]. Biological decolorization methods use several classes of microorganisms including bacteria, algae and fungi to degrade the dyes and industrial wastewater. Many researchers have demonstrated partial or complete biodegradation of the dyes using fungi, algae, actionomycetes and pure or mixed cultures of bacteria or their enzymes

Microbial decolorization of dyes has recently received much attention as it is a cost-effective method for dye removal [29, 30]. Bioremediation is a process in which the natural capacity of microbes is enhanced to degrade toxic chemicals and waste [12]. Several reports are available indicating that a variety of microbes have been involved in the bioremediation and biodegradation of dyes, which includes some bacteria, fungi, actionomycetes and algae.

3.3. Bacterial Decolorization

Bacterial decolorization of the dyes is studied extensively, and several bacteria were reported for dye decolorization either alone or in combination. The use of bacteria for the removal of synthetic dyes from industrial effluents offers considerable advantages. The process is relatively inexpensive, the running costs are low and the end products of complete mineralization are not toxic. The various aspects of the bacterial decomposition of synthetic dyes have been previously reviewed. Decolorization of azo dyes under anaerobic conditions is thought to be a relatively simple and non-specific process, involving fission of the azo bond to yield degradation products such as aromatic amines. Initially, the bacteria bring about the reductive cleavage of the azo linkage, which results in dye decolorization and the production of colorless aromatic amines. Till date several bacterial species are reported for dye decolorization as *Pseudomonas* sp. SUK [31]; *Exiguobacterium* sp. RD3 [32]; *Commamonas* sp. VUS [33]; *Pseudomonas aeruginosa* strain BCH [9].

Along with the pure bacterial culture the bacterial consortium is also reported for the efficient decolorization of dye as well as industrial wastewater. The bacterial consortium DAS consisted of *Pseudomonas* sp. LBC2 *Pseudomonas* sp. LBC1 and *Pseudomonas* sp. SUK was reported earlier for removal of color, metals and toxicity form textile effluent. Similary, the bacterial consortium PMB11 was reported for decolorization of Reactive blue 59 and Red HE3B [30, 34]. Decolorization of dyes by bacteria is mainly mediated through the bacterial enzyme systems and lignin peroxidase, azo-reductase, laccase, DCIP reducatse, Tyrosinase are amongst the few dye decolorizing enzymes of the bacteria [9, 31, 35].

3.4. Fungal Decolorization

Fungi, their biology, economic value and pathogenic capabilities are not new to human society. Fungi are involved in the biodegradation of undesirable materials or compounds and convert them into harmless, tolerable or useful products. Various fungal strains are known to degrade a wide variety of recalcitrant compounds, such as xenobiotics, lignin, and dyestuffs, with their extracellular enzymes. Many studies have also demonstrated that many fungal strains are capable of degrading various types of synthetic dyes such as azo, triphenyl methane, polymeric, phthalocyanine and heterocyclic dyes [36]. Many researchers used the lignolytic and nonlignolytic fungi for the decolorization of dye wastewater. The lignolytic white rot fungi are known to be the most efficient microorganisms for dye degradation. The lignolytic fungi, including *Phanerochaete chrysosporium*, *Trichophyton rubrum* LSK-27, *Ganoderma* sp. WR-1, *Trametes versicolor*, *Funalia trogii*, *Irpex lacteus*, etc. were widely used for the decolorization of textile dyes [37-42]. Fungi especially the white-rot fungi produce enzymes laccase, Mn peroxidase and lignin peroxidase (LiP), which are involved in the degradation of lignin in their natural lignocellulosic substrates [43]. Dye decolorization by the fungus is mediated by biosorption as well as biodegradation mechanism. The yeast *S. cerevisiae* and waste yeast biomass is also reported for dye decolorization as well as decolorization of textile effluent [13, 44, 45]. Belsare and Prasad [46] reported that the effluent from bagasse based pulp and paper mills could be decolorized with the white rot fungus *S. commune*. A white rot fungus *Tinctoporia borbonica* has been reported to decolourize the kraft waste liquor to a light yellow color [47]. About 99% colour reduction was achieved after 4 days of cultivation. Various *Penicillium* species were also reported for dye decolorization; *Penicillium ochrochloron* decolorizes Cotton Blue (50 mg l^{-1}) within 2.5 h [48], newly isolated fungal strain *Penicillium* sp. QQ could decolorize azo dyes significantly [49].

3.5. Phytoremediation

Phytoremediation is an emerging technology that uses various plants to degrade, extract, contain, or immobilize contaminants from soil and water. This technology has been receiving attention lately as an innovative, cost-effective alternative to the more established treatment methods used at hazardous waste sites. The use of phytoremediation of removal toxicants is relatively less understood because of lack of detailed information regarding the inherent metabolic pathways adopted by the plants for metabolism of toxicants [50]. Phytoremediation of dyes is the topic of interest nowadays. *Phragmites australis* , a reed which is the component of the wetland community has been studied in detail for the remediation of textile effluent containing dyes, mainly with respect of Acid Orange 7 [15, 51]. Similarly, various other plants are also reported for dye decolorization, *Blumea malcolmii* for decolorization of Direct Red 5B [52]; *Typhonium flagelliforme* for decolorization of *Brilliant Blue* R [53]. The species of *Sorghum vulgare*, *Phaseolus mungo*, *Brassica juncea* is reported to have the potential to decolorize Reactive Red 2 remediate textile effluent contaminated sites [54]. Similarly, hairy roots of *Tagetes patula* L were used previously for Reactive Red 198 decolorization [55]. Although, different plants possess the ability to degrade same dye molecule, the generated metabolites might be different, indicating the pattern of transformation of xenobiotic molecule depends upon the plant species [56].

3.6. Algal Decolorization

Algae are photosynthetic organisms, which distributed in nearly all parts of the world and in all kinds of habitats. Alga can degrade number of dyes, postulating that the reduction appears to be related to the molecular structure of dyes and the species of algae used. Very few reports are available on the use of algae, including *Cosmarium* sp. and *Enteromorpha prolifera* for the decolorization of azo and triphenyl methane dyes [57, 58].

3.7. Continuous Culture Reactors for Decolorization

To increase the applicability of the biological process nowadays continuous culture technique for decolorization are increasing rapidly. Generally, the microbial cell/enzymes are immobilized using suitable immobilization methods prior to be used for decolorization studies. Immobilization keeps gaining in stature as a key technology for the remediation of the hazardous waste [59]. Immobilization systems are applied to the enzymes, cellular organelles, microbial, plant and animal cells. These systems are intended to enclose the biocatalyst into defined space in such a way that they retain their activities and can be utilized over a long period of time [60]. The use of immobilized whole microbial cells or organelles eliminates often tedious, time consuming and expensive steps involved in the isolation and purification of enzymes. It also tends to enhance the stability of the enzymes by retaining their natural catalytic surroundings during immobilization and subsequent continuous operation. Immobilized cells of *Enterobacter agglomerans* were able to reduce azo dyes enzymatically and hence used as a biocatalyst for the decolorization of synthetic medium containing the toxic azo dye Methyl red [61]. Use of the bacterial consortium for the biological treatment of textile dye Acid violet-17 by an up-flow immobilized cell bioreactor was reported earlier [62]. Similary, use of plaster of paris immobilized cells of waste yeast biomass and *S. cerevisiae* MTCC 463 for remediation of textile industry effluent provide an ecofriendly and cost effective dye decolorization alternative [13].

3.8. Decolorization by Enzyme Systems

The microbial decolorization is mainly mediated through the various xenobiotic metabolizing enzyme systems. The biodegradation of dyes using white rot fungi is mainly associated with an involvement of various lignolytic enzymes, such as lignin peroxidase, manganese peroxidase and laccase. Biodegradation of dyes using nonlignolytic fungi was associated with an involvement of billirubin oxidase, laccase and azoreductase [44, 63, 64]. Similarly, various bacterial enzymes viz. Veratrly alcohol oxidase, tyrosinase, DCIP reductase, azoreductase, laccase were also reported for dye decolorization [9, 13, 33, 35].

3.9. Lignin Peroxidase

Lignin peroxidase enzyme belongs to the family of oxidoreductases, specifically those acting on peroxide as an acceptor (peroxidases) and can be included in the broad category of ligninases. The systematic name of this enzyme class is 1,2-bis(3,4-dimethoxyphenyl) propane-1,3-diol:hydrogen-peroxide oxidoreductase. LiP is *N*-glycosylated protein with molecular weight between 38 and 47 kDa. It contains heme in the active site and shows a classical peroxidase mechanism [65]. LiP catalyzes several oxidations in the side chains of lignin and related compounds by one-electron abstraction to form reactive radicals [66, 67]. The cleavage of an aromatic ring structure is also reported [68].

The purified LiP from *Brevibacillus laterosporous* MTCC 2298 and *Acinetobacter calcoaceticus* NCIM 2890 efficiently decolorized the several sulfonated azo dyes [69, 70].

3.10. Laccases

Laccases (EC1.10.3.2) are the most numerous members of multicopper oxidase protein family. It catalyzes the oxidation of substituted phenolic and nonphenolic compounds in the presence of oxygen as an electron acceptor [71]. Phylogenetically, these enzymes have developed from small sized prokaryotic azurins to eukaryotic plasma proteins ceruloplasmin [72]. They contain four histidine rich copper binding domains, which coordinate the types 1, type 2, and type 3 copper atoms that differ in their environment and spectroscopic properties. They are classified into two category viz. the blue laccases (presence of type 1 copper site) and laccases that lack the type 1 copper site. The purified laccase from *Pseudomonas desmolyticum* NCIM 2112 showed 100% decolorization of various dyes, including Direct blue-6, Green HE4B and Red HE7B.

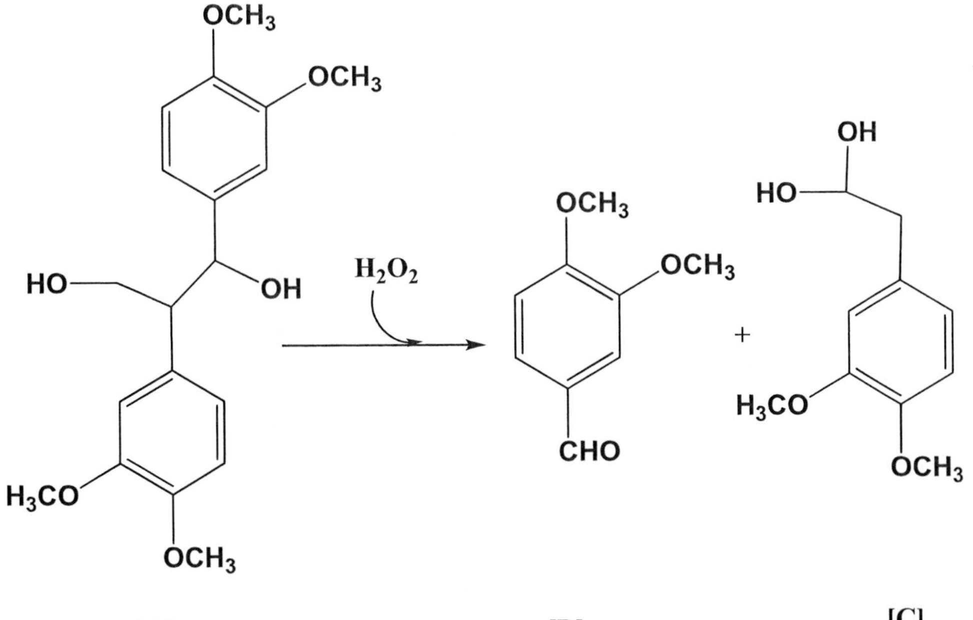

[A] 1,2-bis (3,4-dimethoxyphenyl) propane-1,3-diol; [B] 3,4-dimethoxybenzaldehyde; [C] 1-(3,4-dimethoxyphenyl) ethane-1,2-diol.

Figure 3. Reaction catalyzed by lignin peroxidase.

3.11. Azoreductase

The presence of extracellular oxygen sensitive azoreductase in anaerobic bacteria viz. *Clostridium* and *Eubacterium* that decolorized sulfonated azo dyes during growth on solid or complex media was first reported by Rafii *et al.* [73]. Azoreductases are flavoprotiens (NAD(P)H: flavin oxidoreductase). It is localized intracellular or extracellular site of the bacterial cell membrane. These azoreductases required the NADH or NADPH or FADH as electron donor for the reduction of an azo bond [74]. The induction of azoreductase during decolorization of azo dyes under static condition was reported earlier [32, 75].

3.12. NADH-DCIP Reductase

NADH-DCIP reductase belongs to the bacterial mixed function oxidase system and takes part in the detoxification of xenobiotic compounds [76]. The NADH-DCIP reductase reduces the DCIP using NADH as an electron donor. DCIP is a blue in its oxidized form and becomes colorless after reduction. Significant induction of DCIP reductase during the decolorization of various dyes has been reported previously [9, 13, 30, 31, 77].

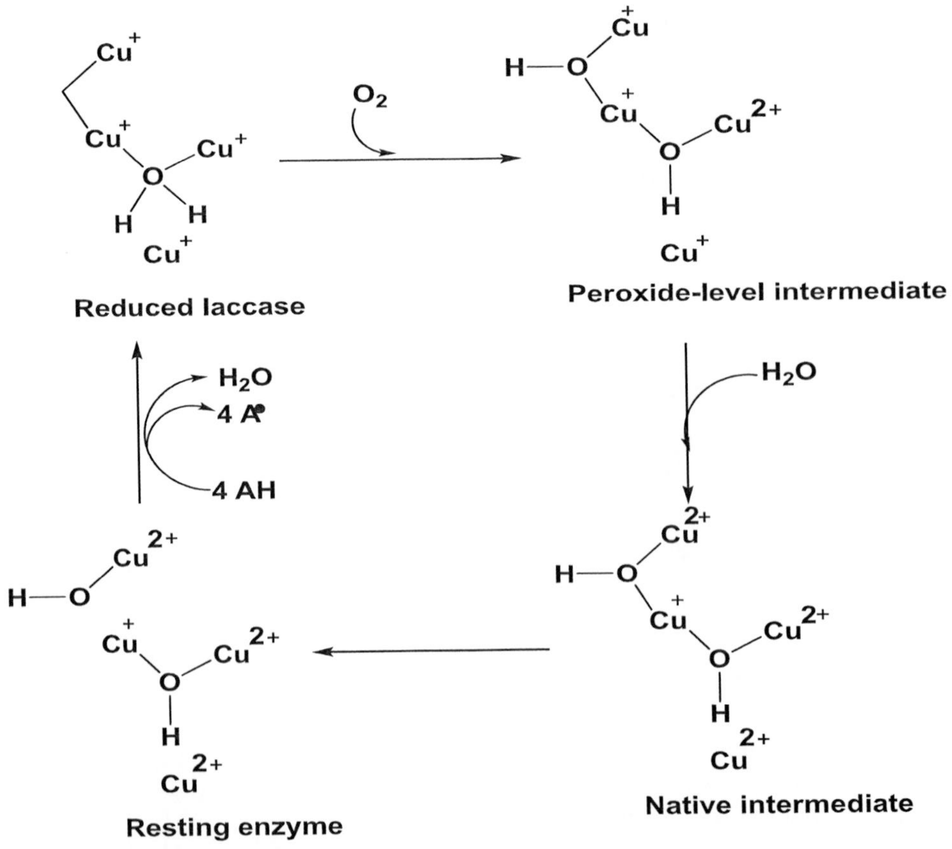

Figure 4. Catalytic cycle of laccases.

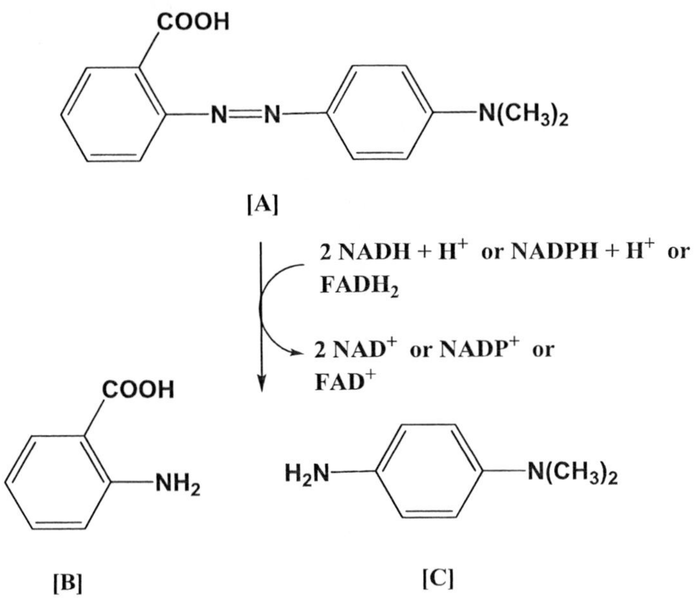

(A = Methyl red; B = 2-Amino benzoic acid; C = p-dimethyl amino aniline).

Figure 5. Reaction catalyzed by azoreductases.

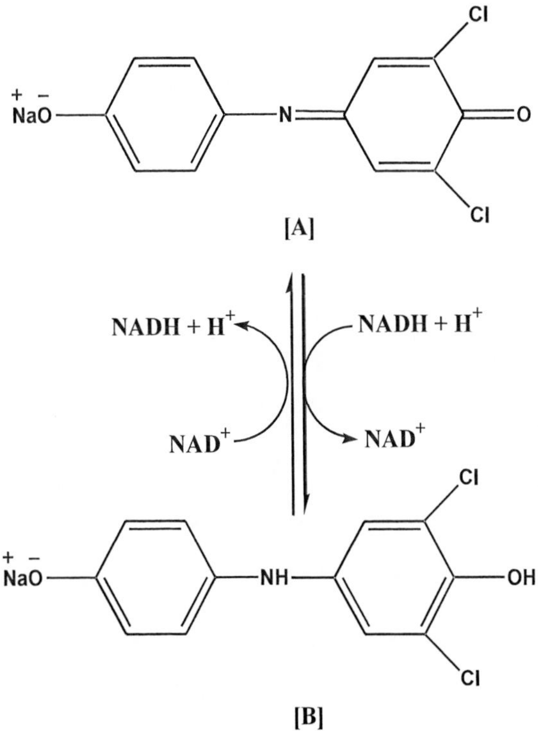

[A] = Oxidized form of DCIP. [B] = Reduced form of DCIP.

Figure 6. Reaction catalyzed by NADH-DCIP reductase.

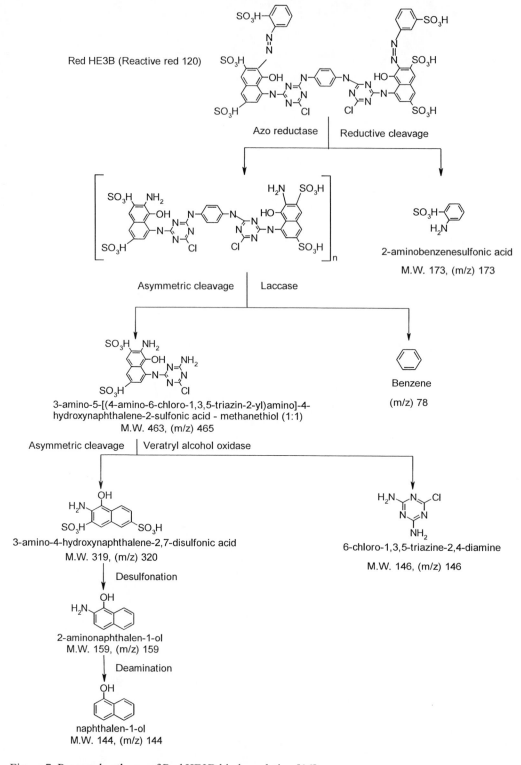

Figure 7. Proposed pathway of Red HE3B biodegradation [16].

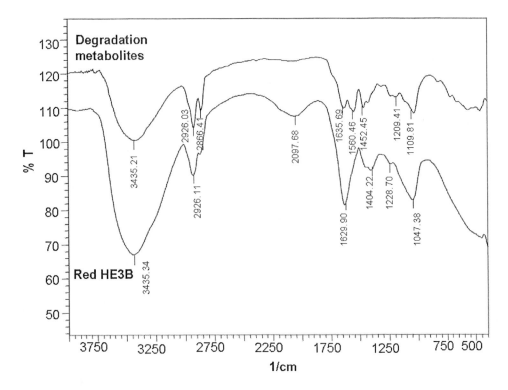

Figure 8. FTIR analysis of Red HE3B and its biodegradation metabolites [16].

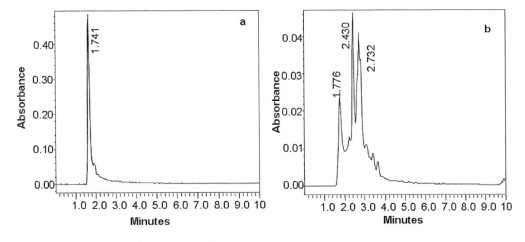

Figure 9. HPLC analysis of Red HE3B and its biodegradation metabolites [16].

3.13. Veratryl Alcohol Oxidase

Veratryl alcohol is a substrate for ligninase, which catalyzes its oxidation to veratraldehyde [78]. The purified veratryl alcohol oxidase from *Comamonas* sp. UVS is also reported for the decolorization of various textile dyes viz. Red HE7B and Direct blue GLL

[79]. Recently, an efficient veratryl alcohol oxidase from *Pseudomonas aeruginosa* strain BCH was reported for the decolorization of various textile dyes [80].

4. ANALYSIS OF THE PRODUCTS FORMED AFTER DEGRADATION OF DYES

The analytical studies are one of the important parameters, which help us to identify different metabolites produces after biological treatment. Researchers have employed various analytical techniques together to identify the dye metabolites; FTIR, GC-MS and HPLC are most commonly used techniques for this purpose. Based on the FTIR analysis one can predict the possible functional groups of a chemical compounds. Hence, FTIR analysis serves as a supportive data to the GC-MS analysis, where one can predict the possible structure of the metabolite based on mass to charge ratio obtained. Similarly, with the help of HPLC analysis one can confirm the biodegradation of parent compound to the different metabolites by comparing peak profile of standard and metabolites. Several researchers have predicted possible metabolic pathway of particular dye molecule after microbial treatment, using GC-MS analysis [16, 31, 32]. The probable products of Red HE3B after treatment with bacterial consortium SDS includes, 2-aminobenzenesulfonic acid (m/z) 173, 3-amino-5[(4-amino-6-chloro-1,3,5-triazin-2-yl)amino]-4-hydroxynaphathalene-2-sulfonic acid-methanethiol (1:1) (m/z) 465, 3-amino-4-hydroxynaphthalene-2-7-disulfonic acid (m/z) 320, 6-chloro-1,3,5-triazine-2,4-diamine (m/z) 146, 2-aminonaphthalene-1-ol (m/z) 159 and naphthalene-1-ol (m/z) of 144 (Figure 7) [16]. The biodegradation of Red HE3B is well supported by the FTIR analysis (Figure 8) and HPLC analysis (Figure 9) [16]. Identification of metabolites after biodegradation experiments help us to predict the role of possible enzyme systems involved in the degradation.

5. TOXICITY OF DYES AND DYESTUFFS

The toxicity of many of these chemicals is known, but limited data are available on biological effects and on the toxicity of fabrics containing these chemicals. An in vitro test capable of detecting the combined effects of chemicals on textile products could give useful information for the development of less toxic textile products. Different textile processes can produce different levels of toxicity in products. Reactive dyes have good technical characteristics but they have been found to cause adverse effects on workers in textile factories and on the environment. Wastewaters and land in an industrial area in India were studied to assess the possible genotoxic health risk and environmental genotoxicity due to textile industry effluents [81]. The toxicity was not caused only by textile dyes but by a large number of different textile chemicals. Allergic dermatoses and respiratory diseases are known to be caused by reactive dyes [82-84]. Contact dermatitis and asthma were also studied by the action of dyes [85] similarly, the change in the immunoglobulin levels of textile industry workers exposed to reactive dyes have been observed [86]. Previous studies have also suggested increased risks of colon and rectum cancers; however, these cancers relate mostly to dyes for synthetic fibers [87]. Besides the toxic effects to the humans these dyes and dyestuff also affects other forms of life badly especially aquatic life. Acute and short term toxicity studies of textile dyestuff and wastewaters were made on a freshwater fish *Gambusia affinis* revealed the significant reduction in mortality and erythrocyte count of fish *Gambusia affinis* [88]. Similarly strong genotoxic effect of textile effluent on the root cells of *Allium cepa* is also previsouly demonstrated [9]. Phytotoxicity studies of dyes and effluents using palnt seedlings are the main and primary toxicity study to assess the toxic nature of dye molecules [30-32]. Toxicology of dyes and dye metabolites is mainly studied with respect to cytogenetic toxicity, genotoxicity, phytotoxicity and oxidative stress studies.

6. Environmental Biomonitoring Using Various Toxicological Assays

The resurgence of genotoxicity studies has led to the development of more than 200 short term assays to evaluate the genotoxicity of unknown environmental agents [89]. However, most animal assays are costly and thus the enforcement agencies are not using them for their routine monitoring [90]. Keeping this in view, plant bioassays, which are considerably less expensive, have been proposed from time to time for pollution monitoring. Some of the plant bioassays, i.e., *Allium cepa*, *Vicia faba* and *Tradescantia paludosa*, have been in use for over 60 years, initially for studying the mutagenic effects of ionizing radiation and chemical mutagens but recently also to evaluate the mutagenicityrclastogenicity of environmental pollutants [90]. On this view, various researchers have used the classical *Allium* test for the assessment of genotoxicity of textile dyes and dye effluents [16, 77].

6.1. Cytotoxicity Analysis

Recently, Jadhav *et al.* [77] has showed that the dye containing wastewater exerts strong cytogenetic effect on the root cells of *Allium cepa*. It was observed that the mitotic index (MI) of the *Allium cepa* was found to be altered after treatment with the dye as well as textile effluent [16, 77]. Decreased mitotic index is the indication of the presence of the cytotoxic compound in the environment [91]. Mitotic index above the control is the indicative of uncontrolled cell growth and formation of tumors [92]. The observation of the *Allium* test indicates that the dyes and textile effluent exert effects on chromosomes and cell division [16, 77, 93].

6.2. Comet Assay (Single Cell Gel Electrophoresis)

Various investigators have used the alkaline version of Single cell gel electrophoresis (SCGE/ Comet assay) for in the area of genetic toxicology for *in vivo/in vitro* evaluation of genotoxicity of different chemicals [94]. The sensitivity of the SCGE or Comet assay allows rapid prediction of genotoxic potential of compounds and has been shown to be useful for in vivo and in vitro biomonitoring of environmental pollutants [95, 96]. The alkaline version of comet assay is very much useful in the medical as well as environmental field for monitoring of the genotoxicity. The alkaline version has also been used successfully to examine the extent of DNA damage in coelomocytes collected from earthworms maintained in different soil samples as an indicator of soil pollution [94, 97]. Assessment of the ecological and genetic impact of dyes and their metabolites produced after biodegradation on plant populations is of great importance as plants are important commercial products and are consumed by people [16]. Comet assay was performed to assess the genotoxic potential of the dye Red HE3B and its biodegradation metabolites obtained after treatment with bacterial consortium. It was reported that the textile dye Red HE3B exerts strong genotoxic effect on the root cells of *Allium cepa*, increase in the tail length is the indication of the nuclear damage to the cells [16]. Similar observations were reported in case of the textile effluent also, indicating that various textile dyes and other material present in the effluent are strong inducers of the DNA damage [98].

6.3. Antioxidant Enzymes (Oxidative Stress Studies)

Along with the cytotoxicity and genotoxicity, the oxidative stress studies are also one of the important parameters for the toxicological assessment. Recently, Phugare *et al.* [16] studied the effect of textile dye and its biodegradation metabolites on the generation of oxidative stress in the root cells of *Allium cepa*. Activities of various antioxidant enzymes viz. super oxide dismutase (SOD), catalase (CAT), ascorbate peroxidase (APX) and guaicol peroxidase (GPX) were studied. Induction in the activites of SOD, APX and GPX were noted which is the indication of generation of the oxidative stress in the root cells of *Allium cepa* after exposure to the textile dye [16]. On the other hand, repression of CAT activity was noted; the induction or the suppression the antioxidant enzymes after exposure to the dye might be associated with the triggering the genetic assembly of the particular gene [16, 99].

6.2. Lipid Peroxidation and Protein Oxidation

Similar to the antioxidant enzyme status; lipid peroxidation and protein oxidation are also important parameters. Lipid peroxidation refers to the oxidative degradation of lipids. It is the process in which free radicals "steal" electrons from the lipids in cell membranes, resulting in cell damage. This process proceeds by a free radical chain reaction mechanism. It most often affects polyunsaturated fatty acids, because they contain multiple double bonds in between which lie methylene CH_2- groups that possess especially reactive hydrogens. As with any radical reaction, the reaction consists of three major steps: initiation, propagation, and termination [100]. Protein oxidation involves the oxidative modification of protein by means of reactive oxygen species and generated oxidative stress. Oxidative modification of protein was also observed under various pathophysiological conditions. The values of lipid peroxidation and protein oxidation were increased significantly in the root cells of the *Allium cepa* after exposure to the textile dye Red HE3B [16]. Significant increase in the lipid peroxidation and protein oxidation in the indication of the potential of the textile dye Red HE3B to generate oxidative stress in the *Allium cepa* root cells [16].

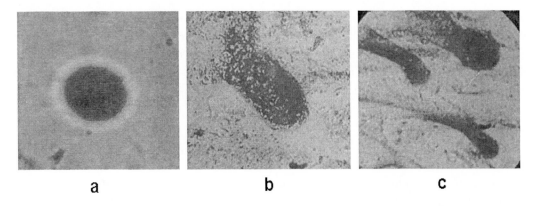

Figure 10. Comet assay analysis of root cells of *Allium cepa* after exposure to water (a); biodegradation metabolites of effluent obtained after treatment with consortium (b) and raw textile effluent (c) [98].

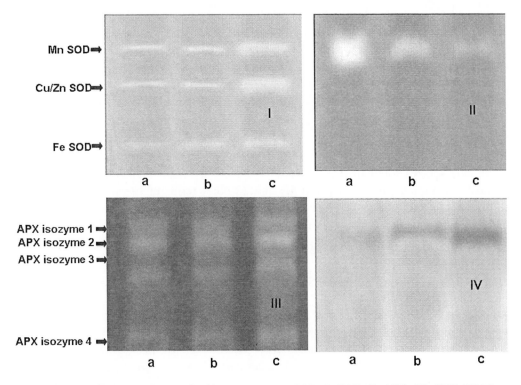

Figure 11. Zymographs of various antioxidant enzymes as SOD- I; CAT- II; APX- III, GPX- IV. The samples are as- control (a); degradation metabolites (treated effluent) (b), untreated textile effluent (c) [98].

6.3. Phytotoxicity Studies

Phytotoxicity studies are one of major assays used for the toxicity analysis of the dyes, effluents and their metabolites. Various researchers have used these studies for the demonstration of the toxicity status of dye and dye metabolites [31, 30, 35, 77]. The seeds of *pheseolus mungo, sorghum vulgare* and *triticum aestivum* are routinely used for the assessment of the phytotoxicity. In the present assay the test seeds are exposed to the water and dyes samples separately and observed for seven days, after seven days the root and shoot length were recorded followed by the statistical analysis. Several studies are reported till date by various researchers for the toxicological impact of the dyes on the environment, and due to the ever increasing water pollution by the textile industries the present issue needs the special attention in the present scenario.

7. CONCLUSION

Many of the countries are experiencing the severe environmental pollution problems because of their rapid industrialization. This phenomenon is common where the polluting industries like textile dying, leather tanning, paper and pulp mills and sugarcane industries thrives as a cluster. The effluent discharge from these industries leads to serious pollution of surface water, groundwater, soil and other natural resources ultimately affecting the livelihood of poor. The wastewater from the textile and paper pulp industries is a major problem of water pollution as they not only contain harmful chemicals but also the color, which severely affect the aquatic life by reducing the light penetration.

The overall survey of the literature reveals that, dyes are the inseparable part of the human activities. One can notice easily that, along with the usefulness of dyes to mankind they have some disadvantages also. The ever increasing demand to population enforces the industrial activities to achieve the target, and textile industry is the leading industry which shares this burden. Thousands of dyes are used by the textile industry which results server pollution of the environment. The pollution of nearby water bodies is the major concern for the textile processing, overall aquatic life and all other forms of life which are surrounded nearby get affected ultimately. Hence in the present scenario the environmental concerns of textiles and textile processing is the hot issue. Several researchers focused their aim to remediate the problems associated with the textile processing; dye decolorization is one of such issues.

The researchers from different streams (Physics, Chemistry and Biology) are working in the area of dye decolorization. Various methods have been employed either alone or in combination to remediate dye containing water till date, including physico-chemical and biological methods. But considering the ecofriendly approach biological methods stands most favorite amongst all other techniques. Microbial as well as plant sources were utilized effectively for the dye decolorization purpose. These methods are adventitious over other methods because it not only decolorizes the dyes but also detoxifies it. Various toxicity assays were set by the researchers to evaluate the toxicological nature of dye as well as its metabolites. Phytotoxicity, genotoxicity and cytotoxicity catch much more attention. Biological processes are mainly mediated through enzyme systems and various dye decolorizing enzymes viz., laccase, lignin peroxidase, azoreductase, veratryl alcohol oxidase and DCIP reductase are studies in detail by the researchers. In present state much more awareness about the environment issues and possible find outs is the need of time.

REFERENCES

[1]   Welham, A. (2000). The theory of dying (and the secret of life). *Society of Dyers and Colourists*, 116: 140-143.

[2]   Zollinger, H. (1987). Color Chemistry-Synthesis, Properties and Applications of Organic Dyes and Pigments. *VCH, New York*, 92-102.

[3]   Van der Zee F, P., Lettinga, G., & Field, J.A. (2001). Azo dye decolorization by anaerobic granular sludge. *Chemosphere*, 44: 1169-1176.

[4]   Ingamells, W. (1993). Color for textiles-A user's handbook. *Society of Dyers and Colourist, West Yorkshire.*

[5]   Guaratini, C.C.I., & Zanoni, M.V.B. (2000). Corantes Textiles. *Quimica Nova.* 23: 71-78.

[6]   http://en.wikipedia.org/wiki/William_Henry_Perkin

[7]   Maguire, R.J. (1992). Occurrence and persistence of dyes in a Canadian river. *Water Science and Technology*, 25: 265-270.

[8]   Selvam, K., Swaminathan, K., & Keo-Sang, C. (2003). Microbial decolorization of azo dyes and dye industry effluent by Fomes lividus. *World Journal of Microbiology and. Biotechnology*, 19: 591-593.

[9]   Jadhav, J.P., Phugare, S.S., Dhanve, R.S., & Jadhav, S.B. (2010). Rapid biodegradation and decolorization of Direct Orange 39 (Orange TGLL) by an isolated bacterium *Pseudomonas aeruginosa* strain BCH. *Biodegradation,* 21: 453-463

[10]   Banat, I., Nigam, P., Singh, D., & Marchant, R. (1996). Microbial decolorization of textile dye containing effluent: a review. *Bioresource Technology,* 58: 217-227.

[11]   Bakshi, D.K., Gupta, K.G., & Sharma, P. (1999). Enhanced biodegradation of synthetic textile dye effluent by Phenerochaete chrysoporium under improved culture. *World Journal of Microbiology and. Biotechnology,* 15: 507-509.

[12]   Senan, R.C., & Abraham, T.E. (2004). Bioremediation of textile azo dyes by aerobic bacterial consortium. *Biodegradation,* 15: 275-280.

[13]   Phugare, S.S., Patil, P.S., Govindwar, S.P., & Jadhav, J.P. (2010). Exploitation of yeast biomass generated as a waste product of distillery industry for remediation of textile industry effluent. *International Biodeterioration and Biodegradation.* 64: 716-726.

[14]   Johnson, R.F., Zenhausen, A., & Zollinger, H. (1978). In: Mark, H.F., Mcketta, J.J., Othmer, D.F. Jr, Standen, A. (eds) Krik-Othmer 2nd edn. Encyclopedia of chemical technology, vol 2. Wiley, Hoboken, pp 868–910.

[15]   Davis, R.J., Gainer, J.L., O'Neal, G., & Wu, I.W. (1994). Photocatalytic decolorization of waste water dyes. *Water Environment Research,* 66: 50-53.

[16]   Phugare, S.S., Kalyani, D.C., Patil, A.V., & Jadhav, J.P. (2011). Textile dye degradation by bacterial consortium and subsequent toxicological analysis of dye and dye metabolites using cytotoxicity, genotoxicity and oxidative stress studies. *Journal of Hazardous Materials*, 186:713-723.

[17]   Raffi, F., Hall, J.D., & Cerniglia, C.E. (1997). Mutagenicity of azo dyes used in foods, drugs and cosmetics before and after reduction by Clostridium species from the human intestinal tract. *Food and Chemical Toxicology,* 35:897-901.

[18]   http://www.google.co.in/imghp?hl=en&tab=wi

[19]   Barton, D.A., Lee, J.W. Buckley, D.B., & Jett, S.W. (1996). Biotreatment of Kraft mill condensates for reuse. In: Proc. Tappi Minimum Effluent Mills Symp., Atlanta, GA., USA pp. 270–288.

[20]   Nagarathnamma, R., Bajpai, P., & Bajpai, P.K. (1999). Studies on decolourization, degradation and detoxification of chlorinated lignin compounds in kraft bleaching effluents by *Ceriporiopsis subvermispora*. *Process Biochemistry,* 34: 939-948.

[21]   Yun, M.A., Yeon, K.M., Park, J.S., Lee, C.H., Chun, J., & Lim, D.J. (2006). Characterization of biofilm structure and its effect on membrane permeability in MBR for dye wastewater treatment. *Water Research,* 40: 45-52.

[22]   Joo, D.J., Shin, W.S., Choi, J.H., Choi, S.J., Kim, M.C., Han, M.H., Ha, T.W., & Kim, Y.H. (2007). Decolorization of reactive dyes using inorganic coagulants and synthetic polymer. *Dyes and Pigments,* 73: 59-64.

[23]   Crini G. (2006). Non-conventional low-cost adsorbents for dye removal: A review. *Bioresource Technology,* 97: 1061-1085.

[24]   Bizani, E., Fytianos, K., Poulios, I., & Tsiridis, V. (2006). Photocatalytic decolorization and degradation of dye solutions and wastewaters in the presence of titanium dioxide. *Journal of Hazardous Materials,* 136:85-94.

[25]   Gultekin, I., & Ince, N.H. (2006). Degradation of aryl-azo-naphthol dyes by ultrasound, ozone and their combination: Effect of α-substituents. *Ultrasononic Sonochemistry,* 13: 208-214.

[26]   Okitsu, K., Iwasaki, K., Yobiko, Y., Bandow, H., Nishimura, R., & Maeda, Y. (2005). Sonochemical degradation of azo dyes in aqueous solution: a new heterogeneous kinetics model taking into account the local concentration of OH radicals and azo dyes *Ultrasononic Sonochemistry,* 12: 255-262.

[27]   Daneshvar, N., Oladegaragoze, A., & Djafarzadeh, N. (2006). Decolorization of basic dye solutions by electrocoagulation: An investigation of the effect of operational parameters. *Journal of Hazardous Materials,* 129: 116-122.

[28]   Chen, K.C., Wu, J.Y., Liou, D.J., & Hwang, S.C.J. (2003). Decolorization of the textile dyes by newly isolated bacterial strains. *Journal of Biotechnology.* 101:57-68

[29]   Moosvi, S., Keharia, H., & Madamwar, D. (2005). Decolorization of textile dye Reactive Violet by a newly isolated bacterial consortium RVM 11.1, *World Journal of Microbiology and. Biotechnology*, 21: 667-672.

[30]   Patil, P.S., Shedbalkar, U.U., Kalyani, D.C., & Jadhav, J.P. (2008). Biodegradation of Reactive Blue 59 by isolated bacterial consortium PMB11, *Journal of Industrial Microbiology and Biotechnology*, 35: 1181-1190.

[31]   Kalyani, D.C., Patil, P.S., Jadhav, J.P., & Govindwar, S.P. (2008). Biodegradation of reactive textile dye Red BLI by an isolated bacterium *Pseudomonas* sp. SUK1. *Bioresource Technology,* 99: 4635-4641

[32]   Dhanve, R.S., Shedbalkar, U.U., & Jadhav, J.P. (2008). Biodegradation of diazo reactive dye navy blue HE2R (Reactive blue 172) by an isolated *Exiguobacterium* sp. RD3. *Biotechnology and Bioprocess Engineering,* 13: 53-60.

[33]   Jadhav, U.U., Dawkar, V.V., Ghodake, G.S., & Govindwar, S.P. (2008). Biodegradation of Direct Red 5B, a textile dye by newly isolated *Comamonas* sp. UVS. *Journal of Hazardous Materials*, 158: 507-516.

[34] Patil, P.S., Phugare, S.S., Jadhav, S.B., & Jadhav, J.P. (2010). Communal action of microbial cultures for Red HE3B degradation. *Journal of Hazardous Materials*, 181: 263-270.

[35] Telke, A.A., Kalyani, D.C., Dawkar, V.V., & Govindwar, S.P. (2009). Influence of organic and inorganic compounds on oxidoreductive decolorization of sulfonated azo dye C.I. Reactive Orange 16. *Journal of Hazardous Materials*, 172: 298-309.

[36] Chulhwan, P., Lee, Y., Kim, T.H., Lee, B., Lee, J., & Kim, S. (2004). Decolorization of three acid dyes by enzymes from fungal strains. *Journal of Microbiology and Biotechnology,* 14: 1190-1195.

[37] Novotny, C., Svobodova, K., Kasinath, A., & Erbanova, P. (2004). Biodegradation of synthetic dyes by *Irpex lacteus* under various growth conditions. *International Biodeterioration and Biodegradation,* 54: 215-223.

[38] Zille, A., Gornacka, B., Rehorek, A., & Cavaco-Paulo, A. (2005). Degradation of azo dyes by *Trametes villosa* laccase over long periods of oxidative conditions. *Applied and Environmental Microbiology,* 6711-6718.

[39] Nilsson, I., Moller, A., Mattiasson, B., Rubindamayugi, M.S.T., & Welander, U. (2006). Decolorization of synthetic and real textile wastewater by the use of white-rot fungi. *Enzyme and Microbial Technology*, 38: 94-100.

[40] Yesiladal, S.K., Pekin, G., Bermek, H., Arslan-Alaton, I., Orhon, D., & Tamerler, C. (2006) . Bioremediation of textile azo dyes by *Trichophyton rubrum* LSK-27. *World Journal of Microbiology and. Biotechnology,* 22: 1027-1031.

[41] Revankar, M.S., & Lele, S.S. (2007). Synthetic dye decolorization by white rot fungus, *Ganoderma* sp. WR-1. *Bioresource Technology*, 98: 775-780.

[42] Park, C., Lee, M., Lee, B., Kim, S.W., Chase, H.A., Lee, J., & Kim, S. (2007). Biodegradation and biosorption for decolorization of synthetic dyes by *Funalia trogii*. *Biochemical Engineering Journal,* 36: 59-65.

[43] Duran, N., Rosa, M.A., D'Annibale, A., & Gianfreda, L. (2002). Applications of laccases and tyrosinases (phenoloxidases) immobilized on different supports: a review. *Enzyme and Microbial Technology*, 31: 907-931.

[44] Jadhav, J.P., & Govindwar, S.P. (2006). Biotransformation of Malachite green by *Saccharomyces cerevisiae* MTCC 463. *Yeast,* 23: 315-323.

[45] Jadhav, J.P., Parshetti, G.K. Kalme, S.D., & Govindwar, S.P. (2007). Decolourization of azo dye methyl red by Saccharomyces cerevisiae MTCC 463. *Chemosphere,* 68: 394-400

[46] Belsare, D.K. & Prasad, D.Y. (1988). Decolourization of effluent from the bagasse based pulp mills by white rot fungus *Schizophyllum commune. Appllied Microbiology and Biotechnology,* 28: 301-304.

[47] Fukuzumi, T. (1980) Microbial decolourization and defoaming of pulping waste liquors. In: Kirk, T.K. Chang H.M. and Higuchi, T. (Eds.), Lignin Biodegradation, Vol. 2, CRCPress, Boca Raton, FL., pp. 161-177.28, 301-304.

[48] Shedbalkar, U.U., Dhanve, R.S., & Jadhav, J.P. (2008). Biodegradation of triphenylmethane dye cotton blue by *Penicillium ochrochloron* MTCC 517. *Journal of Hazardous Materials*, 157: 472-479.

[49] Gou, M., Qu, Y., Zhou, J., Ma, F., & Tan, L. (2009). Azo dye decolorization by a new fungal isolate, *Penicillium* sp. QQ and fungal-bacterial cocultures. *Journal of Hazardous Materials,* 170: 314-319.

[50] Chaudhry, Q., Zandstra, M.B., Gupta, S., & Joner, E.J. (2005). Utilizing the synergy between plants and rhizosphere organisms to enhance the breakdown of the organic pollutants in the environment. *Environmental Science and Pollution Research,* 12: 34-48.

[51] Carias, C.C., Novais, J.M., & Martin-Dais, S. (2007). *Phragmatis australis* peroxidases role in the degradation of the azo dyes. *Water Science and Technology,* 56: 263-269.

[52] Kagalkar, A.N., Jagtap, U.B., Jadhav, J.P., Bapat, V.A., & Govindwar, S.P. (2009). Biotechnological strategies for phytoremediation of the sulfonated azo dye Direct Red 5B using *Blumea malcolmii* Hook. *Bioresource Technology,* 100: 4104-4110.

[53] Kagalkar, A.N., Jagtap, U.B., Jadhav, J.P., Govindwar, S.P., & Bapat, V.A., (2010). Studies on phytoremediation potentiality of *Typhonium flagelliforme* for the degradation of Brilliant Blue R. *Planta,* 232: 271-285.

[54] Ghodake, G.S., Telke, A.A., Jadhav, J.P., & Govindwar, S.P. (2009). Potential of *Brassica juncea* in order to treat textile effluent contaminated sites. *International Journal of Phytoremediation,* 11: 297-312.

[55] Patil, P.S., Desai, N., Govindwar, S.P., Jadhav, J.P., & Bapat, V.A. (2009). Degradation analysis of Reactive Red 198 by hairy roots of *Tagetes patula* L. (Marigold). *Planta,* 230: 725-735.

[56] Page, V., & Schwitzguebel, J.P. (2009). The role of cytochrome P450 and peroxidases in detoxification of sulphonated anthraquinones by rhubarb and common sorrel plants cultivated under hydropnic conditions. *Environmental Science and Pollution Research,* 16: 805-816.

[57] Jinqi, L., & Houtian, L. (1992). Degradation of azo dyes by algae. *Environmental Pollution,* 75: 273-278.

[58] Ozer, A., Akkaya, G., & Turabik, M. (2005). Biosorption of acid red 274 on *Enteromorpha prolifera* in a batch system. *Journal of Hazardous Materials,* 126: 119-127.

[59] Plecas, I., & Dimovic, S. (2004). Immobilization of industrial waste in cement clay matrix. *Bulletin of Materials Science,* 27: 175-178.

[60] Peinado, R.A., Moreno, J.J., Villalba, J.M., Gonzalez-Reyes, J.A., Ortega, J.M., & Mauricio, J.C. (2006). Yeast biocapsules: A new immobilization method and their applications. *Enzyme and Microbial Technology,* 40: 79-84.

[61] Moutaouakkil, A., Zeroual, Y., Dzayri, F.Z., Talbi, M., Lee, K., & Blaghen, M. (2004). Decolorization of azo dyes with *Enterobacter agglomerans* immobilized in different supports by using fluidized bed bioreactor. *Current Microbiology,* 48: 124-129.

[62] Sharma, D.K., Saini, H.S., Singh, M., Chimni, S.S., & Chadha, B.S. (2004). Biological treatment of textile dye Acid violet-17 by bacterial consortium in an up-flow immobilized cell bioreactor. *Letters in Applied Microbiology,* 38: 345-350.

[63] Pajot, H.F., Figueroa, L.I.C., & Farina, J.I. (2007). Dye decolorizing activity in isolated yeasts from the eco-region of Las Yungas (Tucuman, Argentina). *Enzyme and Microbial Technology,* 40: 1503-1511.

[64] Zhang, X., Liu, Y., Yan, K., & Wu, H. (2007). Decolorization of anthraquinone type dye by billirubin oxidase producing nonlignolytic fungus *Myrothecium* sp. IMER1. *Journal of Bioscience and Bioengineering,* 104: 104-110.

[65] Tien, M., Kirk, T.K., Bull, C., & Fee, J.A. (1986). Steady-state and transient-state kinetic studies on the oxidation of 3, 4-Dimethoxybenzyl alcohol catalyzed by the

ligninase of *Phanerochaete chrysosporium* burds. *Journal of Biological Chemistry*, 261: 1687-1693.

[66] Tien, M., & Kirk, T.K. (1983). Lignin-degrading enzyme from the hymenomycete *Phanerochaete chrysosporium* burds. *Science,* 221: 661-663.

[67] Kersten, P.J., Tien, M., Kalyanaraman, B., & Kirk, T.K. (1985). The ligninase from *Phanerochaete chrysosporium* generates cation radicals from methoxybenzenes. *Journal of Biological chemistry*, 260: 2609-2612.

[68] Umezawa, T., & Higuchi, T. (1987). Mechanism of aromatic ring cleavage of h-O-4 lignin substructure models by lignin proxidase. *FEBS Letters,* 218: 255-260.

[69] Gomare, S.S., Jadhav, J.P., & Govindwar, S.P. (2008). Degradation of sulfonated azo dyes by the purified lignin peroxidase from *Brevibacillus laterosporus* MTCC 2298. *Biotechnology and Bioprocess Engineering,* 13: 136-143.

[70] Ghodake, G.S., Kalme, S.D., Jadhav, J.P., & Govindwar, S.P. (2009). Purification and partial characterization of lignin peroxidase from *Acinetobacter calcoaceticus* NCIM 2890 and its application in decolorization of textile dyes. *Applied Biochemistry and Biotechnology*, 152: 6-14.

[71] Sharma, P., Goel, R., & Capalash, N. (2007). Bacterial laccases. *World Journal of Microbiology and. Biotechnology*, 23: 823-832.

[72] Claus, H., & Filip, Z. (1997). The evidence of a laccase-like activity in a *Bacillus sphaericus* strain. *Microbiological Research,* 52: 209-215.

[73] Rafii, F., Franklin, W., & Cerniglia, C.E. (1990). Azoreductase activity of anaerobic bacteria isolated from human intestinal microflora. *Applied and Environmental Microbiology*, 56: 2146-2151.

[74] Russ, R., Rau, J., & Stolz, A. (2000). The function of cytoplasmic flavin reductases in the reduction of azo dyes by bacteria. *Applied and Environmental Microbiology*, 66: 1429-1434.

[75] Dawkar, V.V., Jadhav, U.U., Ghodake, G.S., & Govindwar, S.P. (2009). Effect of inducers on the decolorization and biodegradation of textile azo dye Navy blue 2GLby *Bacillus* sp. VUS. *Biodegradation,* 20: 777-787.

[76] Salokhe, M.D., & Govindwar, S.P. (1999). Effect of carbon source on the biotransformation enzymes in *Serratia marcescens. World Journal of Microbiology and. Biotechnology*, 15: 229-232.

[77] Jadhav, J.P., Kalyani, D.C., Telke, A.A., Phugare, S.S., & Govindwar, S.P. (2010). Evaluation of the efficacy of a bacterial consortium for the removal of color, reduction of heavy metals, and toxicity from textile dye effluent. *Bioresource Technology,* 101: 165-173.

[78] Sannia, G., Limongi, P., Cocca, E., Buonocore, F., Nitti, G., & Giardina, P. (1991). Purification and characterization of a veratryl alcohol oxidase enzyme from the lignin degrading basidiomycete *Pleurotus ostreatus. Biochimica et Biophysica Acta,* 1073: 114-119.

[79] Jadhav, U.U., Dawkar, V.V., Tamboli, D.P., & Govindwar, S.P. (2009). Purification and characterization of veratryl alcohol oxidase from *Comamonas* sp. UVS and its role in decolorization of textile dyes. *Biotechnology and Bioprocess Engineering*, 14: 369-376.

[80] Phugare, S.S., Waghmare, S.R., & Jadhav, J.P. (2011). Purification and characterization of dye degrading of veratryl alcohol oxidase from *Pseudomonas*

aeruginosa strain BCH. *World Journal of Microbiology and. Biotechnology*, DOI 10.1007/s11274-011-0714-6.

[81]   Mathur, N., Bathnagar, P., Nagar, P., & Bijarnia, M.K. (2005). Mutagenicity assessment of effluents from textile/dye industries of Sanganer, Jaipur (India): a case study. *Ecotoxicology and Environmental safety,* 61: 105-113.

[82]   Estlander, T. (1988). Allergic dermatoses and respiratory diseases from reactive dyes. *Contact Dermatitis,* 18: 290-297.

[83]   Hatch, K.L., & Maibach, H.I. (1995). Textile dye dermatitis: A review. *Journal of the American Academy of Dermatology*, 32: 631-639.

[84]   Manzini, B.M., Motolese, A., Conti, A., Ferdani, G., & Seidenari, S. (1996). Sensitization to Reactive Textile Dyes in Patients with Contact Dermatitis. *Contact Dermatitis,* 34: 172-175.

[85]   Thoren, K., Meding, B., Nordlinder, R., & Belin, L. (1980). Contact Dermatitis and Asthma from Reactive Dyes. *Contact Dermatitis*, 15: 186-189.

[86]   Park, H.S., Lee, M.K., Kim, B.O., Lee, K.J., Roh, J.H., Moon, Y.H., & Hong, C.S. (1991). Clinical and Immunologic Evaluations of Reactive Dye-Exposed Workers. *Journal of Allergy and Clinical Immunology,* 87: 639-649.

[87]   De Roos, A.J., Ray, R.M., Gao, D.L., Wernli, K.J., Fitzgibbons, E.D., Ziding, F. Astrakianakis, G., Thoma, D.B., & Checkoway, H. (2005). Colorectal cancer incidence among female textile workers in Shanghai, China: A Case -cohort analysis of occupational exposures. *Cancer Causes and Control*, 16: 1177-1188.

[88]   Sharma, S., Sharma, S., Singh, P.K., Swami, R.C., & Sharma, K.P. (2009). Exploring fish bioassay of textile dye wastewaters and their selected constituents in terms of mortality and erythrocyte disorders. *Bulletin of Environmental Contamination and Toxicology,* 83: 29-34.

[89]   Kilbey, B.J., Legator, M., Nichols, W., & Ramel, C. (1984). Eds., Handbook of Mutagenicity Test Procedures, Elsevier, Amsterdam.

[90]   Grover, I.S., & Kaur, S. (1999). Genotoxicity of wastewater samples from sewage and industrial effluent detected by the *Allium* root anaphase aberration and micronucleus assays. *Mutation Research,* 426: 183-188.

[91]   Chakraborty, R., Mukherjee, A.K., & Mukherjee, A. (2009). Evaluation of genotoxicity of coal fly ash in *Allium cepa* root cells by combining comet assay with the *Allium* test. *Environmental Monitoring and Assessment,* 153: 351-357.

[92]   Hoshina, M.M. (2002). Evaluation of a possible contamination of the waters of the Claro river-municipality of Rio Claro, part of the Corumbatai river basin, with the mutagenicity tests using *Allium cepa*. 52f. Monograph (Bachelor's and Teaching degrees) - State University of Sao Paulo, Rio Claro, SP (in Portuguese).

[93]   Roychoudhury, A., & Giri, A.K. (1989). Effects of certain food dyes on chromosomes of *Allium cepa*. *Mutation Research,* 223: 313-319.

[94]   Rojas, E., Lopez, M.C., & Valverde, M. (1999). Single cell gel electrophoresis assay: methodology and applications. *Journal of Chromatography B,* 722: 225-254.

[95]   Szeto, Y.T. (2007). Single-cell gel electrophoresis: a tool for investigation of DNA protection or damage mediated by dietary antioxidants. *Journal of the Science of Food and Agriculture,* 87: 2359-2381.

[96]   Saghirzadeh, M., Gharaati, M.R., Mohammadi, S., & Ghiassi-Nejad, M. (2008). Evaluation of DNA damage in the root cells of *Allium cepa* seeds growing in soil of

high background radiation areas of Ramsar, Iran. *Journal of Environmental Radioactivity*, 99: 1698-1702.

[97] Verschaeve, L., Gilles, J., Schoctors, J., Van Cleuvenbergen, R., & DeFrie, J. (1993). The single cell gel electrophoresis technique or comet test for monitoring dioxinpollution and effects, in: H. Fiedler, H. Frank, O. Hutzinger, W. Parzefall A. Riss, S. Safe (Eds.), Organohalogen Compounds II Federal Enviromental Agency, Austria, p. 213.

[98] Phugare, S.S., Kalyani, D.C., Surwase, S.N., & Jadhav, J.P. (2011) .Ecofriendly degradation, decolorization and detoxification of textile effluent by a developed bacterial consortium. *Ecotoxicology and Environmental safety*, doi:10.1016/j.ecoenv.2011.03.003.

[99] Achary, V.M.M., Jena, S., Panda, K.K., & Panda, B.B. (2008). Aluminum induced oxidative stress and DNA damage in root cells of *Allium cepa* L. *Ecotoxicology and Environmental safety,* 70: 300-310.

[100] http://en.wikipedia.org/wiki/Lipid_peroxidation.

In: Non-Conventional Textile Waste Water Treatment
Editor: Ahmed El Nemr

ISBN: 978-1-62100-079-2
© 2012 Nova Science Publishers, Inc.

Chapter 2

TEXTILE DYES XENOBIOTIC AND THEIR HARMFUL EFFECT

Amany El Sikaily, Azza Khaled, Ahmed El Nemr[*]

Environmental Division, National Institute of Oceanography and Fisheries
Kayet Bey, El Anfoushy, Alexandria, Egypt

ABSTRACT

Dyes are xenobiotic compounds that make the world more beautiful through colored substances. However, the release of this colored wastewater represents a serious environmental problem and a public health concern. Textile dyeing effluents containing recalcitrant dyes are polluting waters by their color and formation of toxic or carcinogenic intermediates such as aromatic amines that formed from azo dyes degradation. Therefore, elimination of dyes from textile dyeing effluents currently represents a major ecological concern.

1. INTRODUCTION

Dyes are used primarily to give color in textile, leather, paints, cosmetic, and food industries. At the end of the nineteenth century, many natural dyes (e.g. Madder produces red anthraquinone dye in its roots, most important being alizarin; Weld produces yellow flavanoid colorants from foliage and flowers, most important being luteolin) have been largely replaced by synthetic dyes that were developed, provided a broader range of color possibilities and more colorfast and less expensive [1, 2]. In addition to that natural colorants (eco-friendly dye) need large quantities of raw material to obtain the same depth of color synthetic dyes; limited success in coloration of synthetic fibers (polyester has a 45% share of the global textile market); nearly all natural dyes need application with a mordant (salts of Cr, Sn, Zn, Cu, Al, Fe) to secure sufficient wash and light fastness and to give good build-up;

---

[*] E-mail: ahmedmoustafaelnemr@yahoo.com; ahmed.m.elnemr@gmail.com

their effluent contains heavy metals far in excess of allowable limits; extremely desirable to develop new methods of fixation using non-metal mordants [3].

However, the most frequently reported causes of unexpected side effects of clothes are textile dyes, and some dyes formerly used for food like Butter Yellow are known to be carcinogenic. It is actually difficult to routinely detect the exact composition of dyes, because the chemicals used are generally not declared in textiles [4]. Moreover, the manufacturing modifications in developed countries and the banishment of strongly allergenic, mutagenic, or carcinogenic dyes in Europe, Indian and the United States may be counter balanced by the high numbers of imported clothing generally treated with historically older and cheaper dyes from the Far East or underdeveloped countries.

The dyeing processes have in general a low yield, and the percentage of the lost dye in the effluents can reach up to 50% [5, 6]. From the available bibliography it can be estimated that approximately 75% of the dyes, discharged by Western European textile processing industries, belong to the classes of the reactive (~36%), acid (%25~)and direct dyes (~15%) [7]. In these classes, the azo dyes (aromatic moieties linked together by azo (-N=N-) chromophores) are the most important chemical class of synthetic dyes and pigments, representing between 60 to 80 % of the organic dyes referenced in the Color Index [8]. This was the reason of the use of azo dyes in this work.

2. CLASSIFICATION AND CHARACTERISTICS OF DYES

There are over than 13,000 marketed under different names (more than 100 for some of them), that it is sometimes difficult to rapidly and accurately recognize a specific dye. Color Index System Dyes are indicated in the color index (CI), with two systems. A numeric one, with five numbers, corresponds to the CI number, for example, CI 73000; CI 60730 and CI 73300. The second system is a CI generic name, indicating its application class, its hue and a number which indicates its chronological discovery, CI Vat Blue 1; CI Acid Violet 43 and CI Vat Red 41, respectively for the previous molecules. According to their chemical structures and the CI system, dyes can be classified into 17 groups: nitro dyes, triphenylmethane derivatives, xanthenes, acridine derivatives, quinoline derivatives, azines, anthraquinones, indigoid dyes, phthalocyanines dyes, oxydation bases, insoluble azo dye precursors, and azo dyes (classes XII–XVII). In practice, according to the process of dying, dyes are classified into the following types: acid, basic, mordant, direct, reactive, vat, disperse, sulfur and azo dyes (Figure 1).

2. PURITY OF DYES

The influence of the impurities, commonly encountered in commercial dyes, is less studied. According to Lyon [9] these impurities present in dyes are: (i) diluents such as inorganic salts, starch and dispersing agents, (ii) by-products formed during manufacture, and (iii) dyes of different constitution and color that are added for shading. Because of this, a priori unexpected dyes can be employed as yellow, red, orange, or red dyes for black or blue garments. For example, Serisol Black L 1944, used to dye black 'velvet' clothes, contains five disperse dyes, namely Blue 124, Blue 106, Red 1, Yellow 3, and Blue 1. Moreover, a commercial 'pure' dye often comprises one or two major components, and frequently other chemicals and/or impurities. Disperse Yellow 3 is generally pure, Disperse Red 153 or Disperse Blue 35 contain two major fractions, and Disperse Red 1 comprises one major compound and at least two other minor substances. These impurities can also be responsible for sensitization. On the other Hand, these impurities affect on the ozonation degradation of the dye [10]. Zhang *et al.* [11] studied the effects of impurities on the ozonation degradation of the azo dye C.I. Reactive Red 120. They compared the results obtained for unpurified (75%) and purified (90%) dyes, and concluded that the presence of impurities affects mostly the biodegradability of the dye. They also suggested that dyes need to be purified before ozonation treatment if detailed information on the oxidative processes and by-production formation are required.

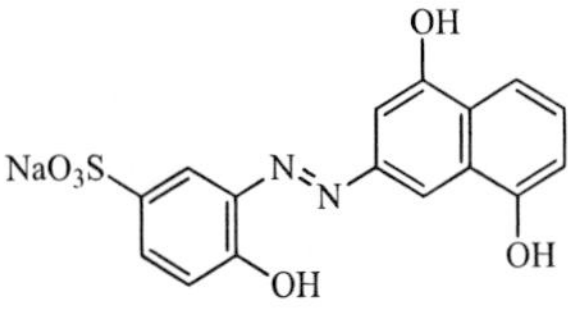

Mordant Black 9 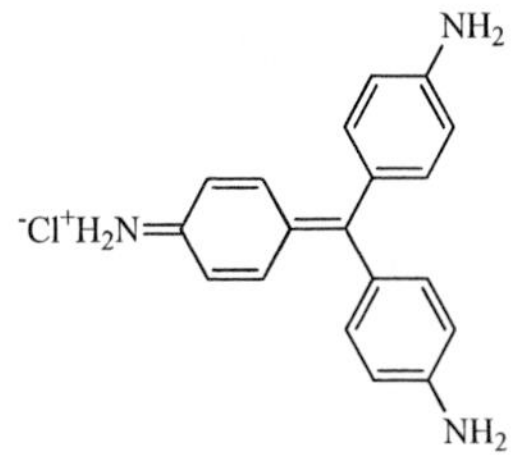 Basic Red 9 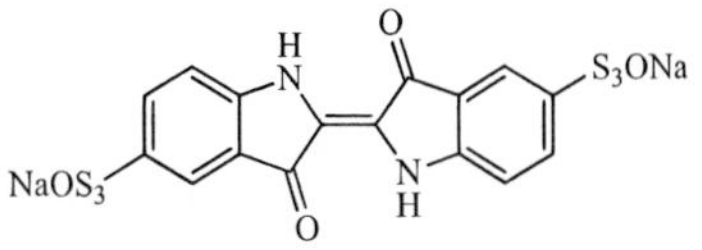 Acid Blue 74

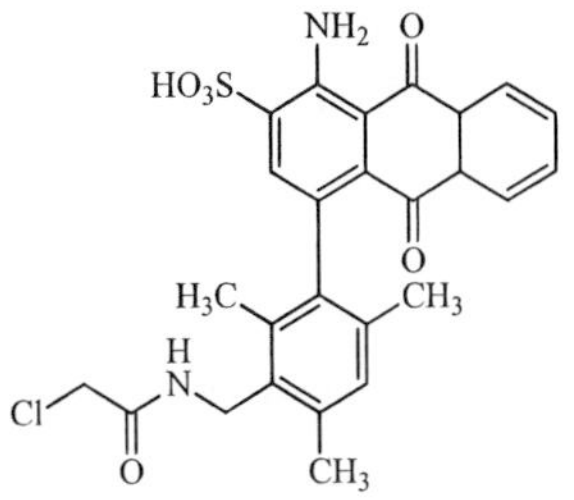

Acid Blue 225 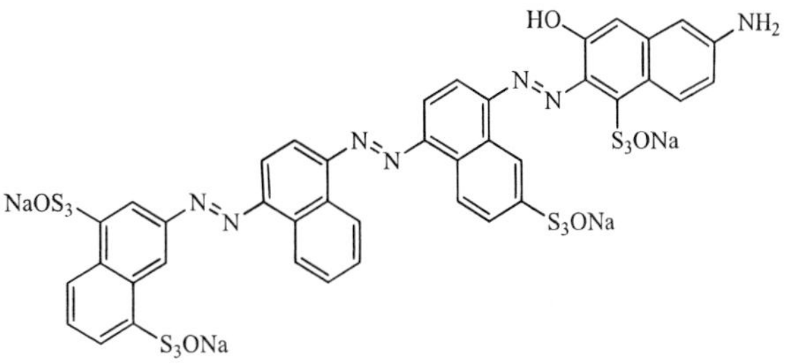 Direct Blue 71

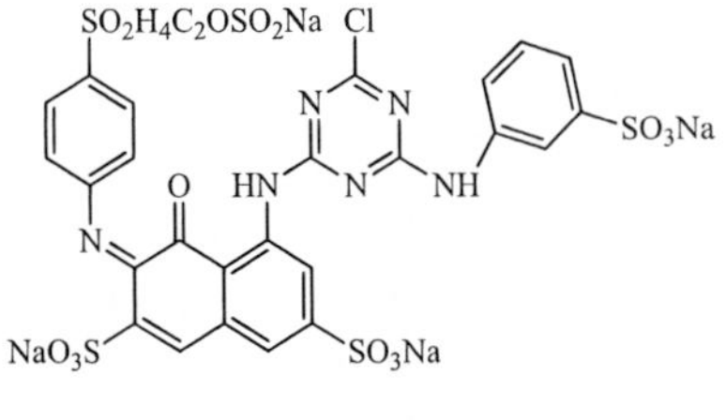

Remazol Red RB 133 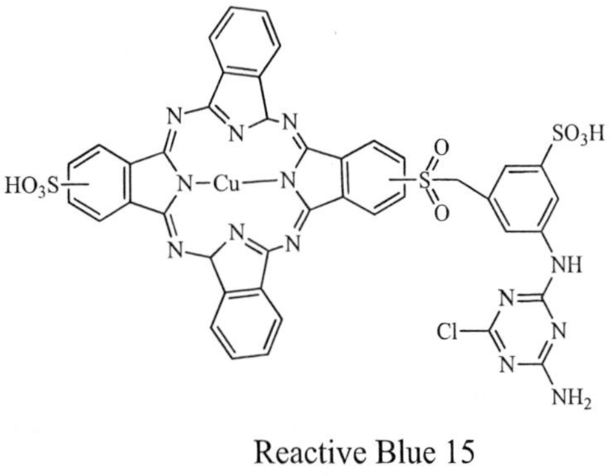 Reactive Blue 15

Figure 1. Examples of common commercial dyes.

3. TEXTILE DYES

The large variety of dyes and chemicals used in an attempt to make more attractive popular shades of fabrics for a competitive market render them very complex [12]. During the last decade, environmental issues associated with dyestuff production and application have grown significantly and are indisputably among the major driving forces affecting the textile dye industry today [13]. Considerable amounts of dyes have been noticed in textile wastewaters, due to their incomplete use and washing operations. The dyes disposed off, can be found in dissolved state or in suspension in the wastewater. These dyestuffs are highly structured polymers and are very difficult to decompose biologically [14]. The most obvious impact of the discharge of dye colored effluent is the persisting nature of the color. It is stable and fast, difficult to degrade, toxic, rendering the water unfit for its intended use. Further, the color removal is also not adequate by the conventional chemical and biological treatment. Such dyestuffs can reach the aquatic environment, primarily dissolved or suspended in water, since the conventional treatment of wastewaters from textile mills and dyestuff factories are unable to remove most of the azo and other dyes effectively. The resulting dye effluents may contain some components or moieties that could be toxic, carcinogenic or mutagenic to aquatic life [15]. Ecological and toxicological problems due to the discharge of textile wastewaters, in natural water bodies, have been one of the most important water pollution problems. Since large quantities of dyes are used, such pollution due to dyes may occur on a significant scale. The International Agency for Research on Cancer (IARC) has classified various dyes like Benzidine as being associated with cancer in humans [16]. Benzidine is known to be carcinogenic to a variety of mammalian species, including humans. In tests on laboratory animals, two benzidine dyes, Direct Blue 6 and Direct Black 38, have been reported to be such potent carcinogens that hepatocellular carcinomas and neoplastic liver nodules occurred in rats after only 13 weeks of exposure [17].

Nowadays, there are more than 100,000 dyes and pigments commercially available, being produced annually about 7×10^5 - 1×10^6 tons [18, 19]. They are used extensively in the dye and printing industries that produce large quantities of colored liquid effluents, since 10-15% of the dyes used are lost in the wastewaters [20-23]. Based on the chemical structure, about 60-70% of all known dyes produced are azo dyes, making them the largest group of synthetic colorants [24, 25], with more than 3000 different structures [26]. This class is characterized by one or more azo groups (–N=N–) substituted with benzene or naphthalene groups, in general, it possesses groups –SO_3H, to increase dyes solubility, and auxochroms groups (like –COOH, –OH, –NH_2, –NHR, –NR_2) that intensify the color and increase dyes ability to bind to fibers [19]. Dyes are not completely degraded by conventional wastewater treatment processes, producing metabolites, like aromatic amines, that can be toxic and mutagenic [27-32], which lead to more restrictive measures in order to eliminate those compounds from the effluents, before they are discharged in the environment [8], and to the application of alternative degradation processes, such as chemical oxidation with strong oxidants [23, 33]. As the degradation of azo dyes may lead to the formation of aromatic amines that can be cytotoxic [34]; highly carcinogenic [32], or organochloride compounds, well known by their very low biodegradability and toxicity [28]. Therefore, removal of dyes from textile dyeing effluents currently represents a major ecological concern. Due to their high brilliance, low concentrations of dyes are highly visible and therefore, undesired in industrial effluents. The chemical structures of dye molecules are designed to resist fading on exposure to light or chemical attack and they prove to be quite resistant towards microbial degradation. Azo dyes, which are the largest group of synthetic dyes and pigments with industrial application due to their relatively simple synthesis, display strongly adverse effects on growth of methanogenic bacterial cultures [35]. This toxicity may be due mainly to the azo functional group itself rather than to the products of reductive cleavage [36] although it lead to the formation of aromatic amines, commonly known to be mutagenic and carcinogenic potential [37-40].

4. CLASSES OF DYES

Dyes can be classified according to chemical structure and/or according to their usage or application (See Chapter 1). Dye chemists usually classify dyes according to chemical structure (i.e., azo dyes, anthraquinone dyes, and phthalocyanine dyes), while dye users or technologists usually classify dyes according to their usage or application (e.g., reactive dyes for cotton and disperse dyes for polyester). Dye classification by usage or application is the principal method adopted by the *Color Index* which is edited every three months [41]. The *Color Index* assigns CI generic names to commercial dyes. The CI name is defined as "a classification name and serial number which when allocated to a commercial product allows that product to be uniquely identified within any *Color Index* Application Class". This designation makes it possible to classify commercial dyes according to the chemical constitution of their essential colorant. That is, commercial dyes are given the same CI generic name if the chemical constitution of their essential colorant is the same. The *Color Index* does not claim, however, that preparations listed under the same CI generic name have identical application fastness or toxicological properties. Moreover, it should not be assumed that one commercial dye can replace another in every respect. There are many kinds of dyes according to the dyeing process, including acidic dyes, azoic (naphthol) dyes, metal-complex dyes, basic (cationic) dyes, direct dyes, disperse dyes, reactive dyes, solvent dyes, sulfur dyes, mordant dyes and vat dyes, which are characterized by their distinct chemical and physical properties (Table 1) [41]. Acid dyes are highly water-soluble anionic dyes, due the presence of sulfonic acid groups or carboxylic acid groups, forming ionic interactions between the protonated functionalities of fibers ($-NH_3^+$) and the negative charge of the dyes; Van-der-waals, dipolar and hydrogen bonds are also formed. Acid dyes have a high affinity for wool, other protein fibers (silk), polyamides (modified acrylics) and other animal fibers when high wet-fastness is needed. Dyeing process increased by lowering the acidity of solution. Chemically, the acid dyes consist of azo (including preformed metal complexes), anthraquinone, and triarylmethane compounds with a few azine, xanthene, ketone imine, nitro, nitroso, and quinophthalone compounds [42]. Basic dyes, sometimes referred as cationic dyes, have high brilliance and intensity of colors are highly visible even at low concentration, mainly used to dye wool and silk, modacrylic, nylon, and polyester [43, 44]. They are usually the salts of organic bases where the cation form of the molecule has the color. Basic dyes are water soluble and yield colored cations in solution. The principal chemical classes are diazahemicyanine, triarylmethane, cyanine, hemicyanine, thiazine, oxazine, and acridine. Direct dyes are water-soluble anionic dyes, containing sulfonic acid groups, which have a high affinity for cellulosic fibers due to their flat shape and length which bind cellulose fibers and maximize the Van-der-Waals, dipole and hydrogen bonds.

Most of the dyes in this class are azo compounds with some stilbenes, phthalocyanines, and oxazines. Only 30% of the 1600 structures are still in production due to their lack of fastness during washing [42].

Disperse dyes are substantially water-insoluble nonionic dyes with polar functionality like $-NO_2$ and $-CN$ that improve water solubility. This type of dye is insoluble in water, but soluble within the fibers, so the excess dye is less difficult to extract once the dyeing process is complete [4]. They are the most important class of dye for dyeing hydrophobic synthetic fibers such as polyester and acetates. Reactive dyes were introduced at the end of the 1950s and they account for more than 10% of the world's production of dyes. They form a covalent bond with $-OH$, $-NH$ or $-SH$ groups in cellulosic fibers (cotton and silk), wool, and nylon [42] and are widely used for the production of clothes. They differ from all other classes of dyes in that they bind to the textile fibers through stable covalent bond which results in excellent color fastness [45]. This property as well as the simplicity of the dyeing process, means that reactive dyes, are widely used on cellulosic fibers. The most common structures of reactive dyes are azo, triphendioxazine, phthalocyanine, formazan, and anthraquinone. A marked advantage of reactive dyes over direct dyes is that their chemical structures are much simpler; their absorption spectra show narrower absorption bands, their favorable characteristics such as bright color, water fast, simple application techniques with low energy consumption. Solvent dyes (non-ionic dyes) are water-insoluble dyes devoid of polar solubilizing groups such as sulfonic acid, carboxylic acid, or quaternary ammonium, used for dyeing substrates in which they can dissolve as plastics, varnish, ink, gasoline, oils, and waxes, but not often used for textile processing. The most common structures are diazo compounds that undergo some molecular rearrangement; triarylmethane, anthraquinone and phthalocyanine dyes are also used. Sulfur dyes are complex molecules containing sulfur obtained from the reaction between selected organic intermediates such as 4-aminophenol or *p*-phenylenediamine and molten sulfur or polysulfide. The actual structures of sulfur dyes are unknown, but it is assumed that they possess sulfur-containing heterocyclic rings representing about 15% of the global dye production.

Vat dyes are insoluble in water. These dyes require oxygen to develop their color. Vat dyes become solubilized by alkali reduction (sodium dithionite in the presence of sodium hydroxide). The fabric absorbs the dye, which then must be re-oxidized by hydrogen peroxide to its insoluble form to reveal the color. The most common structures are anthraquinones or indigoids [42]. The reducing agent normally used for vat dyes is not very stable to air or heat, so an excess of it is needed to ensure good color. Additionally, the sodium dithionite oxidizes into sodium sulphate, sulphate ions, and thiosulphate ions, which are all toxic substances. Because vat dyes are more difficult to control, there is an increased chance of rejection of the dyed goods [4]. These dyes are no longer produced in the United States due to environmental concerns [46].

All molecules absorb electromagnetic radiation, but differ in the specific wavelengths absorbed. Some organic molecules have the ability to absorb light in the visible spectrum (400-800 nm) and, as a result, they become colored. The dyes are molecules with delocalized electron systems with conjugated double bonds that contain at least one of the two radicals groups (the chromophore and the auxochrome).

Table 1. Chemistry, dyeing principle and function of dyes

Name	Dyeing principle, Function	Chemistry
Dyes		
Reactant-Type dyes	Covalent binding to the fibers	Water soluble
Disperse dyes	Balanced distribution, carriers, chemical fibers	Lipophilic azo dyes
Acid and base dyes	Binding via ion exchange	
Mordant agents	Fixation via ion exchange	
Direct dyes	Deposition in cavities	Water soluble
Vat dyes	Redox dyeing process, high degree of fastness in use	Anthraquinones
Sulphur dyes	Diazotized amine, coupled on fiber	Azo dyes
Development dyes (naphthols)	Not readily soluble	Azo dyes, Anthraquinones
Dyeing auxiliaries		
Dye accelerators (carriers)	Chemical fibers, disperse dyes	Aromatics
Leveling agents	Uniform coloration	Surfactants
Crease prevention agents		Polyglycol ethers
After-treatment agents	Color fastness	Surfactants, resins
Binding agents	Pigment dyeing	Copolymers
Thickening	Pigment printing	Copolymers
Dispersing agents	Pigment dyeing	Polymers, surfactants
Fixation accelerators	Pigment printing	Oxethylates

Dyes are characterized by chemical structure, by their chromophore. Typical dyes are aromatic complex or hetero-aromatic compounds that either contains azo bonds, or feature indigoid, triaryl methane, anthrachinoid, or phtalocyanoid carbon skeletons. They are substituted with various electron withdrawing or electron donating groups like hydroxy, amino, nitro, halogens or sulfonate.

According to dyeing properties, Dyes are classified into disperse, reactive, and direct for application purposes. The dyeing properties in turn reflect solubility and chemical reactivity towards the fabric to be dyed. Although dye molecules display a high structural variety, they are degraded by only few different enzymes. These biocatalysts have one common mechanistic feature. They are all redox-active molecules and thus, exhibit relatively wide substrate specificities [47, 48].

(a) The chromophore: is a group of unsaturated organic radicals enables them to absorb and reflect incident electromagnetic radiation within a very narrow band of visible light; which provide the color, and it is usually an electron-withdrawing group. The most important chromophores are: azo, Quinonoid, tri-aryl methane, nitro, and nitroso groups as illustrated in Figure 2 [49].

(b) The auxochrome: is an electron-donating substituent which increases the overall polarity of dye molecule that can intensify the color of the chromophore by altering the overall energy of the electron system and provides solubility and improve the color fastness properties of dyed fiber. The most important acidic and basic auxochromes are (carboxyl and sulphonic group) and (amino, substituted amino, and hydroxyl group) respectively as illustrated in Figure 3. Based on the chemical structure or chromophore, 20-30 different dye groups can be identified. Azo (monoazo, disazo, triazo, polyazo), anthraquinone, phthalocyanine and triarylmethane dyes are quantitatively the most important (Table 2).

| Azo group | nitro group | nitroso group | tri-aryl methane group |

| Quinonoid group | Anthraquinone | Triarylmethane | Phthalein |

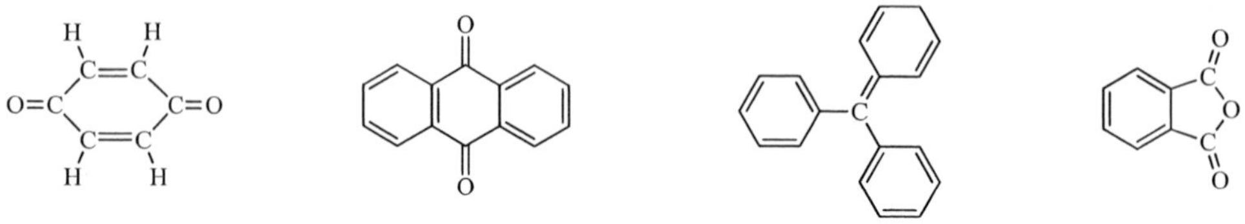

Figure 2. The most important chromophore groups.

HOOC—   HO₃S—   —OH   —NH₂

Figure 3. The most important auxochrome groups.

5. MODE OF DETOXIFICATION

One single enzyme or a whole group of enzymes may be responsible for decolorization, and low-molecular weight compounds like cofactors, co-substrates or mediators may be involved as well. Biochemical transformation of the dye may either occur outside the cell if the enzymes are excreted into the medium or inside the cell (Figure 4), provided that the dye is readily transported into the cell, demonstrating the impact of its bioavailability.

Important oxidative enzymes used for dye decolorization:

6. IDENTIFICATION OF XENOBIOTIC

Xenobiotics are characterized as compounds foreign to specific ecological systems which are often of anthropogenic origin and display high persistence in the environment. They may consist of aromatic ring systems substituted by electron-withdrawing groups like azo, nitro, or halogens (Figure 5) [50]. An examination of the fate of foreign compounds (xenobiotics) in biological systems is a natural outgrowth of man's curiosity about his environment and how it can affect these actions. While the majority of modern day studies concern the fat of drugs in man and animals there are extensive investigations on the fat of organic compounds in plants, animals and microorganisms (www.Issx.org/).

$$Dye + O_2 \xrightarrow{\text{Peroxidase}} \text{Oxidized dye} + H_2O$$

$$Dye + O_2 \xrightarrow{\text{Laccase}} \text{Oxidized dye} + H_2O$$

$$Dye + O_2 \xrightarrow{\text{Monooxygenase}} \text{Oxidized dye} + H_2O$$

$$Dye + O_2 \xrightarrow{\text{Dioxygenase}} \text{Bis-hydroxylated dye}$$

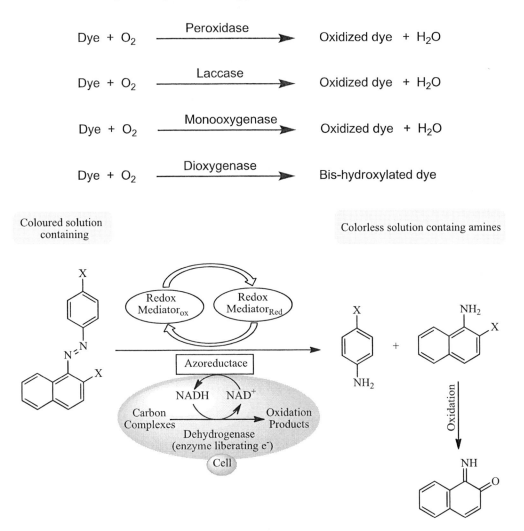

Figure 4. Enzymatic transformation of colored solution to colorless solution.

6.1. Classification of Xenobiotics

The different types of xenobiotics could be implicated in different ways where they might be classified structurally, whether organic or inorganic, classified by their source natural or synthetic, by the type of compound (solvents, paints, pesticides, etc), pharmaceuticals and abused substances, they could be also classified by mechanism of action (enzyme induction or inhibition or formation of free radicals, etc.), or by the target organ as being neurotoxin, hepatotoxin. Many of the xenobiotics undergo biotransformation in the liver. This includes metabolism of the chemical, which undergoes detoxification, activation, or conjugation and then excretion into urine or bile [51].

Table 2. Classification of dyes based on the chromophore present

Class	Chromophore	Example
Nitro dyes		 Acid Yellow 24
Nitroso dyes		 Fast Green O
Azo dyes		 Methyl Orange
Trimethylmethane dyes		 Basic Violet
Phthalein dyes		 Phenolphthalein
Indigo dyes		 Acid Blue 71
Anthraquinone dyes		 Reactive Blue 19

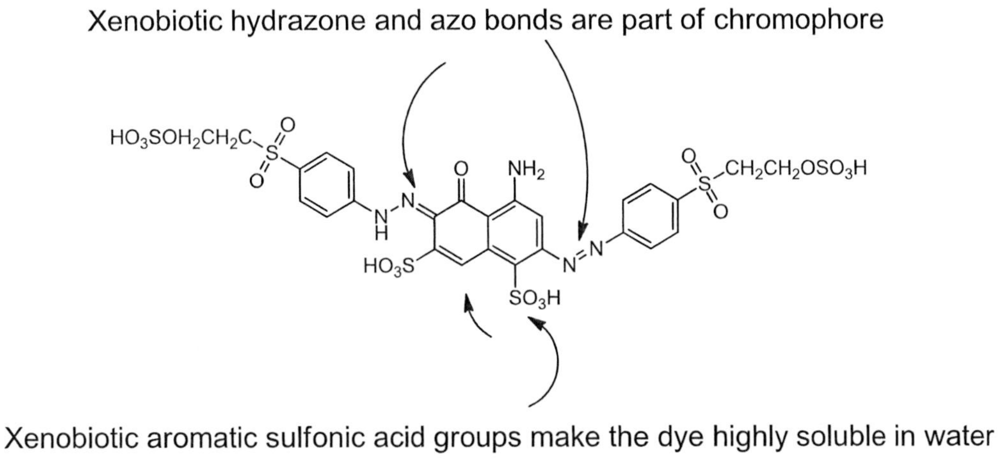

Xenobiotic hydrazone and azo bonds are part of chromophore

Xenobiotic aromatic sulfonic acid groups make the dye highly soluble in water

Figure 5. A typical reactive dye structure with its chromophore, containing azo/keto-hydrazone groups, the reactive centers and its solubilizing components (Remazol Black Bm a reactive azo dye).

6.2. Mineralization of Xenobiotic Compounds

Although the fate of xenobiotic compounds in nature is essentially determined by co-metabolism and complex interactions within microbial communities our knowledge of the naturally existing catabolic potential has largely been obtained from defined mixed cultures or more importantly from single bacterial strains that can grow at the expense of the chemical. Even with compounds exhibiting high xenobiotic character single bacterial strains have been described that harbor complete catabolic sequences. A case in point is 2,4,6-trinitrophenol (PA) or 2,4-DNP. Part of the catabolic sequence is given in Figure 6.

Since catabolism is initiated through hydrogenolytic denitration Gram-positive bacteria, that can utilize 2,4-DNP, can easily be selected in the presence of an auxiliary H donor under N-limiting conditions. Furthermore, spontaneous mutants can be selected which also utilize PA as sole source of carbon, nitrogen and energy. Identification of H^--picrate, $2H^-$-picrate, H^--2,4-dinitrophenol and 4,6-dinitrohexanoate as metabolites indicate that not only initial denitration but also ring cleavage depends on H^--transfers. Interestingly a F420 dependent two component enzyme system in *Nocardoides simplex* FJ2-1A catalyzes transfer of hydride from NADPH to picrate and 2,4-DNP. These proteins exhibit high homology to the corresponding enzymes of methanogenesis in archeae [52]. This homology has also been verified by identification of the genes of PA catabolism in *Rhodococcus erythropolis* HLPM-1 [53]. Bacteria harboring complete pathways are not only suitable objects for studying the physiology, biochemistry and regulation of xenobiotics degradation. Axenic cultures have also been suggested for remediation of industrial waste streams, exhaust gases and contaminated soil. When used as an inocculum these cultures may complement the catabolic potential existing in the autochthonous microflora. At high substrate concentrations a selective advantage exists, so that these cultures harboring complete catabolic pathways can counteract the co-metabolic misrouting of pollutants by the indigenous microflora. Furthermore, inoccula may complement the genetic pool and thus enhance the evolution of new catabolic pathways for xenobiotic compounds.

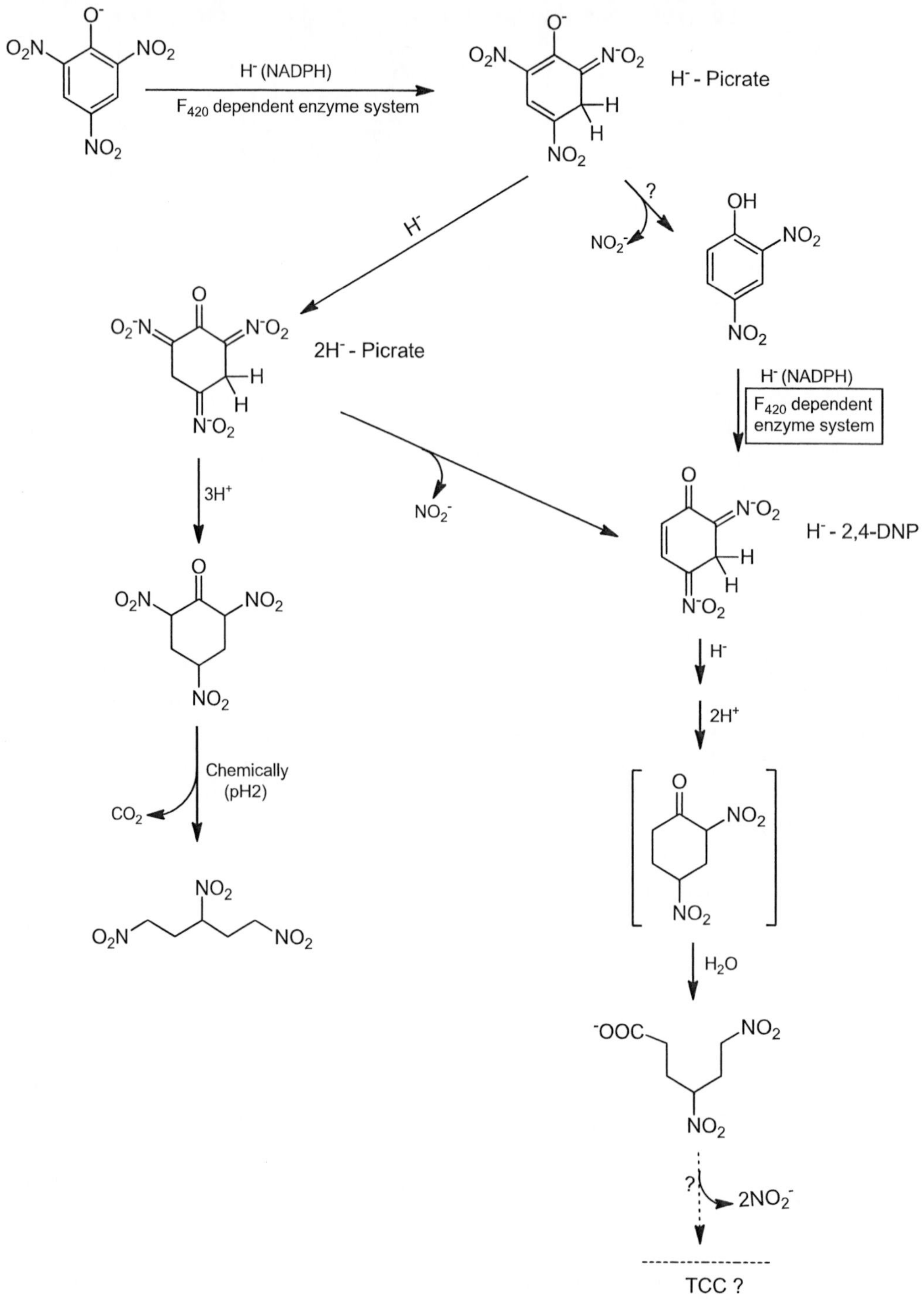

Figure 6. Proposed initial steps of the degradation of picrate and 2,4-dinitrophenol. In *Nocardioides simplex* FJ2-1A a denitrating activity was found with $2H^-$-picrate but not with H^--picrate [52].

7. SUBSTRATE SPECIFICITY OF AZOREDUCTASE FOR DIFFERENT TYPES OF AZO DYES

Azo dyes are a diverse class of chemicals in which various moieties confer a wide range of colors with different shades and intensities. Azo colorants range in shade from greenish yellow to orange, red, violet and brown [42]. The colors depend largely on the chemical structure, whereas different shades rather depend on physical properties. A disadvantage limiting their applications, however, that none of the azo dyes are green. The majority of industrial important azo dyes belong to the following groups: acid dyes, basic dyes, direct dyes, disperse dyes, mordant dyes, reactive dyes, and solvent dyes. The number and position of sulfonate and other substituent groups on the azo dye particularly affect the rate of decolorization. Acid dyes exhibit low color removal due to the number of sulfonate groups present in the dye, while the direct dyes; being independent of the sulfonate groups exhibit high levels of color removal [54]. Methyl red with a mono-azo bond and lacking a sulfonate group is relatively easily degraded, while acid red 151 and congo red with two azo bonds are difficult to cleave [55]. Similarly, the decolorization rates observed in case of acid red and acid orange 8 were lower than those of other dyes containing sulfonate groups [55], which attributed to their complicated chemical structures consisting of polyaromatic and sulfonate groups, due to steric interference and increased difficulty for azo reductases to form enzyme substrate complexes. Likewise, dyes with methyl, methoxy, sulfo, or nitro groups in their structures and substituent groups in the molecule also affect azoreductase activity [6, 56, 57]. On the other hand, azo compounds with a hydroxyl group or with an amino group are more likely to be degraded at faster rates than those with a methyl, methoxy, sulfo, or nitro groups [58]. Zimmermann et al. [59] suggested that a hydroxy group in the ortho position of the naphthol ring is necessary for the azo reductase reaction, and charged groups in the proximity of the azo group could cause hindrance in the reaction. Another polar substituent on the dye molecule inhibits the reaction by lowering its affinity to the enzyme, while the electron withdrawing substituent on the phenyl ring increases the rate of the reaction. The dye reduction rate is affected by electron density in the region of the azo dye group.

Walker and Ryan [60] mentioned that the reduction rate increase by the substitution of electron withdrawing groups in the para position of the phenyl ring, relative to the azo bond. Hydrogen bonding, in addition to the electron density in the region of the azo bond, has a significant effect on the rate of reduction [61]. It was also shown that carboxylated dyes were reduced slower than sulfonated dyes due to the higher electronegativity of the sulfo group, which renders the azo group more accessible to electrons [62]. Likewise, Martins et al. [63] reported that dyes with low polarity and having an electron-donating methyl substituent group in the ring are quite recalcitrant. Thus, it can be concluded that the decolorization of azo dyes is highly dependent on the specificity of azo reductase for different types of azo dyes.

8. HARMFUL EFFECT OF AZO DYE

The majority of azo dyes (food and textile) have LD50 values between 250-2,000 mg/kg body weight, whereas few azo dyes showed LD50 values below 250 mg/kg body weight, indicating that for a lethal dose many grams of azo dyes have to be consumed in a single dose. As azo dyes are highly water soluble, they do not accumulate in the body, but are metabolized in the liver and excreted in the urine. As azo dyes are very strong colors and become hyperactive to level to cause allergies.

8.1. Allergic Reactions to Textiles

Intolerance reactions to wool may occur when wearing textiles. However, real allergic reactions are relatively rare [64-66]. Attributing an allergy to a particular azo dye is a complex and difficult process, because of each azo dye is marketed under several different names and azo dyes are very often containing impurities. In German dermatological clinics contact allergies are attributed in around 1-2% of the cases to textiles. The majority of sensitizing dyes, present in clothes, practically all belong to the group of disperse dyes, which has been developed for use on synthetic fibers. Certain disperse dyes in particular have been identified as the trigger. In this context, skin-tight garments made of chemical fibers constitute a special hazard potential. Under the heading "stocking dye allergy", this phenomenon was described in the literature in the 1970s; in the 1990s the so-called "leggings allergy" was described. What is important is the fastness of the dye. The explanation is probably that the attachment of molecules from disperse dyes is weak, as they are more easily available for skin contact. In conjunction with textile-induced dermatitis 49 dyes are described as contact allergens and about two-thirds of them are dispersing dyes [67-71]. In clinical patch tests the following azo dyes have shown sensitizing properties [7]: Disperse Red (DR) 1, 17; Disperse Orange (DO) 1, 3, 76; Disperse Yellow (DY) 3, 4; Disperse Blue (DB) 124; Disperse Black (DB) 1, 2. In Germany, disperse azo dyes like Disperse Blue 1, 35, 106 and 124, Disperse Yellow 3, Disperse Orange 3, 37, 76 and Disperse Red 1 have been associated with contact dermatitis, resulting from exposure to textiles colored with these dyes. In most cases the dermatitis resolved, once the sensitizing "textile" had been discarded. These dyes are no longer recommended for coloring of textiles, which come into contact with the skin [72]. On the other Hand, none disperse azo dyes, used for coloring of natural fibers were investigated in 1,814 patients attending the clinic patch tests [73]. 0.88% of the patients reacted positive to the following dyes: Direct Orange 34 (8 patients), Acid Yellow 61 (5 patients), Acid Red 359 (2 patients) and Acid Red 118 (1 patient). Remazol Black B (Reactive Black 5) was investigated for sensitization potential in experimental animals and was found to be negative. However, a few cases of allergic reactions have been observed in man. The manufacturing processes for textile fabrication are complex and additional procedures such as bleaching can also lead to allergenic products.

8.2. Chromosomal Aberration of Textiles

Over the last two decades, there has been a tremendous increase in awareness of the toxic and carcinogenic effects of many polluting chemicals that were not considered hazardous in the past [74]. Unlike the naturally occurring organic compounds that are readily degraded upon introduction into the environment, some of the synthetic chemicals are extremely resistant to biodegradation by native microorganisms [75]. Many of the recalcitrant compounds are major environmental pollutants, such as munitions waste, pesticides, organochlorines, polychlorinated biphenyls, polycyclic aromatic hydrocarbons, wood preservatives, synthetic polymers, and synthetic dyes which pose a major carcinogenic risk [76, 77]. Majority of human cancers are known to arise as a direct consequence of environmental exposure to mutagenic and carcinogenic agents, mainly through diet, habit and occupation [78]. The formation of many DNA adducts in human is directly related to exposure to carcinogens associated with life style, contact with many pollutants. Recently, increasing attention has been paid to the development of monitoring methods by which human exposure to mutagens and carcinogens can be detected and several biomarkers were also developed for this purpose [79]. The textile dyeing industries discharge large volume of effluents posing a great threat to the environment and the ecosystem, due to their possible toxicity and carcinogenicity; this is because many dyes are comprised of known carcinogens, such as benzidine and other aromatic hydrocarbons derivatives of toluene, naphthalene, phenol and aniline [80].

Ragunathan *et al.* [81] had studied the chromosome aberrations in human peripheral blood lymphocytes of persons occupationally exposed to a mixture of dye chemicals for long time. The frequencies of chromosomal aberrations were determined using lymphocytes of non-smokers and smokers working in textile dye industry. The authors had analyzed 52 workers exposed to complex chemical mixtures and 25 individuals selected as a control group in the same area not working in the textile dye industry. Cytogenetic monitoring of human population exposed to chemicals has proved to be useful for detecting the possible mutagenic effects of chemicals used. Comparison between workers and the control group reveal that the individual exposed to textile dye industry showed substantial clastogenic effects in peripheral lymphocytes. The frequency of total chromosome aberrations increased with age on workers having smoking habits (20.33 ± 0.73) compared to control (5.33 ± 0.88). Results from chromosome aberration assay indicate that dye industry workers showed statistically significant higher incidence of DNA damage in smokers of higher age group compared to non smokers. Meanwhile, several authors reported significant differences in the frequencies of sister chromatin exchange (SCE) occurred between smokers and non-smokers exposed to toxicologically harmful agents [82-84]. As previously knowing that benzidine (BN) based azo dyes are widely used in textile dyeing where benzidine has long been recognized as a human urinary bladder carcinogen and tumorogenic in a variety of laboratory animals [85]. Since benzidine is used as a reactant in dye synthesis, workers could be directly exposed to the carcinogen [86]. Rats, dogs and hamsters have shown that animals administered with BN and BN based dyes excrete potentially carcinogenic aromatic amines and their *N*-acetyled derivatives in their urine [87]. The effluents of dye industry also reduce the rate of seed germination and growth of crop plants [88]. Pelclova *et al.* [89] studied the chromosome analysis of peripheral lymphocytes of workers exposed to rotogravure printing dyes, they showed an increased incidence of aberrant cells and chromatid breaks. Recent evidence showed that textile dye stuffs caused frame shift mutation in *Salmonella* mutagenicity assay [90] and sulphur dyes used in the textile industry induced a significant DNA damage on tadpoles exposed to various concentrations [91].

8.3. Mutagenicity

8.3.1. Textile Dyes

Because of the wide spread use and potential carcinogenicity of certain dyes, there has been a growing interest in assessing the hazards associated with dyes available in local markets. Most of such dyes, being openly sold in the markets have no information regarding their chemical nature, purity, toxicity or possible mutagenicity [13]. Most textile dyes in use are so called "existing substances" which have been placed on the market before 1983. Many of them have therefore not been adequately tested until now [92]. Unlimited and uncontrolled use of such dyes can lead to grave consequences in terms of human health and ecological balance. Central Pollution Control Board has listed the dye and dye intermediates industry as one of the heavily polluting industries. Assessment of genotoxicity of dyes is therefore of utmost importance. Several experimental investigations have shown that textiles and wastewater from textile finishing companies (TFCs) contain mutagenic substances [93, 94]. The systematic backtracking of the flows of wastewater from the production plants of three textile processing companies led to the identification of textile dyes as a cause of the high mutagenic effects [95-97]. The International Agency for Research on Cancer (IARC) has classified various dyes like Benzidine as being associated with cancer to a variety of mammalian species, including humans [16]. Two benzidine dyes, Direct Blue 6 and Direct Black 38, in tests on laboratory animals, have been reported to be such potent carcinogens those hepatocellular carcinomas and neoplastic liver nodules occurred in rats after only 13 weeks of exposure [14]. Testing of some dyes for mutagenicity using *Salmonella* assay were done by many authors [98-100]. Several of them have been found to be carcinogenic. Various short-term screening methods have played important roles in studying the mechanisms of mutagenesis and carcinogenesis, and have provided useful information for assessing the genetic effects of chemicals on humans. Microorganisms have demonstrated several attributes that make them attractive for use in quick screening of effluents and chemicals for toxicity.

Mutagenicity testing of chemicals in Ames assay is based on the knowledge that a substance that is mutagenic in the bacterium is likely to be a carcinogen in laboratory animals, and thus, by extension, present a risk of cancer to humans. The Ames test has several advantages over the use of mammals for testing compounds. Mutagenicity assays are relatively cost effective, only a few days are required for testing a compound and the test is performed with microgram quantities of the material. Such assays are performed on approximately 100 million organisms rather than on a limited number of animals [13]. A total of seven dyes were tested by Mathur *et al.* [13]. The selected dyes were used in their crude form and no further purification was attempted, because authors wanted to test the potential danger that these dyes represent in actual use. Three of these were processing dyes or Cremazoles (Orange 3R, Brown GR and Blue S1) while remaining four were direct dyes (Violet, Congo red, Royal blue and Bordeaux). Only the Violet dye had recorded a Mutagenicity ratio less than 2.0 at all tested concentrations (2-100 µl and no dose related increase in number of revertant colonies was observed. On the other hand, Bordeaux dye showed higher number of revertants and can be classified as highly mutagenic or extremely mutagenic (12,000 induced revertants, per 100 µl of dye), while both Congo red and Royal blue dyes were positively mutagenic and can be classified as moderately mutagenic (700-1200 induced revertants, per 100 µl of dye). These observations are in accordance with several studies that report mutagenicity of a number of dyes like Direct Black 38, Acid Red

26, etc [99, 100]. Unlimited and uncontrolled use of such dyes can lead to grave consequences in terms of human health and ecological balance. All the three tested Cremazoles dyes were so toxic that they inhibited the growth of bacteria, at higher dose levels. Blue S1 was extremely mutagenic (15,000 induced revertants, per 100 μl of dye), while Orange 3R and Brown GR were moderately mutagenic (1200-1400 induced revertants, per 100 μl of dye). Strain TA 100 of *Salmonella typhimurium*, detects base pair substitution mutations, concluded that all of these six dyes cause genetic damage through base pair substitution mutations (Table 3). Some research groups used the Ames and other bacterial tests, as well as mammalian cell test systems and *in vivo* assays (e.g. induction of micronuclei in bone marrow cells) to investigate possible mutagenic effects of dyes used for textile finishing [101-105]. Most of these investigations focused on anthraquinone and azo dyes.

Jäger *et al.* [92] selected 53 dye products for mutagenicity testing in the bacterial reverse mutation assay with *Salmonella typhimurium* (Ames test) (Table 4). A sample was classified as mutagenic if it caused more than a doubling of the number of revertant colonies per plate in comparison to the control in at least one strain either with or without the metabolic activation system and/or a concentration-related increase over the range tested.

The mouse lymphoma assay (MLA) was applied to dye stuffs which proved to be Ames positive. The results showed that about 28% (15 out of 53) of the dye samples were positive in the Ames test. 15 samples showed positive results with TA98, 2 with TA100. The Mutagenicity of 9 Ames positive textile dye products were further investigated in the mouse lymphoma assay (MLA) (OECD 476). 67% (6 out of 9) induced genotoxic effects in the MLA. The induction rates (IR) were between 2.1 and 132 in the bacterial reverse mutation assay (Table 5) and in the range between 2.1 and 15.2 in the MLA (Table 6). The results confirm previous findings that dye products are marketed which are not sufficiently tested and which show mutagenic effects in *invitro* tests. Friedman *et al.* [106] and MacGregor *et al.* [107] investigated formulated textile dye products in the bacterial reverse mutation assay. Their respective findings of 32 and 29% dyes positive in *S. typhimurium* are in good agreement with Jäger *et al.* [92]. These and other published data on single dye ingredients or dye products were used to evaluate other dye products used by textile finishing companies [108].

Table 3. Absorbance maximum and mutagenicity ratio of dyes (1 g/100 ml) with strain TA 100 of *Salmonella typhimurium*

Dyes	Absorbance	Peak	Mutagenicity Ratio				
			2μl	5 μl	10 μl	50 μl	100 μl
Orange 3R	0.7791	490.0	0.	1.1	7.2	3.4	2.5
Brown GR	1.1201	454.5	1.7	2.1	9.2	4.4	3.5
Blue S1	2.1387	594.5	61.9	74.2	92.4	73.7	7.4
Violet	2.1106	536.0	-	-	-	-	-
Congo Red	0.9250	485.5	-	0.8	1.7	2.6	3.5
Royal Blue	0.9929	581.5	-	0.4	2.6	3.0	5.8
Bordeaux	1.0613	512.5	8.4	10.0	11.8	15.0	17.1

As the bacterial Mutagenicity assays can be carried out in 48 hrs, they have been suggested as rapid pre screens for distinguishing between carcinogenic and non-carcinogenic chemicals, allowing many thousands of compounds in our environment, not previously tested, to be screened for potential hazard. A good co-relation has been obtained by several groups, for a number of carcinogenic aromatic amines in their ability to induce mutation in strain and the ability to induce a response in animals. Thus Ames test can easily and quickly assess mutagenic potential of these dyes. Besides, the dyes can be compared on the basis of their mutagenic potencies. This bioassay can thus be used as an initial screening test to analyze various dyes and dye containing effluents, which are causing major damage to the aquatic environment. Further, excessive use of synthetic chemical dyes should be restricted. They should be replaced by vegetable dyes, which are eco-friendly.

8.3.2. Arylamins

8.3.2.1. Monoarylamines

Monoarylamines, less or more substituted, can have a weak carcinogenic potential. The prototype of these single ring aromatic amines is aniline (Figure 7), which can induce splenic carcinoma by feeding at high doses for a long term. Other monoarylamines (substituted anilines) like *o*-toluidine, *o*-anisidine, and *p*-cresidine are genotoxic upon metabolic activation and induce carcinoma of spleen or urinary bladder. Occupational exposure to dyestuffs (including *o*-toluidine) is associated with an increased risk of bladder cancer. *o*-Toluidine has been classified by EPA as a Group B2, probable human carcinogen [109]. An increased risk of bladder cancer has been reported among workers exposed to dyestuffs and dyestuff intermediates (including *o*-toluidine). However, no population of workers exposed only to *o*-toluidine has been described. Occasional cases of bladder tumors have been reported in workers exposed primarily to *o*-toluidine and other chemicals [110, 111]. *o*-Anisidine is used in the manufacture of dyes. Workers in the dye industry may be occupationally exposed to it. Acute (short-term) exposure to *o*-anisidine results in skin irritation in humans. Workers exposed to *o*-anisidine by inhalation for 6 months developed headaches, vertigo, and effects on the blood. Animal studies have reported effects on the blood from chronic (long-term) dermal exposure to *o*-anisidine. No information is available on the reproductive, developmental, or carcinogenic effects of *o*-anisidine in humans. Animal studies have reported tumors of the urinary bladder from oral exposure to *o*-anisidine.

Table 4. List of dye products tested in the bacterial reverse mutation assay (TA98 and TA100)

Dye Name	IR-TA98	IR-TA100	Dye Name	IR-TA98	IR-TA100
Astrazon Red FBL	negative	negative	Lanasol Rot B	negative	-3.6
Bemaplex Schwarz C-2B	-111.0	negative	Lanasol Gelb 4G	negative	negative
Blanc Minerprint 51	negative	negative	Levafix Blau E-GRN 01	negative	negative
Bleu Cibanone 83962 MD liq	negative	negative	Levafix Brillantrot E-BA Granulat	negative	negative
Bleu Imperon K-RR	negative	negative	Lumacron Black SEF	+41.8	negative

			300%		
Bleu Terasil 3R-02	-35.5	negative	Lumacron Red PGA	+5.9	negative
Brun Cibanone 2RMP	-4.3	negative	Noir Acramin FBB 01	negative	negative
Brun Cibanone BR MD liq. 40%	-6.6	negative	Noir Indanthren G sfx	negative	negative
Brun Indanthren HRR sfx	negative	negative	Olive Cibanone 2R MD	+2.4	negative
Chromafix Black GR	negative	negative	Orange Imperon K-G	negative	negative
Chromafix Tyrqoise G 150%	negative	negative	Orange Minerprint 3RL	-10.7	negative
Cibanon, Türkis P-GR	negative	negative	Ostacelová Cerven E-LB 180	negative	negative
Dianix gelb SE-5G	negative	negative	Procion Blau H-ERD	negative	negative
Erionyl Red A-2BF	negative	negative	Remazol Black N-150	negative	negative
Evercion Blue H-EGN 125%	negative	negative	Rouge Imperon K-B	+9.0	negative
Evercion Blue H-ERD	negative	negative	Rouge Terasil P3G	-77.7	negative
Evercion Navy Blue H-ER	+>132	negative	Saturnová MODR L4G 300	negative	negative
Evercion Red H-E3B	negative	negative	Saturnové Bordo LB 140	negative	negative
Evercion Red H-E7B	negative	negative	Saturnová SED LCG	negative	negative
Evercion Yellow ESL	negative	negative	Sirius Grau K-CGL	-6.0	negative
Evercion Yellow H-E4G	negative	negative	Sirius Orange K-FCN	negative	negative
Evercion Yellow H-E4R	negative	negative	Terasil Blue 3RL-02 150%	negative	negative
Foron Brillant Red E-2BL 200	negative	negative	Turquoise Cibacrone P-GR Liq. 50%	+2.6	negative
Helizarin Gris BT conc. 96	negative	negative	Vert Otan Cibanone 323 IR-01 liq	negative	negative
Imcosol Grau 4G 200%	negative	negative	Violet Cibacrone P-2R liq 33%	negative	negative
Jaune or Cibanone RK MPATE	negative	negative	Violet Imperon K-B	negative	negative
Lanasol Red 6G	negative	-5.8			

TA98-: *S. typhimurium* strain TA98 without metabolic activation; TA98+: *S. typhimurium* strain TA98 with metabolic activation.

TA100-: *S. typhimurium* strain TA100 without metabolic activation; TA100+: *S. typhimurium* strain TA100 with metabolic activation.

Table 5. Dose-response results for the dye products tested positively in the bacterial reverse mutation assay

Sample	Conc. (µg/plate)	IR			
		TA98		TA100	
		without S9	with S9	without S9	with S9
Bemaplex schwarz C-2B	0.5	0.6	0.8	0.9	1.0
	5	1.9	1.4	0.9	0.9
	50	15.2	4.8	1.1	1.0
	500	43.4	25.3	2.3	2.0
	5000	111.3	59.0	6.4	4.6
PC *z		24.0	7.3	4.2	4.7
Bleu terasil 3R-02	0.5	1.1	1.1	1.0	1.0
	5	1.0	1.5	0.9	1.1
	50	3.0	4.9	1.0	1.1
	500	10.4	17.5	1.2	1.5
	5000	35.5	29.7	2.1	2.4
PC *		14.2	10.5	2.5	5.8
Brun Cibanone 2RMP	0.5	1.0	nd	1.2	nd
	5	0.9	nd	1.1	nd
	50	0.8	nd	1.2	nd
	500	1.5	nd	1.5	nd
	5000	4.3	nd	2.0	nd
PC *		17.2	nd	4.3	nd
Brun Cibanone BR MD liq. 40%	0.5	0.9	0.7	1.0	0.8
	5	0.9	0.7	1.2	0.8
	50	1.3	0.8	1.1	0.9
	500	2.4	1.1	1.2	1.0
	5000	6.6	2.9	1.4	1.1
PC *		18.2	5.0	3.3	4.1
Evericon Navy Blue H-ER	0.5	1.0	0.9	0.8	1.0
	5	0.9	1.2	0.8	0.9
	50	4.7	17.9	2.4	6.1
	500	31.2	>132	11.2	>37
	5000	67.4	>132	33.4	>37
PC *		15.3	8.3	3.2	3.9
Lanasol Red 6G	0.5	0.8	0.7	1.0	0.8
	5	0.7	1.0	0.8	0.8
	50	0.7	0.8	0.9	0.8
	500	1.0	0.8	1.3	0.9
	5000	5.5	2.1	5.8	3.4
PC *		14.1	25.7	4.5	3.2
Lanasol Rot B	0.5	0.8	1.5	0.9	0.9
	5	0.6	1.1	0.9	1.0
	50	0.7	1.0	1.1	1.0
	500	0.9	0.9	1.1	1.1
	5000	1.7	1.2	3.6	2.8
PC *		15.4	7.8	4.2	3.5
Rouge Terasil P3G	0.5	1.0	nd	1.1	nd
	5	1.1	nd	1.0	nd

	50	3.3	nd	1.2	nd
	500	15.1	nd	1.3	nd
	5000	77.7	nd	2.5	nd
PC *		17.2	nd	4.3	nd
Lumacron Black SEF 300%	0.5	nd	0.9	nd	nd
	5	nd	1.0	nd	nd
	50	nd	7.3	nd	nd
	500	nd	41.8	nd	nd
	5000	nd	33.8	nd	nd
PC *		nd	nd	nd	nd
Lumacron Red PGA	0.5	nd	0.9	nd	nd
	5	nd	0.9	nd	nd
	50	nd	2.0	nd	nd
	500	nd	5.9	nd	nd
	5000	nd	4.7	nd	nd
PC *		nd	nd	nd	nd
Olive Cibanone 2R MD	0.5	1.5	1.2	0.9	0.9
	5	1.1	1.0	0.9	1.0
	50	1.4	1.3	0.9	1.0
	500	1.5	2.4	1.0	1.1
	5000	1.5	0.8	1.2	1.4
PC *		23.4	12.5	3.0	5.2
Orange Minerprint 3RL	0.5	0.7	0.9	0.9	0.9
	5	0.9	0.9	0.9	0.8
	50	1.6	1.0	1.0	1.1
	500	5.6	1.1	1.1	1.1
	5000	10.7	4.2	1.2	1.1
PC *		17.0	2.2	2.7	5.0
Rouge Imperon K-B	0.5	0.8	1.0	0.9	0.9
	5	0.8	0.9	0.8	0.8
	50	0.9	0.9	0.8	0.9
	500	1.2	1.2	0.9	1.1
	5000	2.5	9.0	0.7	1.7
PC *		15.7	5.8	5.3	4.1
Sirius Grau K-CGL	0.5	0.7	1.1	0.9	0.9
	5	0.9	1.1	1.0	0.8
	50	1.1	1.0	1.0	0.9
	500	3.3	1.1	0.9	1.1
	5000	6.0	2.4	0.9	1.0
PC *		8.9	7.2	3.7	4.9
Turquoise Cibacrone P-GR Liq. 50 %	0.5	0.8	1.0	0.9	1.0
	5	0.8	1.1	0.9	1.0
	50	0.7	1.0	0.9	1.0
	500	0.9	1.0	1.0	0.9
	5000	1.8	2.6	0.9	1.0
PC *		14.2	10.5	2.5	5.8

PC: Positive Control (TA98: Nitrofluorene 1.5 µg/plate; TA98+: 2-Aminoathracene 2.0 µg/plate; TA100: Sodiumazide 0.5 µg/plate; TA100+: 2-Aminoanthracene 2.0 µg/plate); IR: Induction Rate (number of revertants sample/number of revertants control).

Table 6 List of dye products tested in the mouse lymphoma assay (MLA) and the highest induction rates obtained are given

Dye Product Name	without S9	with S9
Astrazon Blue BG 200% 01	positive IR 7.4 with 40 μg ml^{-1}	not tested
Astrazon Blue FGRL 200%	positive IR 2.2 with 50 μg ml^{-1}	not tested
Bemaplex Black C-2B	positive IR 4.1 with 313 μg ml^{-1}	not tested
Bleu Terasil 3R-02	positive IR 15.2 with 2,500 μg ml^{-1}	not tested
Brun Cibanone BR MD liq. 40%	negative	negative
Erionyl Bordeaux A-5B	negative	positive IR 9.5 with 625 μg ml^{-1}
Olive Cibanone 2R MD	negative	negative IR 2.0 with 5,000 μg ml^{-1}
Rouge Imperon K-B	contradictory IR 2.3 with 1,581 μg ml^{-1}	negative
Turquoise Cibacrone PGR liq. 50%	negative	positive IR 3.0 with 5,000 μg ml^{-1}

EPA has not classified *o*-anisidine for carcinogenicity. The International Agency for Research on Cancer [112] has classified *o*-anisidine as a Group 2B, possible human carcinogen.

8.3.2.2. Polycyclic Amines

Several polycyclic arylamines have carcinogenic potential. It is, however, important to note that (even slight) molecular modifications can influence solubility, bioavailability, and metabolism, and the mutagenic and carcinogenic potential of molecules.

The dicyclic arylamine 2-naphthylamine (Figure 8) has demonstrated carcinogenicity in several species, including humans. On the other hand, 1-naphthylamine has not revealed carcinogenic potential in experimentation, but the process for its production can generate 2-naphthylamine and other possibly carcinogenic aromatic amines. 2-naphthylamine is activated in the liver but quickly deactivated by conjugation to glucuronic acid. In the bladder, glucuronidase re-activates it by deconjugation, which leads to the development of bladder cancer [113].

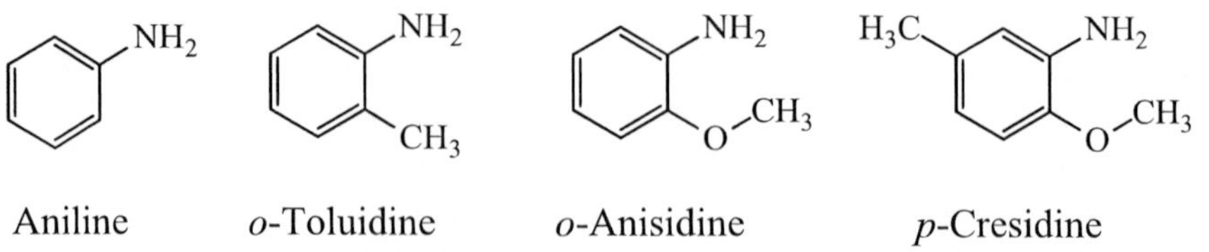

Aniline   *o*-Toluidine   *o*-Anisidine   *p*-Cresidine

Figure 7. Molecular structures of aniline derivatives.

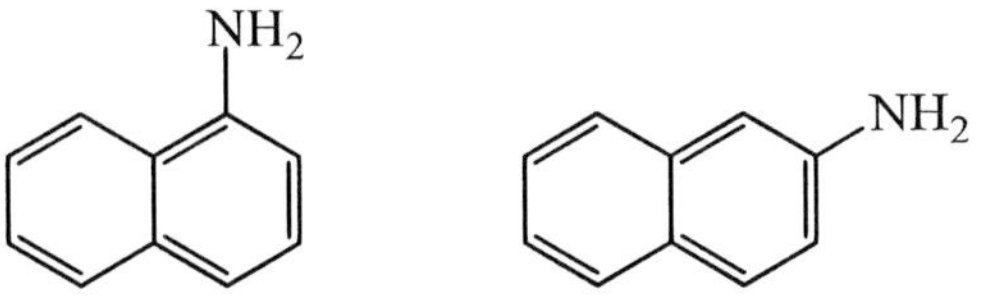

NH₂

1-Naphthylamine   2-Naphthylamine

Figure 8. Molecular structures of naphthylamines.

The biphenyl series comprises molecules with two phenyl rings joined by a carbon-to-carbon bond and an exocyclic amino group. This aromatic amine is a component in the production of dyes. The prototype is 4-aminobiphenyl (xenylamine) and one of the most known is 4,4`-diamino-diphenyl (benzidine) (Figure 9). Case reports and follow-up studies of workers provide evidence that occupational exposure to benzidine is strongly associated with an increased risk of bladder cancer and pancreatic cancer [111, 114]. Metabolized benzidine from dyes known to be carcinogens based on the releasing of free benzidine in humans and in all experimental animal species studied [115-119] as well as benzidine exposure from exposure to benzidine-based dyes is equivalent to exposure to equimolar doses of benzidine [117]. In animals, when administered in the diet or by intraperitoneal injections, benzidine induces urinary bladder carcinomas, mammary carcinoma, and hepatocellular carcinomas. Benzidine derivatives like 3,3`-dimethylbenzidine and 3,3`-dimethoxybenzidine (o-dianisidine) (Figure 10), are used as dyes or intermediates for dyestuffs or pigments (e.g., Trypan Blue, Acid Red 14, and Direct Blue 1, 8, 15, 76, 98, 218, and Pigment Orange 16), coatings, plastics, or in chemical studies. They are currently suspect carcinogens. Carcinogenicity studies in animals have showed induction of several neoplasms and carcinomas (intestine, lung, mammary, liver, and skin). No adequate studies have been reported in humans. Dyes metabolized into such amines are also reasonably anticipated to be human carcinogens. The evidence that dyes metabolized to benzidine are human carcinogens is supported by studies showing that all benzidine-based dyes tested cause cancer in experimental animals [16, 120]. Direct black 38 administered in diet or drinking water caused malignant liver and mammary-gland tumors in mice and malignant liver, colon, and bladder tumors in rats. Direct blue 6 administered in the diet for 13 weeks caused malignant liver tumors in rats but not in mice. In a similar study, direct brown 95 caused neoplastic nodules in the liver and one malignant liver tumor in rats after 13 weeks.

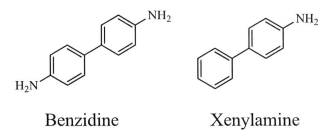

Benzidine   Xenylamine

Figure 9. Structures of Benzidine and Xenylamine.

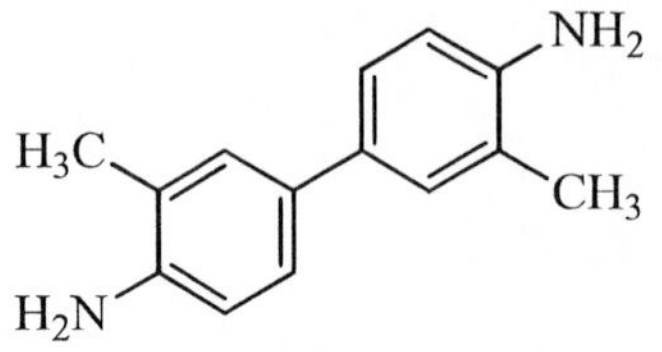

3,3'-Dimethylbenzidine 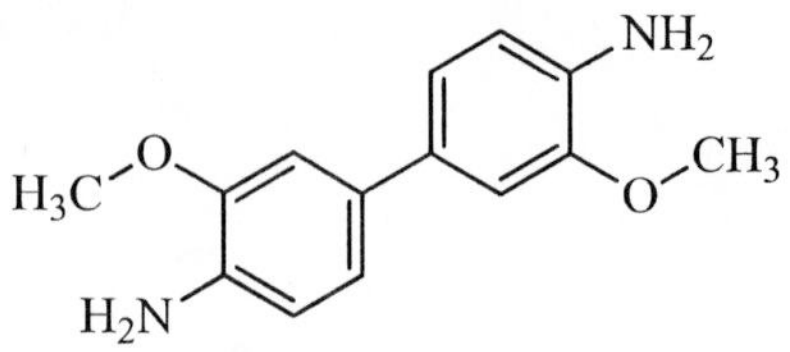   3,3'-Dimethoxybenzidine

Figure 10. Structures of 3,3'-Dimethylbenzidine and 3,3'-Dimethoxybenzidine.

8.3.3. Azo Compounds

Azo dyes are widely used in the food, pharmaceutical, cosmetic, textile, and leather industry. They are synthetic compounds characterized by one (mono-azo) or several intramolecular –N=N– bonds. Azo dyes, if they are systemically absorbed, can be metabolized by the way of azoreductases of intestinal microflora by liver cells and skin surface bacteria. This metabolism leads to aromatic amines that can be hazardous. In the 1930s, some azo derivatives like 4-dimethyl aminoazobenzene (Butter Yellow, CI Solvent Yellow 2, CI 11020) and o-aminoazotoluene were experimentally found to be directly carcinogenic to liver and bladder after feeding. Other complex azo dyes like Direct Black 38 or Direct Blue 6 (Figure 11) release the aromatic amine benzidine.

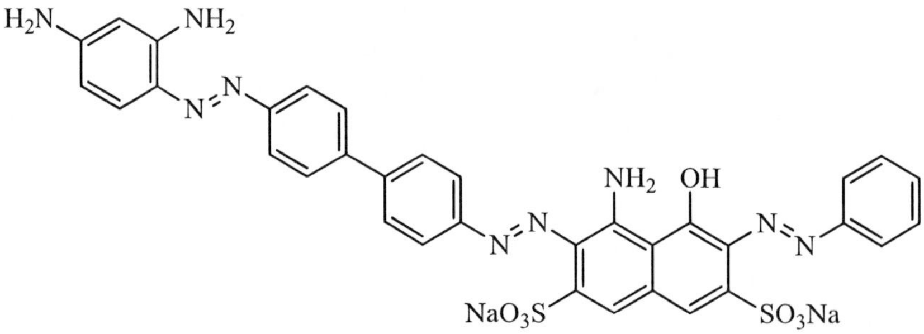

Direct Black 38

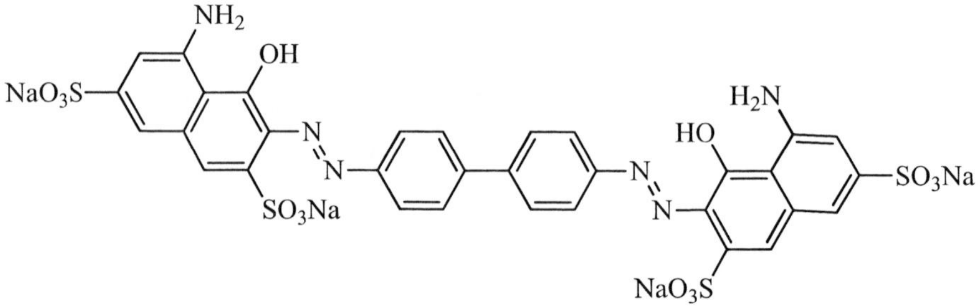

Direct Blue 6

Figure 11. Structure of Direct Black 38 and Direct Blue 6 (notice the benzidine precursor at the center of the molecules).

8.3.3.1. Anthraquinone Derivatives

2-Aminoanthraquinone (CAS 117-79-3) (Figure 12) is used as an intermediate in the industrial synthesis of anthraquinone dyes: Vat Blue 4, 6, 12, and 24, and Pigment Blue 22. It is a carcinogen in animals, inducing hepatocellular carcinomas and lymphomas. 1-Amino-2-methylanthraquinone (CAS 82-28-0) is used as a dye and a dye intermediate, for example, for Solvent Blue 13 and Acid Blue 47. It is a liver and kidney carcinogen in animals. Disperse Blue 1, used for semipermanent hair colorations and for coloring fabrics and plastics, induced urinary bladder carcinomas and sarcomas in rats. They are reasonably anticipated to be human carcinogens.

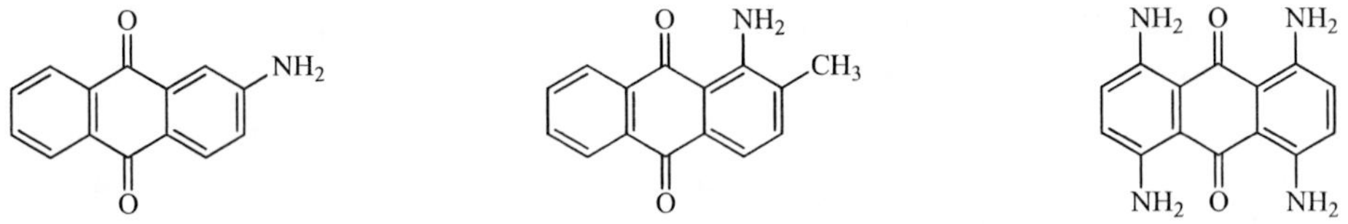

| 2-Aminoanthraquinone | 1-Amino-2-methylanthraquinone | Disperse Blue 1 |

Figure 12. Structures of 2-Aminoanthraquinone, 1-Amino-2-methylanthraquinone, and Disperse Blue 1.

8.3.3.2. Other Compounds Magenta and Basic Red 9 (CAS 569-61-9)

A common constituent of Magenta, have been used to dye textile fibers, to prepare printing inks, and in biological stains. In workers engaged in the manufacture of Magenta, there was a marked excess of cancer of the urinary bladder. It is possible that the workers were also exposed to *o*-toluidine. CI Basic Red 9 (Figure 13) was, however, an inducer of hepatocellular carcinoma in mice and rats after oral administration, and induced local sarcomas after subcutaneous administration.

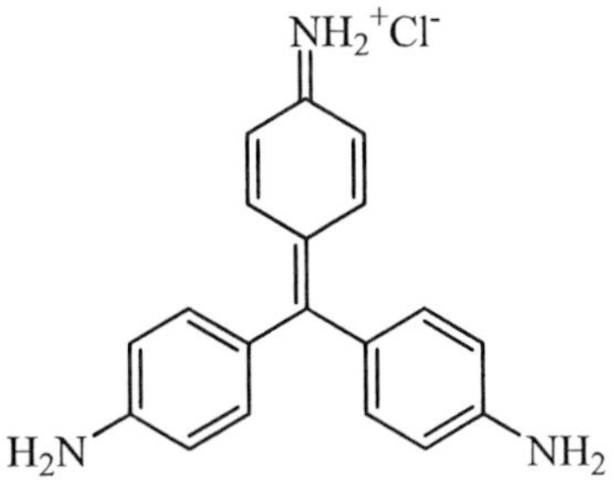

Figure 13. Structure of Basic Red 9 mono-hydrochloride.

9. DEVELOPMENT OF ENVIRONMENTALLY SAFE TEXTILE AUXILIARIES

The enormous hurdles of developing and applying bioremediation technologies in the area of biodegradation of xenobiotic compounds are not only due to the lack of organisms that harbor appropriate catabolic pathways. More importantly the complexity of mixtures of pollutants is generally found in practice limits applicability. In spite of enormous research efforts to overcome these constraints up to now the success in bioremediation is limited to rather simple structures and mixtures of pollutants. Therefore, pollution prevention at the source based on alternative ways of chemical production and more importantly on the design of safer chemicals should be applied already during the conceptual and developmental stage of new chemical substances. This 'Benign by design' chemistry must focus primarily on compounds which have been identified as priority pollutants of soil and groundwater. Therefore, the development of new biodegradable commodity chemicals will be discussed. It will be confined on potential substitutes of textile auxiliaries, which in the past have proven highly persistent. In fact there is a need for new environmentally benign chemicals to replace old ones which exhibited high persistence or toxic potential. Some of these are shown in Figure 14. Some initiatives were taken to derive general rules to predict biodegradability of a new compound to be synthesized. These can be summarized under the generic term Quantitative Structure Activity Relationship (QSAR). The aim is to use descriptors that influence biodegradability and describe the chemical and physical properties of a new substance. Prediction of biodegradability would avoid expensive and time consuming degradation tests or even futile chemical syntheses. Therefore, particularly in the US, ecological data for new chemicals are supplemented with data from QSAR modeling systems to provide an improved risk assessment [121]. The problem with these QSAR systems is that the modeling is based on rather small sections of the whole variety of the interactions between organisms, organic pollutant and the environment.

Therefore, the following strategy for the development of environmentally benign textile auxiliaries has been proposed

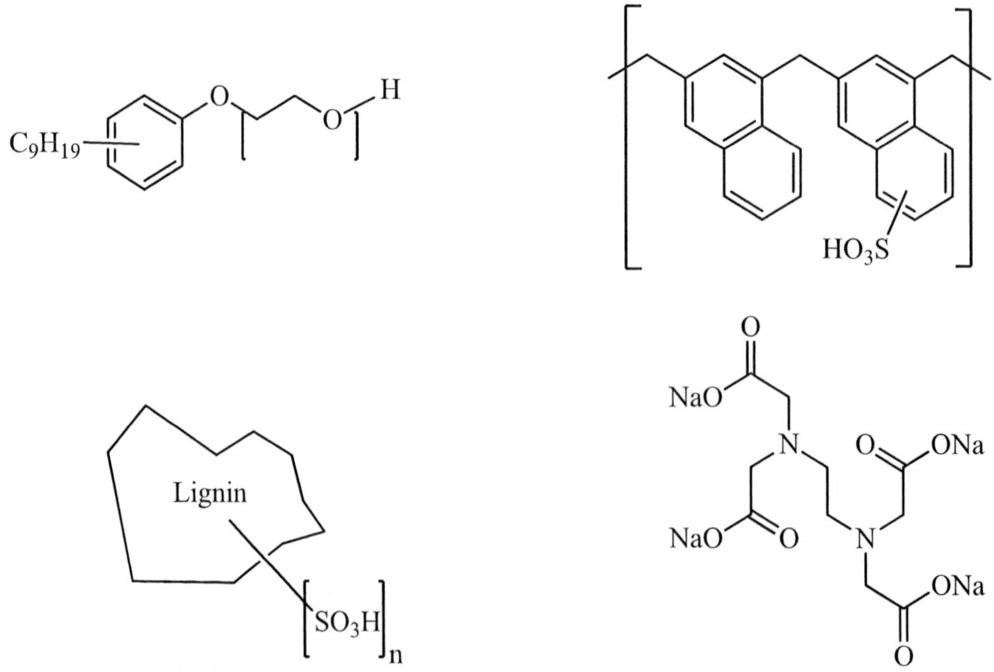

Figure 14. Examples of recalcitrant textile auxiliaries.

i. On the basis of known natural compounds structural analogs should be identified which resemble chemical structures or functional elements of target compounds that appear to be indispensable for technical performance.

ii. Readily available building blocks have to be selected and combined through hydrolysable links such as ester, amide or acetal bonds. These biologically weak links would guarantee that the new product can be cleaved by ubiquitously present exohydrolases of microorganisms. Thus even high molecular weight or highly polar synthetic compounds can be expected to be assimilated and completely mineralized.

iii. After optimizing the technical performance final biodegradability of a new compound has to be verified in standardized test systems.

10. CONCLUSION

Synthetic dyes released into the environment cause considerable water and soil pollution because they may be toxic, carcinogenic, mutagenic, and clastogenic to living organisms. Over the last two decades, awareness and concern about the environmental and health hazards of synthetic dyes is increasing in the global community. In order to minimize future environmental impact by xenobiotics it may be more economic to develop new synthetic compounds that fit in the naturally existing catabolic potential of the microorganisms. In future this approach may replace pipe technologies with microorganisms adapted to the chemicals. The development of new textile auxiliaries, this benign by design strategy implies the use of natural or close to natural building blocks and their combination through biologically weak links like ester, amide or acetyl bonds. In order to satisfy the requirements on the technical performance and (eco) toxicological safeness of the new chemical an intense dialogue between chemists, toxicologist and microbiologists is necessary.

REFERENCES

[1] Lauro, G. J., & Francis, F. J. (1999). Natural food colorants: science and technology, *Proceedings of a symposium.Institute of Food Technologists*, 336.

[2] Delgado-Vargas, F., Jimenez, A. R., & Parades-Lopez, O. (2000). Natural pigments: carotenoids, anthocyanins, and betalains - characteristics, biosynthesis, processing, and stability. *Critical Reviews in Food Science and Nutrition*, 40: 193-195.

[3] Hancock, M. (1997). *Potential for colourants from plant sources in England and Wales.* 1997, ST0106. Arable Crops & Horticulture Division, Mary Hancock, Adas Boxworth Boxworth, Cambridge Cb2 8nn.

[4] Slater, K. (2005). *Environmental impact of textiles: Production, processes and protection.* Cambridge, UK: Woodhead Publishing Ltd.

[5] Pierce, J. (1994). Color in textile effluents - the origins of the problem. *Journal of Society Dyers and Colour*, 110: 131-134.

[6] Pearce, C.I., Lloyd, J.R., & Guthrie, J.T. (2003). The removal of colour from textile wastewater using whole bacterial cells: a review. *Dyes and Pigments*, 58: 179-196

[7]　Øllgaard, H., Frost, L., Galster, J., & Hansen, O. C. (1999). *Survey of azo-colorants in Denmark: Consumption, use, health and environmental aspects*. Danish Technological Institute, Environment, Ministry of Environment and Energy, Danish Environmental Protection Agency, Denmark.

[8]　Vandevivere, P.C., Bianchi, R., & Verstraete, W. (1998). Treatment and reuse of wastewater from the textile wet-processing industry: Review of emerging technologies. *Journal of Chemical Technology and Biotechnolgy*, 72(4): 289- 302.

[9]　Lyon, H.O. (2002). Dye purity and dye standardization for biological staining. *Biotechenic and Histochemistry Journal,* 77: 57-80.

[10]　Paprocki, A., dos Santos, H.S., Hammerschitt, M.E., Pires, M., Azevedo, C.M.N. (2010). Ozonation of azo dye acid black 1 under the suppression effect by chloride ion. *Journal of the Brazilian Chemical Society,* 21(3): 452-460.

[11]　Zhang, F.F., Yediler, A., Liang, X.M., & Kettrup, A. (2004). Effects of dye additives on the ozonation process and oxidation by-products: a comparative study using hydrolyzed C.I. Reactive Red 120. *Dyes and Pigments*, 60(1): 1-7.

[12]　Rajagopalan, S. (1990). Water pollution problem in Textile Industry and Control, in: *Pollution Management in Industries,* Trivedy, R.K. (Ed.), Environmental Pollution, Karad, India pp 21-45.

[13]　Mathur, N., Bhatnagar, P., & Bakre, P. (2005). Assessing mutagenicity of textile dyes from pali (Rajasthan) using Ames bioassay. *Applied Ecology and Environmental Research*, 4(1): 111-118.

[14]　Neppolian, B., Sakthivel, S., Arbindo, B., Palanichamy, M., & Murugesan, V. (1999). Degradation of textile dye by solar light using TiO2 and ZnO photocatalyst. *Journal of Environmental Science and health,* A 34(9): 1829-1838.

[15]　Suzuki, T., Timofei, S., Kurunczi, L., Dietze, U., & Schuurmann, G. (2001). Correlation of aerobic biodegradability of sulfonated azo dyes with the chemical structure. *Chemosphere*, 45: 1-9.

[16]　IARC, International Agency for Research on Cancer (1982). Some Industrial Chemicals and Dyestuffs. *IARC Monographs on the Evaluation of Carcinogenic Risk of Chemicals to Humans*, vol. 29. Lyon, France: 416 pp.

[17]　Robens, J.F., Dill, G.S., Ward, J.M., Joiner, J.R., Griesemer R.A., & Douglas, J.F. (1980): Thirteen-week subchronic toxicity studies of Direct Blue 6, Direct Black 38 and Direct Brown 95 dyes. *Toxicology and Applied Pharmacology*, 54: 431-442.

[18]　Robinson T., McMullan, G., Marchant R., & Nigam, P. (2001). Remediation of dyes in textile effluent: a critical review on current treatment technologies with a proposed alternative. *Bioresource Technology*, 77: 247-255.

[19]　Rai, H.S., Bhattacharyya, M.S., Singh, J., Bansal, T.K., Vats, P., & Banerjee, U.C. (2005). Removal of dyes from the effluents of textile and dyestuff manufacturing industry: A review of emerging techniques with reference to biological treatment. *Critical Reviews in Environmental Science and Technology*, 35(3): 219-238.

[20]　Banat, I.M., Nigam, P., Singh, D., & Marchant, R. (1996). Microbial decolorization of textile-dye-containing effluents: A review. *Bioresource Technology*, 58(3): 217-227.

[21]　Tan N.C.G., Borger, A., Slender, P., Svitelskaya, A.V., Lettinga, G., & Field, J.A. (2000). Degradation of azo dye Mordant Yellow 10 in a sequential anaerobic and bioaugmented aerobic bioreactor. *Water Science and Technology*, 42(5-6): 337-344.

[22] Tan, N.C.G. (2001). Integrated and Sequential Anaerobic/Aerobic Biodegradation of Azo Dyes. Ph.D. Dissertation, Wageningen University, Wageningen, Netherlands.

[23] Anjaneyulu, Y., Chary N.S., & Raj, S.S. (2005). Decolourization of industrial effluents - Available methods and emerging technologies-A review. *Review of Environmental Science and Biotechnology*, 4(4): 245-273.

[24] Carliell, C.M., Barclay, S.J., Naidoo, N., Bucley, C.A., Mulholland D.A., & Senior, E. (1995). Microbial decolourisation of a reactive azo dye under anaerobic conditions. *SA Water,* 21(1): 61-69.

[25] Van der Zee, F.P. (2002). Anaerobic Azo Dyes Reduction. Ph.D. Dissertation, Wageningen University, Wageningen, Netherlands.

[26] Greeves, A.J., Churchey, J.H., Hutching, M.G., Philips D.A.S., & Taylor, J.A. (2001). A chemometric approach to understanding the bioelimination of anionic, water-soluble dyes by biomass using empirical and semi-empirical molecular descriptors. *Water Research*, 35(5): 1225-1239.

[27] Chung, K.T., & Cerniglia, C.E. (1992). Mutagenicity of azo dyes: structure-activity relationships. *Mutation Research*, 277(3): 201-220.

[28] Jung, R., Steinle D., & Anliker, R. (1992). A compilation of genotoxicity and carcinogenicity data on aromatic aminosulphonic acids. *Food Chemistry and Toxicology*, 30(7): 635-660.

[29] Oh, S.W., Kang, M.N., Cho, M.W., & Lee, M.W. (1997). Detection of carcinogenic amines from dyestuff or dyed substrates. *Dyes Pigments*, 33(2): 119-135.

[30] Slokar, Y.M., & Marechal, A.M. (1998). Methods of decoloration of textile wastewater. *Dyes Pigments*, 37(4): 335-356.

[31] Rieger, P.-G., Meier, H.M., Gerle, M., Vogt, U., Groth, T., & Kanckmuss, H.J. (2002). Xenobiotics in the environment: Present and future strategies to obviate the problem of biological persistence. *Journal of Biotechnology*, 94(1): 101-123.

[32] Pinheiro, H.M., Thomas, O., & Touraud, E. (2004). Aromatic amines from azo dye reduction: status review with emphasis on direct UV spectrophotometric detection in textile industry wastewaters. *Dyes and Pigments*, 61: 121-139.

[33] Hao, O.J., Kim H., & Chiang, P.C. (1999). Decolorization of wastewater. *Critical Reviews in Environmental Science and Technology*, 30(4): 449-505.

[34] Bhaskar, M., Gnanamani, A., Ganeshjeevan, R.J., Chandrasekar, R., Sadulla, S., & Radhakrishnan, G. (2003). Analyses of carcinogenic aromatic amines released from harmful azo colorants by *Streptomyces* sp. SS07. *Journal of Chromatography A*, 1018: 117-123.

[35] Hu, T.L., &Wu, S.C. (2001). Assessment of the effect of azo dye RP2B on the growth of a nitrogen fixing cyanobacterium *Anabaena* sp. *Bioresource Technology*, 77: 93-95.

[36] Razo-Flores, E., Donlon, B., Lettinga, G., & Field, J.A. (1997). Biotransformation and biodegradation of N substituted aromatics in methanogenic granular sludge. *FEMS Microbiology Review*, 20: 525-538.

[37] Chung, K.T., Fulk, G.E., & Andrews, A.W. (1981). Mutagenicity testing of some commonly used dyes. *Applied Environmental Microbiology*, 42: 641-648.

[38] Chung, K.T. (1983). The significance of azo reduction in the mutagenesis and carcinogenesis of azo dyes. *Mutation Research*, 114: 269-281.

[39] Rafii, F., Moore, J.D., Ruseler-van Embden, J.G.H., & Cerniglia, C.E. (1995). Bacterial reduction of azo dyes used in foods, drugs and cosmetics. *Microecology and Therapy*, 25: 147-156.

[40] Benigni, R., Giuliani, A., Franke, R., & Gruska, A. (2000). Quantitative structure-activity relationships of mutagenic and carcinogenic aromatic amines. *Chemical Review*, 100: 3697-3714.

[41] Color Index (2001). *The Society of Dyers and colourists*, American Association of Textile Chemists and Colourists, vol. 1-5, 3th Ef., Bradford

[42] Christie, R. (2001). *Colour Chemistry*. The Royal Society of Chemistry, Cambridge, United Kingdom.

[43] Chu, H.C., & Chen., K.M. (2002). Reuse of activated sludge biomass: removal of basic dyes from wastewater by biomass. *Process Biochemistry*. 37: 595-600.

[44] Fu, Y., & Viraraghavan, T. (2002). Removal of Congo red from an aqueous solution by fungus *Aspergillus niger*. *Advances in Environmental Resource*, 7: 239-247.

[45] Klemola K. (2008). *Textile Toxicity: Cytotoxicity and Spermatozoa Motility Inhibition Resulting from Reactive Dyes and Dyed Fabrics*. Kuopio University Publication Company, Faculty of Natural and Environmental Sciences, 241: 1-67.

[46] Collier, B.J., & Tortora, P.G. (2001). *Understanding Textiles,* (6th ed.). Upper Saddle River, NJ: Prentice Hall.

[47] Duran, N., & Esposito, E. (2000). Potential applications of oxidative enzymes and phenoloxidase-like compounds in wastewater and soil treatment: A review. *Applied Catalysis B*, 28: 83-99.

[48] Mester, T., & Tien, M. (2000). Oxidative mechanism of ligninolytic enzymes involved in the degradation of environmental pollutants. *International Biodeterioration and Biodegradation,* 46: 51-59.

[49] Gohl, E.P.G., & Vilensky, L.D. (1983). *Textile science*. Longman Cheshire Pty Ltd, Melbourne, 218 p.

[50] Knackmus, H.J. (1996). Basic knowledge and perspectives of bioelimination of xenobiotic compounds. *Journal of Biotechnology*, 51: 287-295.

[51] Harrison, RJ (2000). Chemicals and gases. *Primary Care*, 27(4): 917-982.

[52] Ebert, S., Fischer, P., & Knackmuss, H.J. (2001). Converging catabolism of 2,4,6-trinitrophenol (Picric acid) and 2,4-dinitrophenol by nocardioides simplex FJ2-1A. *Biodegradation*, 12: 367-376.

[53] Russ, R., Walters, D.M., Knackmuss, H.J., & Rouviere, P.E. (2000). Identification of genes involved in picric acid and 2,4-dinitrophenol degradation by mRNA differential display. In: Spain, J.C., Hughes, J.B., Knackmuss, H.J. (Eds.), *Biodegradation of Nitroaromatic Compounds and Explosives*. CRC Press, Boca Raton, FL, pp. 127–143.

[54] Hitz, H.R., Huber, W., & Reed, R.H. (1978). The absorption of dyes on activated sludge. *Journal of the Society of Dyers and Colorists,* 94: 71-76.

[55] Seesuriyachan, P., Takenaka, S., & Kuntiya, A. (2007). Metabolism of azo dyes by Lactobacillus casei TISTR 1500 and effects of various factors on decolorization. *Water Research*, 41: 985-992

[56] Blumel, S., Knackmuss, H.J., & Stolz, A. (2002). Molecular cloning and characterization of the gene coding for the aerobic azoreductase from Xenophilus azovorans KF46F. *Applied and Environmental Microbiology*, 68: 3948-3955.

[57] Chen, H., Wang, R.F., & Cerriglia, C.E. (2004). Molecular cloning, overexpression, purification, and characterization of an aerobic FMN-dependent azoreductase from Enterococcus faecalis. *Protein Expression and Purification*, 34: 302-310.

[58] Nigam, P., Banat, I.M., Singh, D., & Marchant, R. (1996). Microbial process for the ecolorization of textile effluent containing azo, diazo and reactive dyes. *Process Biochemistry*, 31: 435-442

[59] Zimmermann, T., Kulla, H., & Leisinger, T. (1982). Properties of purified orange II-azoreductase, the en zyme initiating azo dye degradation by Pseudomonas KF46. *European Journal of Biochemistry*, 129: 197-203.

[60] Walker, R., & Ryan, A.J. (1971). Some molecular parameters influencing rate of reduction of azo compounds by intestinal microflora. *Xenobiotica*, 4-5: 483-486.

[61] Beydilli, M.I., Pavlostathis, S.G., & Tincher, W.C. (2000). Biological decolorization of the azo dye Reactive Red 2 under various oxidation-reduction conditions. *Water Environmental Research*, 72: 698-705.

[62] Kulla, H.G. (1981). Biodegradation of synthetic organic colorants. In: Leisinger, T., Hutter, R., Cook, A.M., & Nuesch, J. (eds) *Microbial degradation of xenobiotics and recalcitrant compounds*: FEMS Symposium no. 12. London, UK: compounds: FEMS Symposium no. 12. London, UK: X Swiss Society of Microbiology on behalf of the Federation of European Microbiological Societies

[63] Martins, M.A., Cardoso, M.H., Queiroz, M.J., Ramalho, M.T., & Campos, A.M.O. (1999). Biodegradation of azo dyes by the yeast Candida zeylanoides in batch aerated cultures. *Chemosphere*, 38: 2455–2460.

[64] Feinman, S.E., & Doyle, E.A. (1988). Sensitization to dyes in textiles and other consumer products. *Journal of Toxicology. Cutaneous and Ocular Toxicology*, 7: 195-222.

[65] Hornstein, O.P. (1989). Textilverträglichkeit bei Hautkrankheiten. *Melliand Textilberichte*, 3: 222-227.

[66] Maurer, S., Seubert, A., Seubert, S., & Fuchs, T.H. (1995). Kontaktallergie auf Textilien. *Dermatosen*, 43: 63-68.

[67] Hatch, K.L. (1984a). Chemicals and textiles Part I: Dermatological problems related to fiber content and dyes. *Textile Research Journal*, 54: 664-682

[68] Hatch, K.L. (1984b): Chemical and textiles Part II: Dermatological problems related to finishes. *Textile Research Journal*, 54: 721-732

[69] Hatch, K.L., & Maibach, H.I. (1985). Textile dye dermatits. *Journal of American Academy of Dermatology*, 12: 1079-1092.

[70] Hatch, K.L. and Maibach, H.I. (1995). Textile dye dermatitis. *Journal of American Academy of Dermatology*, 32: 631-639.

[71] Hatch, K.L. (1995). Textile dye contact allergens. In: *Current Problems in Dermatology*. Surber, Elsner, Bircher (eds) 22: 8-16.

[72] Platzek, Th. (1995). *How serious is the actual health hazard caused by textiles?* Melliand Sonderdruck, Berlin, Germany.

[73] Seidenari, S., Mamzini, B.M., Schiavi, M.E., & Motolese, A. (1995). Prevalence of contact allergy to non-disperse azo dyes for natural fibres: A study in 1814 consecutive patients. *Contact Dermatitis*, 133: 118-122.

[74] King, B.R., Long, G.M., & Sheldon, H.K. (1997). *Practical environmental bioremediation: The field guide*. Boca Raton: CRC.

[75] Fernando, T., & Aust, S.D. (1994). Biodegradation of toxic chemicals by white rot fungi, In G. R. Chaudhry (Ed.), *Biological degradation and bioremediation of toxic chemicals,* (pp. 386-402), London: Chapman and Hall.

[76] Preussman, R. (1984): In *N-Nitroso compounds: Occurrence, biological effects and relevance to human cancer* (Eds: O' Neill, von Borstel, Miller, Long and Bartsch) IARC Science Publication (57) International agency for research on cancer, Lyon, 3-15.

[77] Pointing, S.B. (2001): Feasibility of bioremediation by whiterot fungi. *Applied Microbiology and Biotechnology*, 57: 20-33.

[78] Moutchen, J. (1985). *Introduction to genetic toxicology*, Wiley New York, 184.

[79] Hulka, B.S., Wilcosky, T.C., & Griffith, J.D. (1990). *Biological markers in epidemiology*, New York, Oxford University Press.

[80] Singh, H. (2006). Fungal decolorization and degradation of dyes. In H. Singh (Ed.), *Mycoremediation: Fungal bioremediation* (pp. 420–483). Hoboken: Wiley.

[81] Ragunathan, I., Palanikumar, L., Panneerselvam, N. (2007) Cytogenetic studies on the peripheral lymphocytes of occupationally exposed textile dye industry workers. *Medicine and Biology*, 14(1): 43-46.

[82] Lambert, B., Lindblad, A., Holmberg, K., & Francesconi, D. (1982). The use of sister chromatid exchanges to monitor human populations for exposure to toxicologically harmful agents. In Wolff. S (Ed) *Sister chromatid exchange*, Wiley-Interscience, NewYork, 149-182.

[83] Nagaya, T., Ishikawa, N., & Hata, H. (1989). Sister chromatid exchanges in lymphocytes of workers exposed to trichloroethylene. *Mutation Research*, 22: 279−282.

[84] Carbonell, E., Puig, M., Xamena, N., Creus, A., & Marcos, R. (1990). Sister chromatid exchange in lymphocytes of agricultural workers exposed to pesticides. *Mutagenesis*, 5: 403-405.

[85] Haley, T.J. (1975). Benzidine revisited: A review of the literature and its congeners. *Clinical Toxicology*, 8: 13-42.

[86] Mirkova, E.T., & Lalchev, S.G. (1990). The genetic toxicity of the human carcinogens benzidine and benzidine based dyes: chromosomal analysis in exposed workers. *Progress in clinical and biological research*, 340: 397-405.

[87] Nony, C.R., & Bowmann, M.C. (1980). Trace analysis of potentially carcinogenic metabolites of an azo dye and pigment in hamster and human urine as determined by two chromatographic procedures. *Journal of Chromatographic Science,* 18: 64.

[88] Nirmalarani, J., & Janardhanan, K. (1988). Effect of south India viscose factory effluent on seed germination, seedling growth and chloroplast pigment content in five varieties of maize (Zea mays). *Madras Agriculture Journal*, 75: 41.

[89] Pelclova, D., Rossner, P., & Pickova, J. (1990). Chromosme aberrations in rotogravure printing plant workers. *Mutation Research*, 245: 299-303.

[90] Wollin, K.M., & Gorlitz B.D. (2004). Comparisons of genotoxicity of textile dye stuffs in Salmonella mutagenicity assay in vitro micronucleus assay and single cell gel, comet assay. *Journal of Environmental Pathology, Toxicology and Oncology*, 23: 267-278.

[91] Rajaguru, P., Kalpana, R., Hema, A., Suba, S., Baskarasethupathi, B., Kumar, P.A., & Kalaiselvi, K. (2001). Genotoxicity of some sulphur dyes on tadpoles (Rana

hexadactyla) measured using the comet assay. *Environmental and Molecular Mutagenesis*, 38: 316-322.

[92] Jäger, I., Hafner, C., & Schneider, K. (2004). Mutagenicity of different textile dye products in *Salmonella typhimurium* and mouse lymphoma cells. *Mutation Research*, 561: 35-44.

[93] Knasmüller, S., Zöhrer, E., Kainzbauer, E., Kienzl, H., Colbert, B., Lamprecht, G., & Schulte-Hermann R. (1993). Detection of mutagenic activity in textiles with Salmonella typhimurium. *Mutation Research*, 299: 45-53.

[94] Yassini, S., Popp, W., Müller, G., & Norpoth, K. (1997). Aromatische Amine in Textilien Ein kanzerogenes Risiko für den Menschen? In: E. Borsch-Galetke & F. Struwe (eds.), 37. *Jahrestagung der Deutschen Gesellschaft für Arbeitsmedizin und Umweltmedizin* e.V., Wiesbaden, 12.-15. Druckerei Rindt, Fulda, pp. 441-443.

[95] Jäger, I. & Meyer, G. (1995). Toxizität und Mutagenität von Abwässern der Textilproduktion, Forschungsbericht 102 06 519 des Bundesministeriums für Umwelt, Naturschutz und Reaktorsicherheit im Auftrag des Umweltbundesamtes, UBA-FB 95-045, 7/95.

[96] Jäger, I. (1999). Biologische Wirkungstests als Instrument zum ökologischen Stoffstrommanagement. *Melliand Textilberichte*, 7-8: 634-637.

[97] OSPAR Commission (2002). Survey of Genotoxicity Test Methods for the Evaluation of Waste Water within Whole Effluent Assessment, ISBN 1-904426-02-6 (www.ospar.org).

[98] Garner, R.C., & Nutman, C.A. (1977). Testing of some azo dyes and their reduction products for mutagenicity using Salmonella typhimurium TA 1538. *Mutation Research*, 44: 9-19.

[99] Venturini, S., & Tamaro, M. (1979). Mutagencity of anthraquinone and azo dyes in Ames Salmonella typhimurium test. *Mutation Research*, 68: 307-312.

[100] Prival, M.J., Bell, S.J., Mitchell, V.D., & Vaughan V.L. (1984). Mutagenicity of benzidine and benzidine congener dyes and selected monoazo dyes in a modified Salmonella assay. *Mutation Research*, 136: 33-47.

[101] Joachim, F., Burrell, A., & Andersen, J. (1985). Mutagenicity of azo dyes in the salmonella/microsome assay using in vitro and in vivo activation. *Mutation Research*, 156: 131-138.

[102] Harrington-Brock, K., Parker, L., Doerr, C., Cimino, M.C., & Moore, M.M. (1991). Analysis of the genotoxicity of anthraquinone dyes in the mouse lymphoma assay. *Mutagenesis*, 6: 35-46.

[103] Kaur, A., Sandhu, R.S., & Grover, I.S. (1993). Screening of azo dyes for mutagenicity with Ames/Salmonella assay. *Environmental Molecular Mutagenesis*, 22: 188-190.

[104] Janik-Spiechowicz, E., Dziubaltowska, E., & Wyszynska, K. (1997). Mutagenic and genotoxic activity detected by Ames, micronucleus and SCE tests under the influence of samples of dyes manufactured in Poland. *International Journal of Occupational Medicine and Environmental Health*, 10: 55-65.

[105] Sharma, M.K., and Sobti, R.C. (2000). Rec effect of certain textile dyes in Bacillus subtilis. *Mutation Research*, 465: 27-38.

[106] Friedman, M., Diamond, M.J., & MacGregor. J.T. (1980). Mutagenicity of textile dyes. *Environmental and Science Technology*, 14: 1145-1146.

[107] MacGregor, J.T., Diamond, M.J., Mazzeno, L.W., & Friedman, M. (1980). Mutagenicity tests of fabric-finishing agents in *Salmonella typhimurium*: Fiber-reactive wool dyes and cotton flame retardants. *Environmental Mutagenesis*, 2: 405-418.

[108] Schneider, K., Hafner, C., & Jäger, I. (2004). Mutagenicity of textile dye products, *Journal of Applied Toxicology*, 24: 83-91.

[109] U.S. Environmental Protection Agency (1997). *Health Effects Assessment Summary Tables*. FY 1997 Update. Office of Research and Development, Office of Emergency and Remedial Response, Washington, DC. EPA/540/R-97-036.

[110] U.S. Department of Health and Human Services (DHHS) (1998). *The 8th Report on Carcinogens. 1998 Summary*. Public Health Service, National Toxicology Program.

[111] US Department of Health and Human Services (2010): Public Health Service, National Toxicology Program. Report on Carcinogens, Eleventh Edition. 2005. Accessed at http://ntp.niehs.nih.gov/ntp/roc/toc11.html on May 13, 2010.

[112] International Agency for Research on Cancer (IARC) (1987). *IARC Monographs on the Evaluation of the Carcinogenic Risk of Chemicals to Humans*. Supplement 7. World Health Organization, Lyon.

[113] Steinberg, G.D. & Kim, H.L. (2007). Bladder Cancer. eMedicine.com. URL: http://www.emedicine.com/MED/topic2344.htm. Accessed on: May 9, 2007.

[114] International Agency for Research on Cancer (IARC) (2010): Monograph: Overall Evaluations of Carcinogenicity to Humans. 2009. Accessed at http://monographs. iarc.fr/ENG/Classification/crthall.php on May 13, 2010.

[115] Rinde, E., & W. Troll. (1975). Metabolic reduction of benzidine azo dyes to benzidine in the rhesus monkey. *Journal of the National Cancer Institute,* 55(1): 181-2.

[116] Lowry, L.K., Tolos, W.P., Boeniger, M.F., Nony, C.R., & Bowman, M.C. (1980). Chemical monitoring of urine from workers potentially exposed to benzidine-derived azo dyes. *Toxicology Letter*, 7(1): 29-36.

[117] Lynn, R. K., Donielson, D.W., Ilias, A.M., Kennish, J.M., Wong, K. & Matthews, H.B. (1980). Metabolism of bisazobiphenyl dyes derived from benzidine, 3,3′-dimethylbenzidine or 3,3′-dimethoxybenzidine to carcinogenic aromatic amines in the dog and rat. *Toxicology and Applied Pharmacology,* 56(2): 248-58.

[118] Martin, C.N., & Kennelly, J.C. (1985). Metabolism, mutagenicity, and DNA binding of biphenyl-based azodyes. *Drug Metabolism Review*, 16(1-2): 89-117.

[119] Nony, C.R., Bowman, M.C., Cairns, T., Lowry, L.K., & Tolos, W.P. (1980). Metabolism studies of an azo dye and pigment in the hamster based on analysis of the urine for potentially carcinogenic aromatic amine metabolites. *Journal of Analytical Toxicology,* 4(3): 132-40.

[120] NCI, (1978). *Thirteen-Week Subchronic Toxicity Studies of Direct Blue 6, Direct Black 38 and Direct Brown 95 Dyes*. Techincal Report Series No 108. DHEW (NIH) Publication No. 78-1358. Bethesda, MD: National Institute of Health.

[121] Zeemann, M. (1995). *EPAs Framework for Ecological Effects Assessment. US Congress*. Office of Technology Assessment. Screening and Testing Chemicals in Commerce, Washington, DC.

In: Non-Conventional Textile Waste Water Treatment
Editor: Ahmed El Nemr

ISBN: 978-1-62100-079-2
© 2012 Nova Science Publishers, Inc.

Chapter 3

BIOREMEDIATION OF TEXTILE DYES WASTEWATER BY MARINE MICROORGANISMS

Nermeen Ahmed El-Sersy[*]

Marine Microbiology Department, Environmental Division, National Institute of Oceanography and Fisheries, Kayet Bey, El Anfoushy, Alexandria, Egypt

ABSTRACT

Today the earth is facing a major environmental problem in the form of pollution increases. Production of textile involves bleaching, mercerizing, carbonizing and dying, etc. Polyvinyl, alcohol, gums, cellulose materials, dyes and other substances are present in textile effluent. The expanding use of synthetic dyes such as triphenyl-methane, azo, and anthraquinone is alarming, given that the release of colored compounds into the environment may cause substantial ecological damage, not only due to their color, which may have an impact on photosynthesis in aquatic plants, but also because many dyes and their breakdown products may be toxic and/or mutagenic to living organisms. Biological decolorization and degradation is an environmentally friendly, cost-competitive alternative to chemical decomposition and do not produce large quantities of sludge.

This chapter reports how several marine microorganisms have the ability to bio-decolorize and treat wastewater containing textile dyes.

DEDICATION

All the words are not enough to express my feelings or to show my passion. He's my great father to whom I dedicate this honorable work. He was working as a textile engineer, got his M.Sc. from North Carolina, USA. Finally, He was a chairman of a textile company for twelve years. He is the one who always dreamed of me achieving the highest remarkable scientific degrees. Although he passed away but his dream didn't. It kept inspiring me and

---

[*] E-mail: nermeen_ok@yahoo.co.uk.

encouraging me all the way. Now, if he is somewhere watching me or hearing what I say, it's one thing I want to tell him…,

"I did this work for you, for you I started and for you I kept on going, May this makes you happy as you always made us".

1. TEXTILE DYES

1.1. Synthetic Dyes

Dyes are recalcitrant molecules difficult to be degraded biologically. Synthetic dyes have a wide application in the food, pharmaceutical, textile, leather, cosmetics and paper industries due to their ease of production, fastness and variety in color compared to natural dyes [1, 2]. Dyes have been used increasingly in textile and dyeing industries because of their ease and cost effectiveness in synthesis, firmness, and variety in color compared with natural dyes [3].

Based on the chemical structure of the chromophoric group, synthetic dyes are classified as azo dyes, anthraquinone dyes, triarylmethane dyes, etc. Synthetic dyes, which often contain substitutions such as azo, nitro and sulfo groups, are recalcitrant to bacterial degradation [4].

1.1.1. Azo Dyes

Azo dyes are a group of compounds characterized by the presence of one or more azo groups (-N=N-) in association with one or more aromatic systems [5]. Their color is attributed to the azo-bond, the associate auxochromes and a system of conjugated double bonds (aromatic hydrocarbons). Among many classes of synthetic dyes used in industry, azo dyes are the largest class both in number and amount produced because of their ease of synthesis and versatility [6]. Azo dyes being the most versatile, with the great variety of colors play a prominent role in a wide variety of applications [7].

Many studies indicated that most of the azo dyes are toxic [8] and carcinogenic [9]. Azo dye compounds have been found to be linked to bladder cancer in humans and to hepato-carcinoma and nuclear ancomalies in intestinal epithelial cells in mice [10]. Thus, a number of azo dyes have been classified as carcinogenic [11].

Several amino-substituted azo dyes including 4- phenylazoaniline and N-methyl and N,N-dimethyl 4-phenyl- azoanilines are mutagenic and carcinogenic [12]. The carcinogenecity of an azo dye may be due to the dye itself or to aryl amine derivatives generated during the reductive biotransformation of the azo linkage [13]. In a recent study [14].the azo dye RP2B was found to inhibit the growth of the nitrogen fixing cyanobacterium, *Anabaena* sp.

1.1.2. Release of Azo Dyes into the Environment

Azo dyes are released into the environment as effluent from two major sources, the textile and dyestuff industries. Although dyeing and finishing technologies in textile industries have significantly progressed, fibers only absorb 90% of the dyes with some reminder still released in the wastewater [15]. Because their environmental fate remains largely unknown, they are considered to represent an appreciable hazard [16].

Color produced by synthetic dyes is one of the most obvious indicators of water pollution and the discharge of highly colored synthetic dye effluents can be damaging to the receiving water bodies [17], and may affect their transparency and aesthetics [18]. Over 7×10^5 tons of these dyes are produced annually worldwide [13]. It is estimated that 10 to 15% of the dye is lost in the effluent during process [19]. With the increasing use of a wide variety of dyes, pollution by dye-wastewater is becoming increasingly alarming [20].

1.2. Removal of Dyes

The removal of color from textile industry and dyestuff manufacturing industry wastewater represents a major environmental concern. Dye compounds are difficult to treat because of their ability to resist microbial attack [21]. They are not readily degradable and are typically not removed from water by conventional wastewater treatment systems. The removal of dyes from aqueous effluent has received considerable attention within environmental research.

The elimination of colored effluents in wastewater treatment systems is mainly based on physical or chemical procedures [17]. Although these methods are effective, they suffer from such shortcomings as high cost, formation of hazardous by-products and high-energy requirements [22]. Biological techniques which are cheaper and easier to operate have become the focus in recent studies of dyes degradation and decolorization. El-Sersy, [23] studied the kinetics of B. pumilus N40 cells to catalyze azo dye degradation was investigated during growth on basal medium amended with 100 mg l^{-1} of MR. The results showed that, MR had some inhibitory effect on N40 growth rate. The reduction catalytic function of the cells paralleled biomass formation. After removal of 94% of the color, a sharp increase in the growth rate was observed which indicated MR detoxification.

Among the techniques suitable for decolorization or decomposition of organic pollutants are the following:

i.   Aerobic Activated Sludge or Rotating Biofilm Reactors [24];
ii.   Aerobic-Anaerobic Packed-Bed Reactors [25];
iii. Aerobic-Anaerobic Fluidized-Bed Reactors [26];
iv.   Aerobic-Anaerobic Sequential Batch or Continuous Flow Reactors [27]; and,
v.   Anaerobic Batch Reactors [28].

The effectiveness of microbial treatment of color effluents in wastewater systems depends on the survival, adaptability and activity of the selected microorganisms [22]. In a previous study [29] the combined biological and chemical treatment of highly concentrated reactive azo dye-containing residual dye house liquors with recalcitrant compounds in a sequencing batch reactor was published.

1.2.1. Microbial Degradation of Azo Dyes

Because azo dyes exhibit great structural variety, they are not uniformly susceptible to microbial attack. In addition to azo linkage, the aromatic moieties and sulfonated substitutions contribute to the dyes' resistance to biological or chemical degradations [14]. Thus, the reactive azo dyes have been identified as the most problematic compounds in textile effluents as they are difficult to remove due to their high solubility and low exhaustion [30].

In the natural environment, azo dye can be degraded or transformed by variety of microorganisms, including aerobic and anaerobic bacteria and fungi [31].The biotransformation of azo dyes by environmental microorganisms has been reviewed [32].

A few studies have been conducted to identify bacterial species that are capable of reducing and degrading azo dyes [22]. Most biological degradation of azo dyes is carried out by anaerobic bacteria [33]. Azo dyes degradation by bacteria under aerobic conditions has been also reported [34].

The ability to biodegrade azo dyes has been shown to exist in *Aeromonas Pseudomonas* [35], *Flavobacterium* [32] *Acetobacter liquefaciens* S-1 [36], *Klebsiella pneumoniae* RS-13 [3], *Bacillus sp.* [22], *Rhodococcus* [11], *Shigella* [36] and *Escherichia coli* NO$_3$ [37]. A characterization of dye degrading bacteria and their activity in biofilms has been published [38].

Bacterial degradation of azo dye is often initiated by an enzymatic biotransformation step that involves cleavage of azo bonds with the aid of azo-reductase utilizing NADH as the electron donor, Pandey & Upadhyay [2], used *Pseudomonas fluorescens* to degrade Direct Orange - 102 dye. The dye was subjected to degradation by the bacterium and its metabolic products were identified by UV, 1HNMR and IR spectrophotometry. The dye was first broken down into 3, 7- diamino- 4 hydroxy - naphthalene - 2 sulfonic acid sodium salt. This compound is further degraded into 7-amino -3, 4- dihydroxy - naphthalene- 2- sulfonic acid sodium salt or 3- amino-4-7- dihydroxynaphthalene -2 sulfonic acid sodim salt or 1,3,4,5,6,7,8 - heptahydroxy naphthalene - 2 – sulfonic acid sodium salt. These breakdown compounds were non - toxic in nature. Therefore, *Pseudomonas fluorescens* can be used for bioremediation of textile effluent containing Direct Orange-102 dye. Successful decolourisation and degradation of textile dyes was achieved by Aloius Togo [39] in a biosulphidogenic batch reactor using biodigester sludge from a local municipality waste treatment plant as a source of carbon and microflora that augmented a sulphate reducing bacteria (SRB) consortium. Orange II (O II) was decolourised by 95% within one day (24 h) producing 1-amino-2-naphthol and stoichiometric quantities of sulphanilic acid. The latter was degraded steadily (from _ 290 to 43 µM) over 20 days while 1-amino-2- naphthol disappeared from the reactor within two days. Other azo dyes, Reactive black 5 (RB 5),Reactive red 120 (RR 120), Remazol Brilliant violet 5R (RBV 5R), an anthraquinone dye Reactive blue 2 (RB 2) and an industrial azo dye mixture (Da Gama Textiles, King Williams Town, South Africa) were successfully degraded with the exception of Amido black 10B (AB 10B). The Orange II degrading cultures were freeze dried to investigate the feasibility of commercialising a powdered mixed starter culture for textile effluent bioremediation, but this decreased the dye degrading efficiency. Therefore bioremediation of textile effluent with sludge and SRB can concomitantly treat two wastes while providing a cheaper alternative of the carbon source.). The resulting aromatic amines are further degraded by multiple-step bioconversion occurring aerobically or anaerobically.

Streptomyces strains have been shown to degrade a group of dyes by oxidative mechanisms, probably involving the ligninolytic enzymatic system [40].

Although large number of publication on bacterial and fungal degradation of azo dyes, yeasts on the other hand, are remarkably absent from the literature on dye degradation. Trindade and Angelis [41] referred to azo dye removal by *Rhodotorulla* yeast, presumably by an adsorptive interaction with fully-grown cells. Luo and Liu [42] used a yeast strain, isolated from dye-contaminated soil, in the decolorization and degradation of Direct Orange S. In a recent study, Martins *et al* [43] reported the biodegradation of azo dyes by the yeast *Candida zeylanoides* in batch-aerated cultures.

Fungal species, such as *Phanerochaete chrysosporium*, utilize lignin peroxidase to degrade azo dyes under aerobic conditions [44]. A pure fungal culture has been used to develop bioprocess for mineralization of azo dyes [45]. However, the long growth cycle and moderate decolorization rate limit the performance of the fungal decolorization system [31]. Pratum *et al.* [46], evaluate eleven strains of white rot fungi on their ability to decolorize reactive blue 19 (RB19) and reactive blue 171 (RB171) dyes on agar plates. *Pleurotus sajor-caju* (Fr.) Sing., *Lentinus squarrosulus* Mont., and *Coprimus fimetarus* (L) Fr. showed high decolorization of both RB19 and RB 171. In submerged culture, maximum decolorization of 150 mg l^{-1} of RB19 and 25 mg l^{-1} of RB 171 by *Pleurotus sajor-caju* (Fr.) Sing was observed at 93.31 and 57.53%, respectively. Interestingly, *Pleurotus sajor-caju* (Fr.) Sing, one kind of edible mushroom, showed the ability to decolorize mixed reactive blue dyes at a concentration of 50 mg l^{-1} by 46.15% at a growth period of eleven days. In addition, *Pleurotus sajor-caju* (Fr.) Sing. produced a high level of extracellular lignin peroxidase (LiP) (222.79 ± 11.23 mU mg^{-1} of protein). LiP enzymes play an important role in the biodegradation of reactive dyes and LiP activity is induced by reactive dye. Fungal biomass *Pleurotus sajor-caju* (Fr.) Sing. had the ability to decolorize textile dyeing effluent by 58.42% under aerated conditions for five days after fungal cell mass inoculation. This finding suggests that *Pleurotus sajor-caju* (Fr.) Sing. has potential for application in the treatment of synthetic dyes in industrial wastewater.

In contrast, bacterial decolorization is normally faster, but it may require a mixed bacterial community to degrade azo dyes completely [38].

The most promising strategy seems to be a tandem anaerobic-aerobic treatment by an adapted bacterial consortium, as described by Haug *et al* [47], who achieved through this method, the complete mineralization of Mordant yellow 3. However, several combined anaerobic and aerobic microbial treatments have been suggested to enhance the degradation of textile dyes [15].

The majority of studies on decolorization of industrial effluents containing reactive dyes have been performed with fungi [48]. White rot fungi and specifically *Phanerochaeta chrysosporium* have been attracted attention [49]. Decolorization of textile dyes using *Geotrichum candidum* [50], *Aspergillus sojae* B10 [51] and *Trametes hirsuta* [52] has been reported.

Few studies reported the decolorization of industrial effluents containing dyes by bacteria and actinomycetes. Vitor and Corso, [53] studied microbial decolorization and biodegradation of the Direct Violet 51 azo dye by *Candida albicans* isolated from industrial effluents and study the metabolites formed after degradation. *C. albicans* was used in the removal of the dye in order to further biosorption and biodegradation at different pH values in aqueous solutions. A comparative study of biodegradation analysis was carried out using UV–vis and FTIR spectroscopy, which revealed significant changes in peak positions when compared to the dye spectrum. These changes in dye structure appeared after 72 h at pH 2.50; after 240 h at pH 4.50; and after 280 h at pH 6.50, indicating the different by-products formed during the biodegradation process. Hence, the yeast *C. albicans* was able to remove the color substance, demonstrating a potential enzymatic capacity to modify the chemical structure of pigments found in industrial effluents. Ola *et al.* [1], isolated *Bacillus cereus* from dye industrial waste, that is, effluent and soil samples was screened for its ability to decolorize two reactive azo dye cibacron black PSG and cibacron red P4B under aerobic conditions at pH 7 and incubated at 35°C over a five day period. Different carbon and nitrogen sources were used for the decolorization study. *B. cereus* was able to decolorize cibacron red P4B by (81%) using the combination of ammonium nitrate and sucrose, while it decolorizes cibacron black PSG by (75%) using yeast extract and lactose. Junnarkar *et al.* [54], collected samples from various effluent-contaminated soils in the vicinities of dyestuff manufacturing units of Ahmedabad, India, were studied for screening and isolation of organisms capable of decolorizing textile dyes. A novel bacterial consortium was selected on the basis of rapid decolorization of Direct Red 81 (DR 81), which was used as model dye. The bacterial consortium exhibited 90% decolorization ability within 35 h. Maximum rate of decolorization was observed when starch (0.6 g l^{-1}) and casein (0.9 g l^{-1}) were supplemented in the medium. Decolorization of DR 81 was monitored by high performance thin layer chromatography, which indicated that dye decolorization was due to its degradation into unidentified intermediates. The optimum dye-decolorizing activity of the culture was observed at pH 7.0 and incubation temperature of 37°C. Maximum dye-decolorizing efficiency was observed at 200 mg l^{-1} concentration of DR 81. The bacterial consortium had an ability to decolorize nine other structurally different azo dyes.

1.2.2. Biosorption of Dyes from Effluents

Studies on detoxification of azo dyes have been concentrated on total dye degradation and decolorization and a number of studies in this area have demonstrated promising results [55]. However, many of the studies involving submerged culture technology have been complicated by the dilute nature of the relevant effluents and the rate at which the dyes are degraded by microorganisms. As in the case with heavy metal-bearing effluents, dye-containing effluents are also complicated by the dilute nature of the relevant species. It has been therefore suggested that biosorptive processes circumvent this problem by concentrating the dye onto a solid phase [56].

Although many studies have described microbial degradation of textile dyestuffs and decolorization, very little work has been carried out on the biosorptive capacity of microbial biomass for these materials. Color removal by biological biosorption has been suggested [57].

Figure 1 Shows TEM micrographs of native and dye exposed cells of *B. subtilis* N10. Control cells (a) appeared normal with regular cell wall and no dense areas were observed. Cells exposed to the FB dye (b) showed an irregular wavy cell wall. No dense areas were noticed intracellularly. However, electron dense dark layers were observed throughout the cell wall referring to the adsorbsion and location of the dye on cell wall [23].

Walker & Weatherly [34] reported the biodegradation and biosorption of the acid anthraquinone dye Tectilon Blue (TB4R), by three strains of bacteria, namely, *Bacillus gordonae*, *Bacillus benzeororans* and *Pseudomonas putida*. Junnarkar *et al.* [54], studied the Decolorization of diazo dye Direct Red 81 by a novel bacterial consortium. El-Sersy [58], studied Bioremediation of Methylene blue by *Bacillus thuringiensis* 4G1 In this study *Bacillus thuringiensis* 4G1 was used to decolorize Methylene blue (MB). The decolorization process was optimized by using two sequential experimental designs. Eleven fermentation factors were screened using Plackett-Burman design. Among these factors, the most significant variables influencing MB decolorization were statistically elucidated for optimization and included $MgSO_4.7$ H_2O, glucose and $(NH_4)_2$ SO_4. The optimum concentrations of these variables were predicted by using a second order polynomial model fitted to the results obtained by applying the Box-Behnken design. A verification experiment performed under optimal conditions yielded 98.23% of the predicted decolorization % (100%) with an increase by a factor of 1.3 compared with the results obtained under basal conditions.

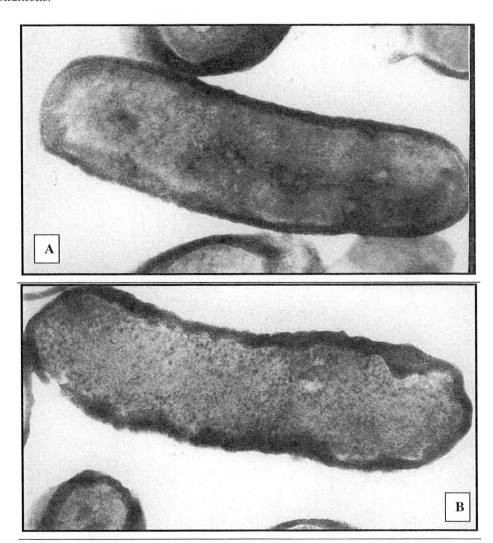

Figure 1. Transmission Electron Micrograph showing native control *B. subtilis* N10 cells (a), and dye exposed cells (b).

In a recent study, El-Sersy *et al.* [59], examined two different azo dyes known as acid fast red (AFR) and Congo red (CR) for their decolorization by five strains of actinomycetes (*Streptomyces globosus*, *Streptomyces alanosinicus*, *Streptomyces ruber*, *Streptomyces gancidicus*, and *Nocardiopsis aegyptia*) under shake and static conditions. *Streptomyces globosus* decolorized AFR by 81.6% under static condition while 70.2% dye removal was achieved under shake conditions. Application of Plackett-Burman statistical design revealed that the main factors that affected biosorption capacity were the starch concentration and the inoculum size. Under static conditions, increasing the inoculum size and decreasing starch concentration increased the biosorption % up to 1.14 fold with time reduction, while increasing both the inoculum size and starch concentration under shake conditions increased the biosorption % up to 1.09 fold only. A trial for the use of potato peel for more economic biomass production of *S. globous* was carried out and (2 g/50 ml) and dried potato peel had the optimum concentration for maximum biomass production (0.3 g/50 ml) which led to considerable biosorption capacity (89.4%).

1.3. Applications of Bacilli

The genus *Bacillus* comprises a heterogenous group of chemoorganotrophic, aerobic and rod-shaped microorganisms, including mesophilic and thermophilic species as well as acidophiles and alkalophiles. Figure 2 illustrates scanning electron micrograph of marine bacillus sp. [23].

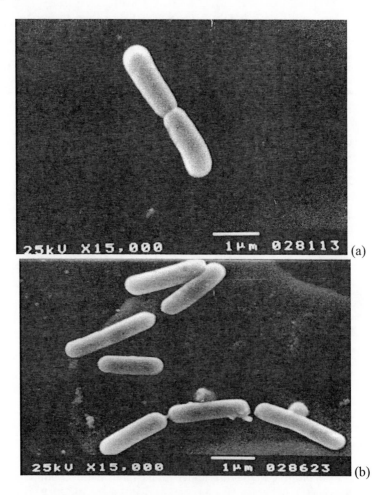

Figure 2. Scanning electron micrograph of (a) *B. pumilus* N40 and (b) *B. subtilis* N10. Bar =1 μm.

One of the main characteristics is the ability of its members to produce heat-resistant-endospores [60]. Figure 3 Illustrates transmission electron micrograph of spore structure of marine bacillus sp. [23].

Members of the genus *Bacillus* are generally grow easy to high cell density and do not require expensive growth factors. They are commercial sources of a number of enzymes [61,62].

The biodegradation of phenantherene, P-aminoazobenzene and methyl red by *Bacillus sp.* has been reported [63]. As well, the catabolism of amine borate by *Bacillus* sp. [64] has been published. Ghosh *et al.* [65] reported a novel approach in composting of cellulosic hospital solid wastes by *Bacillus sp.*, *Bacillus gordonae* and *B. Beneovorans* had a considerable role in the biodegradation and biosorption of the acid anthraquinon dye Tectilon blue [34]. Moreover, Nica *et al* [66] isolated a *Bacillus* species involved in the biodegradation of concrete in sewers.

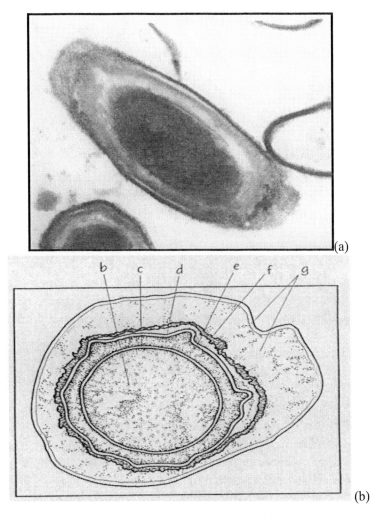

Figure 3. (a) Transmission electron micrographs of uranyl stained cells of *B. pumilus* N40 showing spore location, and (b) a diagram showing endospore structures. Spore core, b; Core wall, c; Cortex, d; Inner membrane, e; Outer membrane, f; Exosporium basal layer, g.

REFERENCES

[1] Ola, I.O., Akintokun, A.K., Akpan, I., Omomowo, I.O., & Areo, V.O. (2010). Aerobic decolourization of two reactive azo dyes under varying carbon and nitrogen source by *Bacillus cereus*. *African Journal of Biotechnology*. 9: 672-677.

[2] Pandey, B.V., & Upadhyay, R.S. (2010). *Pseudomonas fluorescens* can be used for bioremediation of textile effluent Direct Orange-102. *Tropical Ecology,* 51: 397-403.

[3] Wong, P.K., & Yuen, P.Y. (1996). Decolorization and biodegradation of Methyl Red by *Klebsiella pneumoniae* RS-13. *Water Research* 30: (7) 1736-1744.

[4] Shaul, G.M., Holdsworth, T.J., Dempsey, C.R., & Dostal, K.A. (1991). Fate of water soluble azo dyes in the activated sludge process. *Chemosphere* 22: 107-119.

[5] So, K.O. (1989). Decolorization and Biodegradation of Methyl Red by *Acetobacter liquefaciens*. Thesis, The Chinese University of Hong Kong, Hong Kong.

[6] Griffths, J. (1984). Developments in the light absorption properties of dyes-color and photochemical degradation reactions. In: Griffith J (Eds) *Developments in the Chemistry and Technology of Organic Dyes*. P. 1-30. Oxford: Society of Chemical Industry.

[7] Gordon, P.F., & Gregory, P. (1983). *Organic chemistry in colour.* Springer-Verlag, New York, 322.

[8] Holme, I. (1984). Ecological aspects of color chemistry. In Griffiths J (Ed). Developments in the Chemistry and Technology of Organic Dyes. Society of chemistry industry, Oxford, pp. 111-128.

[9] Chung, K.T., Fulk, G.E., & Andrews, A.W. (1981). Mutagenicity testing of some commonly used dyes. *Applied and Environmental Microbiology*. 42: 641-648.

[10] Percy, A.J., Moore, N., & Chipman, J.K. (1989). Formation of nuclear anomalies in rat intestine by benzidine and its biliary metabolites. *Toxicology* 57: 217-23.

[11] Heiss, G.S., Gowan, B., & Dabbs, E.R. (1992). Cloning of DNA from a *Rhodococcus* strain conferring the ability to decolorize sulfonated aze dyes. *FEMS Microbiology Letter* 99: 221-226.

[12] McCann, J., & Ames, B.N. (1975). Detection of carcinogens as mutagens in the Salmonella/microsome test. Assay of 300 chemicals: discussion. Proceeding National Academic Scince USA 73: 950-954.

[13] Spadaro, J.T., Gold, M.H., & Renganathan, V. (1992). Degradation of azo dyes by the lignin-degrading fungus *Phanerochaete chrysosporium. Applied and Environmental Microbiology*, 58: (8) 2397-2401.

[14] Hu, T.L., & Wu, S.C. (2001). Assessment of the effect of azo dye RP2B on the growth of nitrogen fixing cyanobacterium – *Anabaena* sp. *Bioresource Technology*, 77: 93-95.

[15] O'Neill, C., Lopez, A., Eateves, S., Hawkes, F., Hawkes, D.L., & Wilcox, S. (2000). Azo-dye degradation in an anaerobic-aerobic treatment system operating on simulated textile effluent. *Applied Biochemistry and Biotechnology*, 53:249-254.

[16] Weber, E. J., & Adams, R.L. (1995). Chemical and sediment mediated reduction of azo dye disperse blue 79. *Environmental Science Technology* 29: 1163-1170.

[17] Nawar, S.S., & Doma, H.S. (1989). Removal of dyes from effluents using low cost agricultural by-products. *Science Total Environment* 79: 271-279.

[18]   Banat, I.M., Nigam, P., McMullan, G., & Marchant, R. (1997). The isolation of thermophilic bacterial cultures capable of textile dyes decolorization. *Environmental International*, 23: (4) 547-551.

[19]   Vaidya, A.A., & Datye, K.V. (1982). Environmental pollution during chemical processing of synthetic fibers. *Colourage*, 14: 3-10.

[20]   Nigam, P., McMullan, G., Banat, I.M. & Marchant, R. (1996). Decolorization of effluent from the textile industry by a microbial consortium. *Biotechnology Letters*, 18: 117-120.

[21]   Mckay, G., Geundi, M.E.L., & Nassar, M.M. (1988). External mass transport processes during the adsorption of dyes onto bagasse pith. *Water Research*, 22: 1527-1533.

[22]   Sugiura, W., Miyashita, T., Yokoyama, T. & Arai, M. (1999). Isolation of Azo dye-Degrading microorganisms and their application to white discharge printing of fabric. *J. Bioscience Bioengineering*, 88: (5) 577-581.

[23]   El-Sersy, N.A. (2001). Microbial catabolism of some marine organic pollutants: the development of bioremediation system. PhD Thesis, Faculty of Science, Alexandria University.

[24]   Jiang, H., & Bishop, P.L. (1994). Aerobic biodegradation of azo dyes in biofilms. *Water Science Technology*, 29: 525-530.

[25]   Lin, S.H., & Liu, W.Y. (1994). Continuous treatment of textile water by ozonation and coagulation. *Journal Environmental Engineering*, 120: 437-446.

[26]   Seshadri, S., Bishop, P.L. & Agha, A.M. (1994). Anaerobic /aerobic treatment of selected azo dyes in wastewater. *Waste Management*, 14: 127-1 37.

[27]   Oxspring, D.A., McMullan, G., Smyth, W.F. & Marchant, R. (1996). Decolorization and metabolism of the reactive textile dye, Remazol-Black-B, by an immobilized microbial consortium. *Biotechnology Letters* 18: 527-530.

[28]   Carliell, C.M., Barclay, S.J., Naidoo, N., Buckley, C.A., Mulholland, D.A. & Senior, E. (1995). Microbial decolorization of a reactive azo dye under anaerobic conditions. *Water SA*, (Pretoria 21: 61-69)

[29]   Krull, R., Hemmi, M., Otto, P., & Hempel, D.C. (1998). Combined biological and chemical treatment of highly concentrated residual dye-house liquors. *Water Science Technology,* 38: (4-5) 339-346.

[30]   Carliell, C.M., Barclay, S.J., Naidoo, N., Buckley, C.A., Muholland , A., & Senior ,E. (1994). Anaerobic decolorization of reactive dyes in conventional sewage treatment processes. *Water SA*, 20: 341-344.

[31]   Banat, I.M., Nigam, P., Singh, D., & Marchant, R., (1996). Microbial decolorization of textile-dye-containing effluents. *Bioresource Technology*, 58: 2 17—227.

[32]   Chung, K.T., & Stevens, S.E., (1993). Degradation of azo dyes by environmental microorganism and helminths. *Environmental Toxicology Chemistry*, 12: 2121-2132.

[33]   Dudrow, S.F., Boardman, G.D., & Michelsen, D.L. (1996). In: Reife A & Freeman HS (Ed) Environmental Chemistry of Dyes and pigments. Chapter 5, John Wiley & Sons, New York.

[34]   Walker, G.M., & Weatherley, L.R. (2000). Biodegradation and biosorption of acid anthraquinone dye. *Environmental Pollution*, 108: 219-223.

[35]   Ogawa, T., & Yatome, C., (1990). Biodegradation of azo dyes in multistage rotating biological contactor immobilized by assimilating bacteria. *Bull. Environ. Contam. Toxicol.* 44: 561-566.

[36] Ghosh, D.K., Mandal, A., & Chaudhuri, J. (1992). Purification and partial characterization of two azoreductases from *Shigella dysenteriae* Type I. *FEMS Microbiology Letters,* 98: 229-234.

[37] Chang, J.S. & Kuo, T.S. (2000). Kinetics of bacterial decolorization of azo dye with *Escherichia coli* NO3. *Biores. Technology* 75: 107-111.

[38] Coughlin, M.F., Kinkle, B.K., Tepper, A., & Bishop, P.L. (1997). Characterization of aerobic azo dye-degrading bacteria and their activity in bioflims. *Water Science Technology*, 36: 215-220.

[39] Togo, C.A., Cecil, C.Z.M. & Christopher, G.W. (2008). Decolourisation and degradation of textile dyes using a sulphate reducing bacteria (SRB) − biodigester microflora co-culture. *African Journal of Biotechnology*, 7: (2), 114-121.

[40] Pasty-Grigsby, M.B., Paszczynski, A., Goszczynski, S., Crawford, D.L. & Crawford, R.L. (1992). Influence of aromatic substitution patterns on azo dye degradibility by *Streptomyces* sp. and *Phanerochaete chrysosporium. Applied Environmental Microbiology* 58: 3605-3613.

[41] Trindade, R.C. & Angelis, D.F. (1995). Removal of azo dyes by *Rhodotorula*: relationships with PH and substantivity index. 7th. International Symposium on Microbial Ecology, Santos, S. Paulo, Brazil.

[42] Luo, Z., & Liu, M. (1996). Degradation and decoloration of Direct Orange-S waste water by yeast S-36. *Zhongguo Jishui Paishui*, 12: 12-13.

[43] Martins, M.A.M., Cardoso, M.H., Queiroz, M.J., Ramalho, M.T., & Campos, A.M.O. (1999). Biodegradation of azo dyes by the yeast *Candida zeylanoides* in batch aerated cultures.*Chemosphere,* 38: (11) 2455-2460.

[44] Bakshi, D. K., Gupta, K.G., & Sharma, P. (1999). Enhanced biodecolorization of synthetic textile dye effluent by *Phanerochaete chrysosporium* under improved culture conditions. *World Journal Microbiology Biotechnol*ogy, 15: 507-509.

[45] Palma, C., Moreira, M.T., Mielgo, I., Feijoo, G., & Lema, J.M. (1999). Use of a fungal bioreactor as a pretreatment or post-treatment step for continuous decolorization of dyes. *Water Research Technology*, 40 (8): 131-136.

[46] Pratum, C., Jaruwan, W., Chumlong A., & Benjaphorn, P. (2011). Decolorization of reactive dyes and textile dyeing effluent by *Pleurotus Sajor- caju.* International *Journal of Integrative Biology.* 11: (1) 52-57.

[47] Haug, W., Schmidt, A., Nortemann, B., Hempel, D.C., Stolz, A., & Knackmuss, H.J. (1991). Mineralization of the sulfonated azo dye Mordant Yellow 3 by a 6-aminonaphthalene-2-sulfonate degrading bacterial consortium. *Applied Environmental Microbiology*, 57:3144-3149.

[48] Nigam, P., Banat, I.M., Oxspring, D., Marchant, R., Singh, D., & Smyth, W.F. (1995). A new facultative anaerobic filamentous fungus capable of growth on recalcitrant textile dyes as sole carbon source. *Microbios.* 84: 171-185.

[49] Swamy, J., & Ramsay, J.A. (1999). The evaluation of white rot fungi in the decolorization of textile dyes. *Enzyme Microbial Technology*, 24: 130-137.

[50] Kim, S.J., Ishikawa, K., Hirai, M., & Shoda, M. (1995). Characterization of a newly isolated fungus, *Geotrichum candidum* Dec1, which decolorizes various dyes. *Journal Fermentation Bioengineering*, 79: 601-607.

[51] Ryu, B.H., & Weon, Y.D. (1992). Decolorization of azodyes by *Aspergillus sojae* B10. *Journal Microbiology Biotechnology* 2: 215-219.

[52] Abadulla, E., Tzanov, T., Costa, S., Robra, K., Cavaco-Paulo, A., & Gubitz, G.M. (2000). Decolorization and detoxification of textile dyes with a laccase from *Trametes hirsuta*. *Applied Environmental Microbiology*, 66(8): 3357-3362.

[53] Vivian, V., & Carlos, R. C. (2008). Decolorization of textile dye by Candida albicans isolated from industrial effluents. *J Indian Microbiology Biotechnology*, 35:1353–1357.

[54] Junnarkar, N.D., Srinivas, M.N.S., & Bhatt, D. M. (2006). Decolorization of diazo dye Direct Red 81 by a novel bacterial consortium. *World Journal of Microbiology & Biotechnology*, 22: 163–168.

[55] Nigam, P., Banat, I.M., Singh, D., & Marchant, R. (1996 a). Microbial process for the decolorization of textile effluent containing azo, diazo and reactive dyes. *Process Biochemistry*, 31: (5) 435-442.

[56] Bustard, M., McMullan, G., & Mchale, A. P. (1998). Biosorption of textile dyes by biomass derived from *Kluyveromyces marxianus* IMB3. *Bioprocess Engineering*, 19: 427-430.

[57] Banks, C.J., & Parkinson, M.E. (1992). The mechanism and application of fungal biosorption to color removal from raw water. *Journal Chemistry Tech. Biotechnology*, 54: 192-196.

[58] El-Sersy, N. A., (2007). Bioremediation of Methylene blue by *Bacillus thuringiensis* 4G1: Application of statistical designs and surface plots for optimization. *Biotechnology*, 6: No. 1, 34-39.

[59] El-Sersy, N. A., Abou-Elela, G. M., Hassan, S.W., & Abd-Elnaby, H. (2011). Bioremediation of Acid Fast Red dye by *Streptomyces globosus* under static and shacked conditions. *African Journal of Biotechnology*, 10(17): 3467-3474.

[60] Jenkinson, H.F., Kay, D., & Mandelstam, J. (1980). Temporal dissociation of late events in *Bacillus subtilis* sporulation from expression of genes that determine them. *Journal Bacteriology*, 141: 793-805.

[61] El-Helow, E.R., & El-Ahawany, A.M. (1999). Lichenase production by catabolite repression-resistant *Bacillus subtilis* mutants: Optimization and formulation of an agro-industrial by- product medium. *Enzyme Microbiol Technology*, 24: 325-331.

[62] EL-Helow, E.R., Abdel-Fattah, R.Y., Ghanem, M.K., & Mohamed, A.E. (2000). Application of the response Surface methodology for optimizing the activity of an *apr E* - driven gene expression system in *Bacillus subtilis*. *Applied Microbiology and Biotechnology*, 54: 515-520.

[63] Doddamani, H.P., & Ninnekar, H.Z. (2000). Biodegradation of phenantherene by a *Bacillus* species. *Current Microbiology*, 41:11-14.

[64] Sherburn, R.E., & Large, P.J. (1999). Amine borate catabolism by bacteria isolated from contaminated metal – working fluids. *Journal Applied Microbiology*, 87: 668-675.

[65] Ghosh, S., Kapadnis, B.P. & Singh, N.B. (2000). Composting of cellulosic hospital solid waste: a potentially novel approach. *International Biodeterioration and Biodegradation*, 45: 89-92.

[66] Nica, D., Davis, J.L., Kirby, L, Zuo, G., & Roberts, D.J. (2000). Isolation and characterization of microorganisms involved in the biodegradation of concrete in sewers. *International Biodeterioration and Biodegradation*, 46: 61-68.

Chapter 4

BIOTECHNOLOGICAL APPLICATIONS OF FUNGI IN TEXTILE WASTEWATER BIOREMEDIATION

Ola M. Gomaa[*], Reham Fathey, Hussein Abd El Kareem

Radiation Microbiology Department, National Center for Radiation Research and
Technology, Atomic Energy Authority, 3 Ahmad El Zomor st. Nasr City, Cairo, Egypt

ABSTRACT

The textile industry is considered one of the major worldwide industries which produce vast amount of effluent, its major threat lies in the presence of synthetic recalcitrant dyes. While conventional chemical and physical decolorizing techniques were used effectively for a long time, yet biological treatment or "bioremediation" has recently gained an interest due to its cheap and effective decolorization of a wide range of dyes. The process of bioremediation in general could be either a spontaneous process or a controlled process in which the microorganism could act to remove a specific contaminant. Fungi and their enzymes are thought to be one of the preferred tools in bioremediation. Biosorption by fungal cell wall is also an evolving attractive option as it presents a very inexpensive biosorbent. The biosorptive capacity of fungi could be manipulated through pre-treatment with alkalis or acids to increase the available surface area for biosorption. The introduction of genetic engineering in environmental biotechnology may provide an insight to methods for up scaling the textile waste water treatment. The study of the fate of the degraded dyes is also required to ensure the safety of their direct disposal to sewer systems after decolorization. More research is required to elucidate fungal applications in bioremediation since there are deeper implications to fungal cell-dye interaction than just mere color removal of dye molecules.

1. INTRODUCTION

Although the concentration of dyes in waste water is usually lower than the other chemicals present, they often receive the largest attention due to their strong color that render

---

[*] E-mail: ola_gomaa@hotmail.com.

them highly visible even at very low concentrations (less than 1 ppm for some dyes), causing serious aesthetic and pollution problems in wastewater disposal such as water transparency and gas solubility in lakes, rivers and other water bodies [1]. The removal of color from waste water is often more important than the removal of soluble colorless organic substances, which usually contribute the major fraction of biochemical oxygen demand (BOD) [2].

There are more than 8000 chemical products associated with the dyeing process listed in the color index, while over 100,000 commercially available dyes exist with over 7×10^5 metric tons of dyestuff produced annually [3, 4], about 100,000 commercial dyes and dyestuffs are used in the coloring (textile, cosmetic, leather) industries [5,6]. Approximately 10-15% of the dyes are lost in the effluents of textile units, rendering them highly colored [7, 8]. It is estimated that 280,000 tons of textile dyes are discharged in such industrial effluents every year worldwide [9]. Direct discharge of these effluents results in the formation of toxic aromatic amines under anaerobic conditions in receiving media. In addition to their visual effect and their adverse impact in terms of chemical oxygen demand, many synthetic dyes are toxic, mutagenic and carcinogenic [10], therefore, water pollution control is one of the major areas of scientific activity.

The frequently high volumetric rate of industrial effluent discharge in combination with increasingly stringent legislation, make the search for appropriate treatment technologies an important priority [11]. Chemical or physical treatment methods could result in complete destruction of dye molecules, yet they pose other problems in terms of cost and limited applicability, moreover, sometimes large amounts of toxic by-products maybe produced [2]. Therefore, there has been interest in biological methods of dye removal along the past years as a cost effective and applicable alteration to the currently used methods. The term bioremediation is referred to the biological method of treatment [12].

2. TYPES OF BIOREMEDIATION

Under certain conditions, pollutants are degraded over time without human intervention. Generally, this process, termed as natural environmental remediation, is slow [13]. But in some cases human intervention is needed because of inadequate environmental conditions to further stimulate the environmental remediation, this is termed an engineered bioremediation process [13]. The general methods in engineered bioremediation can be categorized into two types. The first type involves the stimulation of indigenous micro-flora for pollutant degradation, which can be achieved through the addition of electron donors, electron acceptors, micro-elements, or chelating agents….etc. In order to ensure a successful bioremediation method, indigenous single or group of microorganisms that is capable of degrading a specific pollutant must be available. This type of engineered bioremediation is termed biostimulation. The second type of engineered bioremediation is the addition of an adequate pollutant-degrading microorganism which is not found in the environment under normal conditions. Therefore, an inocula composed of a specific microorganism (or several) is prepared and administered to the polluted environment and this is termed bioaugmentation [14].

Many microorganisms have been found to be very efficient in dye bioremediation, these microorganisms may be bacteria, algae or fungi and the treatment process may be aerobic, anaerobic or a combination of both. The choice of the treatment process is basically dependent on the dye and the microorganism [15]. Bioremediation could involve partial or complete mineralization of dyes to CO_2 and H_2O [16, 17].

2.1. Fungal Bioremediation of Dyes

Fungi have proved to be a suitable organism for the treatment of textile effluents and in dye removal [2]. The fungal mycelia have an advantage over single cell organisms by solubilising the insoluble substrates by producing extracellular enzymes, due to an increased cell-to-surface ratio; fungi have a greater physical and enzymatic contact with the environment. The extracellular nature of the fungal enzymes is also advantageous in tolerating high concentrations of the toxicants [18].

The potential of using white-rot fungi for the degradation of pollutants has been primarily and extensively researched and has mainly been attributed to their ability to degrade lignin [19, 20]. Hydrocarbons, insecticides, dyes, metals and other have been successfully degraded, detoxified or immobilized by the fungus. Aust [21] state that most white-rot fungi are more resistant to toxic levels of pollutants as compared to other microorganisms. Degradation by white-rot fungi is achieved through the production of ligninolytic enzymes and other organic compounds catalyzing various reactions such as: depolymerization, demethoxylation, de carboxylation, hydroxylation and aromatic ring opening [22].

Many genera of fungi have been employed for the dye decolorization either in living or dead form. Based on the mechanism involved, they can be grouped into biodegradation, biosorption and bioaccumulation. Biodegradation is an energy dependent process and involves the breakdown of dye into various by products through the action of various enzymes. Biosorption is defined as binding of solutes to the biomass by processes which do not involve metabolic energy or transport, although such processes may occur simultaneously where live biomass is used. Therefore, it can occur in either living or dead biomass [23]. Bioaccumulation is the accumulation of pollutants by actively growing cells by metabolism [24].

The enrichment procedures, which were designed to obtain microbial agents suitable for decolorizing dye containing waste water resulted in the isolation of several strains of fungi capable of decolorization; these include the fungal strains *Myrothecium verrucaria* and *Ganoderma* sp. mainly through adsorption to the fungal mycelium and effective for a wide range of dyes, high dye concentrations resulted in low color removal by the two reported strains [25].

Spadaro *et al.* [26] observed that aromatic rings with substituents such as hydroxyl, amino, acetamido, or nitro functions were mineralized to a greater extent than unsubstituted rings in dye decolorization by *Phanerochaete chrysosporium*. In contrast, Paszcczynski *et al.* [27] reported that the substitution pattern of five sulfonated azo dyes did not significantly influence the susceptibility of the dyes to degradation by *Phanerochaete chrysosporium*. *Aspergillus sojae* B-10 was shown to be capable of decolorizing azo dyes in nitrogen-poor media after three to five days of incubation [28]. Wong and Yu [29] reported that dye decolorization by *Trametes versicolor* was dependent on dye structure, anthraquinone dyes were laccase substrate while azo and indigo dyes were not the substrates for the same enzyme. Zhang *et al.* [30] also observed that the color removal efficiency decreased with an increase in the concentration of the cotton bleaching effluent. Yesiladali *et al.* [6] demonstrated that *Trichophyton rubrum* LSK-27 is a promising culture for dye removal applications and can be a potential candidate for treatment of textile effluents under aerobic conditions leading to non toxic degradation of dye compounds. *Phanerocheate chrysosporium* had the ability to decolorize artificial textile effluent by up to 99% within 7 days Robinson *et al.* [5]. Facultative anaerobic fungi are also capable of growing on dyes as sole carbon sources have been reported. They, however, do not seem to be capable of performing decolorization they appear to cleave some of the bonds in these dyes to use as carbon sources, yet do not affect the chromophore centers of the dyes. This capability might be of significance when a consortium of microorganisms is employed in degrading dye-containing effluents when other decolorizers are present [31-33]. Table 1 represents different fungi and their modes of decolorization.

Table 1. Mechanisms of dye removal by fungi

Strain	Dye	Mechanism	Reference
Aspergillus sojae B-10	Amaranth,Congo red,Sudan III	Decolorization	[28]
Trametes versicolor	Anthraquinone, Azo, Indigo	Enzymatic	[29]
Trichophytom rubrum LSK-27	Textile effluent	Degradation	[6]
Phanerocheate chrysosporium	Azo	Enzymatic	[34]
Trametes versicolor *Bjerkandera adusta* *Thelephora sp.*	Azo	Decolorization	[35]
Aspergillus flavus EL-2	Textile effluent	Enzymatic	[36]
Phanerocheate chrysosporium	Triaryl methane dye	Enzymatic	[37]
Rhizopus stolonifer	Bromophenol blue	Biosorption	[38]
Schizophyllum commune *Ganoderma lucidum* *Aspergillus nige*	Solar golden yellow R	Biodegradation	[39]
Kluyveromyces marxianus *Candida spp.* *Candida trpicalis*	Remazol blue,Remazol black B	Bioaccumulation	[24]

2.1.1. Degradation by White Rot Fungi

Many white-rot fungi have been studied for their decolorizing ability. Decolorization of azo dyes by the ligninolytic fungus, *Phanerochaete chrysosporium*, was described for the first time by Cripps *et al.* [34], ever since, *Phanerochaete chrysosporium* and *Colorius versicolor* are considered the most studied fungi [40, 41].

The promising results obtained with *Phanerochaete chrysosporium* opened the door to more studies regarding the potential of other species of ligninolytic basidiomycetes [42]. Novotny *et al.* [43] screened 103 wood-rotting fungal strains for decolorization of azo and other types of textile dyes. Other white rot fungi, such as *Trametes versicolor*, *Bjerkandera adusta*, and *Thelephora sp.*, have also been shown to be efficient in decolorizing different azo dyes [35].

White rot fungi have interesting properties because they are capable of degrading lignin which is a polymeric structure with a lot of aromatic rings [44]. A correlation between dye decolorization and the production of ligninolytic enzymes was implied by Wesenberg *et al.* [45]. The ligninolytic enzymes are extracellularly excreted by the fungi to initiate the oxidation of substrates in the culture media of the fungal cells [46]. Essential extracellular enzymes involved in the degradation of lignin in wood and recalcitrant pollutants in the environment are laccase, lignin peroxidase (LiP), and manganese peroxidase (MnP). All of these enzymes are generally believed to form during secondary metabolism of white rot fungi [47] and are thought to be responsible for decolorizing a variety of dyes [48].

White rot fungi do not require preconditioning to particular pollutants because enzyme secretion depends on the nutrient limitation of nitrogen or carbon source, rather than the presence of a pollutant. The extracellular enzyme system also enables white rot fungi to tolerate high concentrations of pollutants [10].

2.1.2. White Rot Fungi Degradative Enzymes

The main key feature of an enzyme in the degradation process involves generation of activated oxygen forms that can carry out the initial attack on the stable structure. White rot fungi were found to be effective for decolorization applications through the use of the oxidative enzymes: lignin peroxidase (LiP), manganese peroxidase (MnP) and laccase. The catalytic action of these enzymes lies in the oxidation of the aromatic molecules to radicals; nontoxic decolorization becomes possible under various effluent conditions [6, 49]. The advantage of white rot fungi is that they produce and excrete ligninolytic enzymes which are non-specific with respect to their aromatic structure. This means that they are capable of degrading mixtures of aromatic compounds [50].

The application of white-rot fungi in textile waste water treatment on a large scale, however, has been impeded owing to the lack of appropriate reactor systems capable of coping with rather slow fungal degradation, loss of extracellular enzymes and excessive growth of fungi [51]. Also, the fungi need to be supplied with an external carbon source in order to be able to degrade polycyclic aromatic hydrocarbons [44].

(i) Lignin Peroxidase

Lignin peroxidase (LiP) also named ligninase was first discovered in *Phanerochaete chrysosporium* [52], LiP is a classical heme-protein peroxidase containing heme in the active site with molecular weight between 38 and 47 KDa [45]. Due to its high redox potential, LiP is able to directly oxidize non-phenolic lignin units [53]. LiP reacts directly with aromatic substrates by abstracting single electrons from their aromatic rings, leading to the formation of a cation radical and the subsequent cleavage reactions [54]. One of the main characteristics of LiP, also shared by non-ligninolytic peroxidases, is its relative unspecificity for substrates such as phenolic compounds and dyes [55]. Whereas, phenoxy radicals appear as the first product of phenolic substrate oxidation by peroxidases. Aromatic cations are formed after non-phenolic aromatic ring oxidation by LiP [55].

(ii) Manganese Peroxidase

Like LiP, manganese peroxidase (MnP) is a heme-containing peroxidase [56] and is the most common ligninolytic peroxidase produced by almost all white rot basidiomycetes [45]. MnP is a glycoprotein with a heme (ferric protoporphyrin) group and a molecular weight of 32 to 62.5 KDa [57]. It requires the presence of H_2O_2 to oxidize lignin and lignin-related compounds [46].

Manganese is known to catalyze several oxidation reactions important in lignin degradation, including decarboxylation and demethoxylation of aromatic substrates. It plays an important role in the degradation of both phenolic and non phenolic units, acting together with lipids. In contrast, lignin peroxidase degrades only the non-phenolic units and acts with hydrogen peroxide [58].The need of manganese in MnP enzyme results from the enzyme's ability to catalyze the oxidation of Mn (II) to Mn (III) in the presence of Mn (III) stabilizing ligands. The resulting Mn (III) complexes can then oxidize organic substrates [59].

(iii) Laccase

Most white-rot fungi synthesize oxidoreductases such as laccase. Laccase (benzenediol: oxygen oxidoreductase) belong to blue copper oxidase and a molecular weight of 58 KDa [60] are widely distributed among plants, fungi [61] and bacteria [62]. Laccases are generally considered to be remarkably non-specific to their substrates, being able to oxidize a broad range of organic and inorganic substrates by reducing molecular oxygen (instead of H_2O_2) to water by a multicopper system [47, 63]. These substrates including, monoaromatic phenolic substrates diphenols, complex phenol, nonphenolic heterocyclic compounds, diamine, aromatic amines and ascorbate [64-67].

This enzyme normally oxidizes only lignin model compounds with free phenolic groups forming phenoxy radicals. However, in the presence of the artificial substrate ABTS (2, 2 azinobis (3-ethyl benzthiazoline-5-sulphonate) or some other synthetic mediators such as veratryl alcohol and Mn (Π), laccase can oxidize other non-phenolic compounds [68].

Although most laccase isolated from a large number of white-rot fungi share several structural properties, the physiology of production is markedly different even in strictly related organisms [69]. Garzillo et al. [70] observed that laccase production by Pleurotus ostreatus was positively regulated by wheat straw. Trametes trogii required protein nitrogen (yeast extract) to excrete high levels of laccase in shake flask cultures; in the presence of wheat straw, partly because of the strong induction of cellulases, the specific activity of laccase significantly decreased also, syringaldazine is considered as the most potent inducers of extracellular laccase, as well as, 2, 5 xylidine reported to enhance laccase production by a number of basidiomycetes [71, 72].

2.1.3. Degradation by Brown Rot Fungi

A number of fungal cultures are capable of decolorization have been isolated by Ohmomo et al. [73], among which Aspergillus fumigatus showed high decolorizing ability. Other brown rot fungi capable of decolorizing a wide range of structurally different dyes were also isolated and were found to be more effective than Phanerochaete chrysosporium [74].

Also, there are various fungi such as Aspergillus niger [75], Rhizopus arrhizus [76, 77], Rhizopus oryzae [78] which can also decolorize and/or biosorb diverse dyes. But the most famous brown rot fungus used is Aspergillus sp.

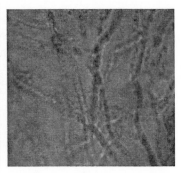

Figure 1. *Aspergillus sp.* growing and accumulating the textile dye. Pictures are captured with a light microscope, 40x magnification. *Aspergillus* was grown in textile waste water for 2 days.

Aspergillus species are a ubiquitious group of filamentous fungi which are commonly isolated from soil, plant debris, and indoor air environments. *Aspergillus niger* grows rapidly on a variety of artificial substrates producing colonies which consist of a compact white or yellow basal felt covered by a dense layer of dark-brown to black conidial heads, their mycelial hypae are septate [79].

Many *Aspergillus* enzymes are used in brewing and textile industries. Several researches suggest that *Aspergillus* fungi could be used to remove toxic and radioactive metals from the environment. *Aspergillus niger* fermentation is generally regarded as safe (GRAS) by the FDA, also *Aspergillus niger* is used to test the efficacy of preservative treatments [80]. In addition, *Aspergillus niger* has been shown to be exquisitely sensitive to micronutrient deficiencies prompting the use of *Aspergillus niger* strains for soil testing [81]. The brown rot fungus *Aspergillus niger* is known to produce glucose oxidase enzyme (GOD) and hydrogen peroxide [82]. *Aspergillus niger* was reported to remove melanoidin from molasses waste water in 3 days, GOD enzyme was suspected to be involved [83]. *Aspergillus sp.* is known for their efficiency in dye decolorization. *Aspergillus sojae* B-10 was able to decolorize Amaranth, Sudan III and Congo red in 5 days, the mechanism of dye decolorization was not reported [28]. *Aspergillus* could decolorize both single and textile effluent. *Aspergillus fumigatus* XC6 was shown to be capable of decolorizing textile dye effluent [10]. *Aspergillus* could grow in textile effluent and accumulate the dyes inside their mycelia [36] as shown in Figure 1.

2.2. Fungal Biosorption of Dyes

Although the use of live microbial cells is considered a safe alternative to conventional chemical and physical treatment methods, yet it has some drawbacks of requiring the appropriate conditions for growth, the need for prior adaptation, the extensive time needed for the dye removal or the toxicity of the resulting aromatic amines. To overcome such drawbacks, fungal biosorption was considered a suitable preference for the simplicity of handling and high performance. Biosorption is considered an interesting option because it acts as an intermediate which brings about the benefits of the cell wall binding properties with the cost effectiveness [84]. Dye biosorption depends mainly on the binding of the dye onto the biomass, the implied mechanism depends qualitatively and quantitatively on the type of biomass, its origin and processing, dead biomass being favored for the lack of nutrients or cultivation conditions, it is also unaffected by the presence of toxic compounds in the media [38]. Waste fungal biomass, which is a by-product of industrial fermentations, can be used as a cheap source of biosorbent. The different groups present on the fungal cell wall are responsible for binding the dye molecules; the dye biosorption process could be accomplished quickly and often is completed in a matter of hours [18]. Moreover, the biosorption sites could be chemically or physically modified to achieve a higher biosorptive capacity through exposure of latent binding sites [24, 85]. A variety of techniques are commonly used for detecting such modifications; usually through Infra Red Spectra (IR) and scanning electron microscopy (SEM). Native fungal pellets have rough and porous surface of interwoven mycelia which provide the surface area for adsorption, thus increasing the biosorptive capacity of fungi [85]. Fungal cell wall is known to contain amine, carboxyl and phosphonate groups [86]. The binding between the dye and the fungal functional groups is known to take place via the formation of Van der Waals interaction and also by ion exchange with other groups [87]. Electrostatic attraction is not the only mechanism involved in biosorption; the adsorption capacity may be increased by heat or autoclaving. The type of pretreatment of fungal biomass determines how the fungal cell wall will be affected, therefore controlling the extent of biosorption and/or the type of adsorbed dye, for example: the pretreatment of *R. arrihzus* with NaOH led to an increase in the biosorptive capacity, the reason was attributed to the removal of proteins and glucans from the cell wall which resulted in changes in the chitin/chitosan ratio generating anionic sites, while the use of autoclaving results in changes of the fibrous nature of the biomass which was caked [87]. It was shown that chemical pretreatments led to the rearrangement of the cell wall components against the treated chemicals, although acid treatment is known to give rise to fragmentation of the cell wall differently from alkali treatment to raise cross-linking reactions [87]. Aksu [24] explained that autoclaving is the major cause for cell wall disruption, thus leading to an increase in biosorption which might also be due to the increase in surface area and opening of more latent sites. Pretreatment of *R. stolonifer* with NaOH increased the biosorptive capacity from 280 to 385 mg g^{-1} for Bromophenol blue [38], heat treatment of *Trametes versicolor* increased the biosorptive capacity from 101 to 152.3 mg g^{-1} for Direct blue 1 [85], while Biosorptive capacity of *Lentinus sajur-caju* increased for Reactive red 120 from 117.8 to 182 mg g^{-1} by heat treatment [88].

Since the type of treatment affects the fungal cell wall-dye interaction through morphological, chemical and biophysical changes, therefore, it is easy to manipulate this interaction towards higher removal levels according to the chemical nature of the adsorbate and the adsorbent employed. The use of native and modified waste fungal pellets is not only effective because of the potential increase in the biosorptive capacity, but also because it encourages the economical use of cheap cast-off biomass as the adsorbent.

2.3. Advances in Bioremediation of Dyes

Although fungal dye decolorization has proved to be efficient, cheap, safe and applicable, yet there are several limitations in terms of dye concentrations, recalcitrance of some dye molecules and the presence of other inhibitory substances in the dye effluent. Therefore, scientists resorted to different methods in the past ten years to enhance the bioremediation process in order to increase the removal capacity or the concentrations of degradative enzymes. Therefore, optimization of the cultivation conditions whereby directly utilizing the purified enzyme in decolorization was one of the approached procedures [89]. The use of crude culture filtrate containing laccase enzyme showed good decolorizing activity [90]. The addition of nitrogen sources and vitamins improved the decolorizing ability of white rot fungi [91]. Different molecular biology approaches were also perceived as mandatory to overcome such drawbacks. With recent advances in biomolecular engineering, the bioremediation processes has become the ultimate solution. Exploring new catabolic pathways that lead to complete mineralization of a recalcitrant compound is considered one of the molecular approaches [92]. Extension of the catabolic pathways may include more substrates such as analogues of the same substrate or the addition of totally new substrates into the existing catabolic pathway [93, 94]. These approaches being either rational design or a directed evolution; has been only applied only to persistent organic pollutants (POPs) through expression of an enzyme, increasing its activity or widening its substrate specificity [95]. The same could be applied for fungal decolorization as an analogous approach. The use of a recombinant strain would add to the ability of decolorization in less time or more dyes. Recombinant *Aspergillus oryzae* expressing a dye-decolorizing peroxidase gene showed high stability in decolorizing 26 repeated 1 day batches [96]. Recombinant enzymes are also very efficient in performance; recombinant dye decolorizing peroxidase (rDyP) was used in the decolorization of anthraquinone dye [97]. An enzymatic manganese peroxidase (MnP) was synthesized as in vitro coupled transcription-translation system; studying the in vitro expression of MnP provided an efficient system for characterizing fungal peroxidases [98]. Generally, studying the molecular and biochemical characterization of a certain decolorizing enzyme reveals more about the decolorizing ability of this enzyme, understanding why and how the enzyme decolorizes would lead to the ability to increase the decolorization process [99].

3. TOXICITY OF BIOLOGICALLY TREATED TEXTILE WASTEWATER

The chemical structure of synthetic dyes used in the textile industry are based primarily on substituted aromatic and heterocyclic groups such as aromatic amines, these aromatic amines are suspected carcinogenic and/or genotoxic compounds[17].Therefore, improper disposal of textile dyes is considered a major environmental problem, which leads to disturbances in the ecosystem [100]. Dye decolorization by fungi does not imply that the resulting by-products are less toxic than the parent compound. On the contrary, it has been shown that reduction and cleavage of azo dyes result in the formation of potentially carcinogenic aromatic amines [101].

In the past, only one method of conventional waste water treatment was employed for color removal, methods such as chemical or physico-chemical treatment (coagulation, electrolysis, ozonation…etc.,) could be considered as inefficient, expensive, or of limited applicability [102]. On the other hand, biological methods are cost effective and applicable [12, 103-105]. Although white rot and brown rot fungi could be employed efficiently in biological treatment of textile dyes, yet biological treatments also have their drawbacks which involve the transfer of the dye onto biomass via adsorption or the incomplete destruction of the dye molecule which leaves carcinogenic by-products as potential hazard [18]. The use of more than one treatment method might provide complete destruction of the dye without producing toxic waste [106]. This new trend is gaining more attention due to the ability to combine the positive outcome of one or more method(s) and/or eliminating the drawbacks of another.

While color removal and complete destruction of dye molecules is important, the toxicity assessment of dyes and dye intermediates has become an extremely important matter, especially that most dyes have no safety data sheet [107]. Therefore, detoxification of the treated effluent should be coupled with color removal [108]. The carcinogenic tests could be performed through detecting microbial changes, phytotoxicity or chromosomal aberrations in mammalian cells [107, 109]. Studies show that biological treatments are efficient for removal of toxicity, however, the combined biological and physical method prove to be the closest to the non-toxic control samples. Fish exposed to non-remediated dye effluent showed high DNA fragmentation, the genotoxicity levels decreased after two remediation processes [110], this confirms that sometimes more than one mode of treatment is required to destruct the possible toxic compounds completely. Jadhav *et al.* [104] stated that a decreased mitotic index could be considered a reliable method to determine the presence of cytotoxic compounds. The level of increase or decrease in the mitotic index could be used efficiently as a biomonitoring technique for environmental toxicity [111]. Vanhulle *et al.* [112] stress on the importance of monitoring toxicity and mutagenicity, besides color to ensure the efficiency of the proposed bioremediation process.

4. CONCLUSION

Fungi have a great potential for textile waste water bioremediation for their ability to adapt and grow in such effluent and for their ability to decolorize different synthetic dyes. Though decolorization is considered the primary concern in the treatment of textile waste water, yet dye decolorization often result in toxic and carcinogenic compounds. Although improving cellular performance of fungi via adaptation and/or bioaugmentation could be employed successfully as a simple and classical tactic, yet it consumes time and requires a series of metabolic and cultural manipulations to obtain the required results. New trends in bioremediation involve combined treatments which ensure complete removal of any toxic by-product which could result in another problem. Different molecular approaches; such as the use of genetically modified microorganisms (GMMs), could be the answer. This directed approach offers a specific target with the use of an engineered microorganism capable of handling all the negative aspects of conventional bioremediation. The resulting microorganism would tolerate the textile waste water constituents, and mineralize the dyes under aerobic conditions. This suggestion is yet faced with the debate of releasing GMMs into the environment; therefore, the need to terminate the viability of these altered microorganisms is a pre-requisite necessity, this would also entail a chain of tests to investigate the appropriateness of this new application in textile waste water plants.

There is a need for a wide scope of answers and long-term view when approaching an environmental dilemma. Environmental scientists will always be faced with new puzzles and the need to look for new solutions.

REFERENCES

[1]   Kritikos, D.E., Xekoukoulotakis, N.P., Psillakis, E., & Mantzavinos, D. (2007). Photocatalytic degradation of reactive black 5 in aqueous solution: Effect of operating conditions and coupling with ultrasound irradiation. *Water Research*, 41: 2236-2246.

[2]   Banat, I.M., Nigam, P., Singh, D., & Marchant, R. (1996). Microbial decolorization of textile-dye containing effluents, A Review. *Bioresource Technology*, 58: 217-227.

[3]   Fu, Y., & Viraraghavan, T. (2001). Fungal decolorization of dye waste waters. A review. *Bioresource Technology*, 79: 251-262.

[4]   Park, C., Lee, M., Lee, B., Kim, S.W., Chase, H.A., Lee, J., & Kim, S. (2007). Biodegradation and biosorption for decolorization of synthetic dyes by *Funalia trogii*. *Biochemical Engineering Journal*, 36: 59-65.

[5]   Robinson, T., Chandran, B., & Nigam, P. (2001). Studies on the decolorization of an artificial textile effluent by white-rot fungi in N- rich and N- limited media. *Applied Microbiology and Biotechnology*, 57: 810-813.

[6]   Yesiladali, S.K., Pekin, G., Bermek, H., Alaton, I.A., Orhon, D., & Tamerler, C. (2006). Bioremediation of textile azo dyes by *Trichophyton rubrum* LSK-27. *World Journal of Microbiology and Biotechnology*, 22: 1027-1031.

[7]   Vaidya, A.A., & Date, K.V. (1982). Environmental pollution during chemical processing of synthetic fibers. *Colourage*, 14: 3-10.

[8]   Boer, C.G., Obici, L., Souza, C.G., & Peralta, R.M. (2004). Decolourization of synthetic dyes by solid state cultures of *Lentinula* (*Lentinus*) *edodes* producing manganese peroxidase as the main lignolytic enzyme. *Bioresource Technology*, 94: 107-112.

[9]   Maas, R., & Chaudhari, S. (2005). Adsorption and biological decolorization of azo dye reactive red 2 in semicontinuous anaerobic reactors. *Process Biochemistry*, 40: 699-705.

[10]   Jin, X.C., Liu, G.Q., & Xu, Z.H. (2007). Decolorization of a dye industry effluent by *Aspergillus fumigatus* XC6. *Applied Microbiology and Biotechnology*, 74: 239-243.

[11]   O'Neill, C., Hawkes, F.R., Hawkes, D.L., Lourenco, N.D., Pinheiro, H.M., & Delee, W. (1999). Color in textile effluents: sources, measurement, discharge consents and simulation. A review. *Journal of Chemical Technology and Biotechnology*, 74: 1009-1018.

[12]   Chen, K.C., Wu, J.Y, Liou, D.J., & Hwang, S.C.J. (2003) Decolorization of the textile azo dyes by newly isolated bacterial strains. *Journal of Biotechnology* 101: 57-68.

[13]   Rittman, B.E., & McCarty, P.L. (2001). *Environmental Biotechnology: Principals and Applications*. New York, NY: McGraw-Hill.

[14]   Alexander, M. (1994). *Biodegradation and Bioremediation*. (Second Edition). San Diego, USA, Academic Press.

[15]   Keharia H., & Madamvar D. (2003). Bioremediation concept for treatment of dye containing waste water: a review. *Indian Journal of Experimental Biology* 41: 1068-1075.

[16]   Mohan, S.V., Prasad, K.K., & Karthikeyan, J. (2002). Treatment of simulated Reactive Yellow 22(Azo) dye effluents using *Spirogyra* species. *Waste Management*, 22: 575-582.

[17] Nyanhongo, G.S., Gomes, J., Gubitz, G.M., Zvauya, R., Read, J., & Steiner, W. (2002). Decolorization of textile dyes by laccase from a newly isolated strain of *Trametes modesta*. *Water Research,* 36: 1449-1456.

[18] Kaushik, P., & Malik, A. (2009). Fungal dye decolourization: recent advances and future potential. *Environment International,* 35: 127-141.

[19] Bumpus, J.A., Tien, M., Wright, D., & Aust, S.D. (1985). Oxidation of persistent environmental pollutants by white rot fungus. *Science,* 288: 1434-1436.

[20] ***Reddy,*** C.A. *(1995).* The potential for white-rot fungi in the treatment of pollutants. **Current Opinion** in **Biotechnology, 6:** *320-328.*

[21] Aust, S.D. (1990). Degradation of environmental pollutants by *Phanerocheate chrysosporium*. *Microbial Ecology*, 20:197-209.

[22] Shah, V., & Nerud, F. (2002). Lignin degrading system of white-rot fungi and its exploitation for dye decolorization. *Canadian Journal of Microbiology*, 48: 857–870.

[23] Tobin, J.M., White, C., & Gadd, G.M. (1994). Metal accumulation by fungi: applications in environment biotechnology. *Journal of Industrial Microbiology,* 13: 126–130.

[24] Aksu, Z., & Donmez, G. (2005). Combined effects of molasses sucrose and reactive dye on the growth and dye bioaccumulation properties of *Candida tropicalis*. *Process Biochemistry*, 40: 2443–2454.

[25] Mou, D.G., Lim, K.K., & Shen, H.P. (1991). Microbial agents for decolorization of dye waste water. *Biotechnology Advances*, 9: 613-622.

[26] Spadaro, J.T., Gold, M.H., & Renganathan, V. (1992). Degradation of azo dyes by the lignin-degrading fungus *Phanerochaete chrysosporium*. *Applied and Environmental Microbiology*, 58: 2397-2401.

[27] Paszczynski, A, Pasti-Grigsby, M.B., Goszczyanski, S., Crawford, R.L., & Crawford, D.L. (1992). Mineralization of sulfonated azo dyes and sulfanilic acid by *Phanerochaete chrysosporium* and *Streptomyces chromofuscus*. *Applied and Environmental Microbiology,* 58: 3598-3604.

[28] Ryu, B.H., & Weon, Y.D. (1992). Decolorization of azo dyes by *Aspergillus sojae* B-10. *Journal of Microbiology and Biotechnology*, 2: 215-219.

[29] Wong, Y., & Yu, J. (1999). Laccase-catalyzed decolorization of synthetic dyes. *Water Research,* 33: 3512-3520.

[30] Zhang, F., Knapp, J.S., & Tapley, K.N. (1999). Decolourisation of cotton bleaching effluent with wood rotting fungus. *Water Research*, 33: 919-928.

[31] Marchant, R., Nigam, P., & Banat, I.M. (1994). An unusual facultatively anaerobic fungus isolated from prolonged enrichment culture conditions. *Mycological Research,* 98: 757-760.

[32] Nigam, P., Banat, I.M., Oxspring, D., Marchant, R., Singh, D., & Smyth, W.F. (1995). A new facultative anaerobic filamentous fungus capable of growth on recalcitrant textile dyes as sole carbon source. *Microbios*, 84: 171-185.

[33] Nigam, P., Singh, D., & Marchant, R. (1995). *An investigation of the biodegradation of textile dyes by aerobic and anaerobic microorganisms.* In: *Environmental Biotechnology: Principles and Applications*, ed. M. Moo-Young. Kluwer Academic. The Netherlands. 278-292.

[34]   Cripps, C., Bumpus, J.A., & Aust, S.D. (1990). Biodegradation of azo and heterocyclic dyes by *Phanerochaete chrysosporium*. *Applied and Environmental Microbiology,* 56: 1114-1118.

[35]   Selvam, K., Swaminathan, K., & Chae, K.S. (2003). Decolouriztion of azo dyes and a dye industry effluent by a white rot fungus *Thelephora sp. Bioresource Technology,* 88: 115-119.

[36]   Gomaa, O., Momtaz, O., Abd El Kareem, H., & Fathy, R. (2011). Isolation, identification, and biochemical characterization of a brown rot fungus capable of textile dye decolorization. *World Journal of Microbiology and Biotechnology*, 27: 1641-1648.

[37]   Gomaa, O., Linz, J., & Reddy, C.A. (2008). Decolorization of Victoria blue by *Phanerochaete chrysosporium. World Journal of Microbiology and Biotechnology* 24: 2349-2356.

[38]   Zeroual, Y, Kim, B.S, Blaghen, M, & Lee, K.M. (2006). Biosorption of bromophenol blue from aqueous solutions by *Rhizopus Stolonifer* biomass. *Water, Air and Soil pollution,* 177: 135-146.

[39]   Asgher, M., Kausara, S., Bhattia, H.N., Shah S.A.H., & Ali M. (2008). Optimization of medium for decolourization of solar golden yellow R direct textile dye by Schizophyllum commune IBL-06. *International Biodeterioration Biodegradation* 61: 189-193.

[40]   Bumpus, J.A., & Brock, B.J. (1988). Biodegradation of crystal violet by the white rot fungus *Phanerochaete chrysosporium. Applied and Environmental Microbiology,* 54: 1143-1150.

[41]   Urra, J., Sepulveda, L., Contreras, E., & Palma, C. (2006). Screening of static culture and comparison of batch and continuous culture for the textile dye biological decolorization by *Phanerochaete chrysosporium. Brazilian Journal of Chemical Engineering,* 23: 281 –290.

[42]   Adosinda, M, Martins, M, Lima, N, Silvestre, A., & Queiroz, M. (2003). Comparative studies of fungal degradation of single or mixed bioaccessible reactive azo dyes. *Chemosphere*, 52: 967-973.

[43]   Novotny, C., Rawal, B., Bhatt, M., Patel, M., Sasek, V., & Molitoris, H.P. (2001). Capacity of *Irpex lacteus* and *Pleurotus ostreatus* for decolorization of chemically different dyes. *Journal of Biotechnology*, 89: 113-122.

[44]   Nilsson, I., Moller, A., Mattiasson, B., Rubindamayugi, M.S., & Welander, U. (2006). Decolorization of synthetic and real textile waste water by the use of white-rot fungi. *Enzyme and Microbial Technology*, 38: 94-100.

[45]   Wesenberg, D., Kyriakides, I., & Agathos, S.N. (2003). White-rot fungi and their enzymes for the treatment of industrial dye effluents. *Biotechnology Advances,* 22: 161-187.

[46]   Mester, T., & Tien, M. (2000). Oxidation mechanism of ligninolytique enzymes involved in the degradation of environmental pollutants. *International Biodeterioration and Biodegradation.* 46: 51-59.

[47]   Hou, H., Zhou, J., Wang, J., Du, C., & Yan, B. (2003). Enhancement of laccase production by *Pleurotus ostreatus* and its use for the decolorization of anthraquinone dye. *Process Biochemistry.* 39: 1415-1419.

[48]   Rani, C., Jana, A.K., & Bansal, A. (2009). Studies on the biodegradation of azo dyes by white rot fungi *Phlebia Radiata*. Proceedings of International Conference on Energy and Environment, ISSN: 2070-3740. March 19-21, 203-207.

[49]   Pointing, S.B. (2001). Feasibility of bioremediation by white-rot fungi. *Applied Micrbiology and Biotechnology*, 57: 20-33.

[50]   Axelsson, J., Nilsson, U., Terrazes, E., Aliage, T.A., & Welander, U. (2006). Decolorization of the textile dyes reactive red 2 and reactive blue 4 using *Bjerkandera* sp. strain BOL 13 in a continuous rotating biological contactor reactor. *Enzyme and Microbial Technology*. 39: 32-37.

[51]   Faisal, I.H., Yamamoto, K., & Fukushi, K. (2006). Development of a submerged membrane fungi reactor for textile waste water treatment. *Desalination*, 192: 315-322.

[52]   Tien, M., & Kirk, T.K. (1983). Lignin-degrading enzyme from hymenomycete *Phanerochaete chrysosporium*. Burds. *Science*, 221: 661-663.

[53]   Sarkar, S., Martinez, A.T., & Martinez, M.J. (1997). Biochemical and molecular characterization of a manganese peroxidase isoenzyme from *Pleurotus ostreatus*. *Biochimica Biophysica Acta*, 1339: 23-30.

[54]   Zheng, Z., & Obbard, J.P. (2002). Oxidation of polycyclic aromatic hydrocarbons (PAH) by the white rot fungus, *Phanerochaete chrysosporium*. *Enzyme and Microbial Technology*, 31: 3-9.

[55]   Martinez, A.T. (2002). Molecular biology and structure-function of lignin-degrading heme peroxidases. *Enzyme and Microbial Technology*, 30: 425-444.

[56]   Zapanta, L.S., & Tien, M. (1997). The roles of veratryl alcohol and oxalate in fungal lignin degradation. *Journal of Biotechnology*, 53: 93-102.

[57]   Hofrichter, M. (2002). Lignin conversion by manganese peroxidase (MnP). Review. *Enzyme and Microbial Technology*, 30: 454-466.

[58]   Hatakka, A. (1994). Lignin-modifying enzymes from selected white-rot fungi: production and role in lignin degradation. *FEMS Microbiology Reviews*, 13: 125-135.

[59]   Asamudo, N.U., Dada, A.S., & Ezeronye, O.U. (2005). Bioremediation of textile effluent using *Phanerochaete chrysosporium*. Review. *African Journal of Biotechnol*, 4: 1548-1553.

[60]   Salomy, S., Mishra, V., & Bisaria, S. (2006). Production and characterization of laccase from *Cyathus bulleri* and its use in decolorization of recalcitrant textile dyes. *Applied Microbiology and Biotechnology*, 71: 646-653.

[61]   Mayer, A.M., & Staples, R.C. (2002). Laccase: new functions for an old enzyme. *Photochemistry*. 60: 551-565.

[62]   Claus, H. (2003). Laccase and their occurrence in prokaryotes. *Archives of Microbiology*, 179: 145-150.

[63]   Hublik, G., & Schinner, F. (2000). Characterization and immobilization of the laccase from *Pleurotus ostreatus* and its use for the continuous elimination of phenolic pollutants. *Enzyme and Microbial Technology*, 27: 330-336.

[64]   Bourbonnais, R., & Paice, M.G. (1990). Oxidation of non-phenolic substrates. An expanded role for laccase in lignin biodegradation. *FEBS Letters,* 267: 99-102.

[65]   Thurston, C.F. (1994). The structure and function of fungal laccase. *Microbiology*. 140: 19-26.

[66] Xu, F. (1996). Oxidation of phenols, anilines, and benzenthiols by fungal laccase: correlation between activity and redox potential as well as halide inhibition. *Biochemistry*. 35: 7608-7614.

[67] Lu, L., Zhao, M., Zhang, B.B., Yu, S.Y., Bian, X.J., Wang, W., & Wang, Y. (2007).Purification and characterization of laccase from *Pycnoporus sanguineus* and decolorization of an anthraquinone dye by the enzyme. *Applied Microbiology and Biotechnology*, 74: 1232-1239.

[68] Podgornik, H., Stegu, M., Zibert, E., & Perdih, A. (2001). Laccase production by Phanerochaete chrysosporium - an artefact caused by Mn (III)?. *Letters in Applied Microbiology*. 32: 407-411.

[69] Tuor, U., Winterhalter, K., & Fiechter, A. (1995). Enzymes of white-rot fungi involved in lignin degradation and ecological determinants for wood decay. *Journal of Biotechnology*, 41: 1-17.

[70] Garzillo, A.M., Di Paolo, S., Burla, G., & Buonocore, V. (1992). Differently- induced extracellular phenol oxidase from *Pleurotus ostreatus*. *Phytochemistry*. 31: 3685-3690.

[71] Bollag, J.M., & Leonowicz, A. (1984). Comparative studies of extracellular fungal laccase. *Applied and Environmental Microbiology*, 48: 849-854.

[72] Bourbonnais, R., Paice, M.G., Reid, I.D., Lanthier, P., & Yaguchi, M. (1995). Lignin oxidation by laccase isozymes from *Trametes versicolor* and role of the mediator 2,2'–azinobis(3-ethylbenzthiazoline-6-sulfonate) in kraft lignin depolymerization. *Applied and Environmental Microbiology*, 61: 1876-1880.

[73] Ohmomo, S., Itoh, N., Watanabe, Y., Kaneko, Y., Tozawa, Y., & Ueda, K. (1985). Continuous decolorization of molasses waste water with mycelia of *Coriolus versicolor* Ps4a. *Agriculture and Biological Chemistry*, 49: 2551-2555.

[74] Knapp, J.S., Newby, P.S., & Reece, L.P. (1995). Decolorization of dyes by wood-rotting basidiomycete fungi. *Enzyme and Microbial Technology*. 17: 664-668.

[75] Fu, Y., & Viraraghavan, T. (1999). Removal of acid blue 29 from aqueous solution by fungus *Aspergillus niger*. In: Nikolaidis, N., Erkey, C., & Smet, B.F. (Eds.). Proceedings of the 31st Mid- Atlantic Industrial and Hazardous Waste Conference. Storrs Conneticut, USA. (published by Technomic Publishing Company, Inc. Lancaster, Pennsylvania), 510-519.

[76] Zhou, J.L., & Banks, C.J. (1991). Removal of humic acid fraction by *Rhizopus arrhizus*: uptake and kenetic studies. *Environmental Technology*, 12: 859-869.

[77] Zhou, J.L., & Banks, C.J. (1993). Mechanism of humic acid colour removal from natural waters by fungal biomass biosorption. *Chemosphere*, 27: 607-620.

[78] Gallagher, K.A., Healy, M.G., & Allen, S.J. (1997). Biosorption of synthetic dye and metal ions from aqueous effluents using fungal biomass. In: Wise, D.L. (Ed.), Global Environmental Biotechnology. Elsevier, UK. 27-50.

[79] Frisvad, J.C., Hawksworth, D.L, Kozakiewicz, Z., Pitt, J.I., Samson, R.A., & Stolk, A.C. (1990). *Proposals to conserve important species names in Aspergillus and Penicillium*. In, Samson, R.A., & Pitt, J.I., (Eds.), *Modern Concepts in Penicillium and Aspergillus classification*. New York, Plenum press, 83-89.

[80] Jong, S.C., & Gantt, M.J. (1987). *Catalogue of fungi and yeasts*, (17th edition). American Type Culture Collection, Rockille. MD.

[81] Raper, K.B., & Fennell, D.I. (1965). *The genus Aspergillus*. Williams and Wilkins Company, Baltimore, MD.

[82]   Fieudrek, J., & Gromada, A. (2000). Production of catalase and glucose oxidase by *Aspergillus niger* using unconventional oxygenation of culture. *Journal of Applied Microbiology,* 39: 85-89.

[83]   Gomaa, O., Abdel Karem, H., Mattar, Z., & Hassanein, H. (2003). Decolorization of molasses waste water by *Aspergillus niger. Egyptian Journal Biotechnology*, 13: 15-28.

[84]   Nigam, P., Armour, G., Banat, I.M., Singh, D., & Marchant, R. (2000). Physical removal of textile dyes from effluents and solid-state fermentation of dye-adsorbed agricultural residues. *Bioresoure Technology,* 72: 219-216.

[85]   Bayramoğlu, G., & Arica, M.Y. (2007). Biosorption of benzidine based textile dyes "Direct Blue 1 and Direct Red 128" using native and heat-treated biomass of *Trametes versicolor. Journal of Hazardous Materials,* 143: 135-143.

[86]   Hughes, M.N., & Poole, R.K. (1989). *Metals and Microorganisms*. London, Chapman and Hall.

[87]   Binupriya, A.R., Sathishkumar, M., Swaminathan K., Ku C.S., & Yun S.E. (2008). Comparative studies on removal of congo red by native and modified mycelial pellets of *Trametes versicolor* in various reactor modes. *Bioresoure Technology,* 99: 1080-1088.

[88]   Arica, M.Y., & Bayramoğlu, G. (2007). Biosorption of Reactive Red-120 dye from aqueous solution by native and modified fungus biomass preparations of *Lentinus sajor-caju. Journal of Hazardous Materials,* 149: 499-507.

[89]   Vanhulle, S., Enaud, E., Trovaslet, M., Nouaimeh, N., Bols, C.M., Keshavarz, T., & *et al*. (2007) Overlap of laccase/cellobiose dehydrogenase activities during decolorization of anthraquinone dyes with close chemical structures by *Pycnoporous strains. Enzyme Microbial Technology,* 40: 1723-1731.

[90]   Zeng X, Cai Y, Liao X, Zeng X, Li W, & Zhang D. (2011). Decolorization of synthetic dyes by crude laccase from a newly isolated *Trametes trogii* strain cultivated on solid agro-industrial residue. *Journal of Hazardous Materials,* 187: 517-525.

[91]   Levin, L., Melignani, E., & Ramos, A.M. (2010). Effect of nitrogen sources and vitamins on ligninolytic enzyme production by some white-rot fungi. Dye decolorization by selected culture filtrates. *Bioresource Technology*, 101: 4554-4563.

[92]   Singh, O.V., & Nagaraji, N.S. (2006). Transcriptomics, proteomics and interactomics: unique approaches to track the insights of bioremediation. Briefings in functional genomics and protemics, 4: 335-362.

[93]   Johri, A.K., Dua, M., Singh, A., Sethunathan, N., & Legge, R.L. (1999). Characterization and regulation of catabolic genes. *Critical Reviews in Microbiology*, 25: 245-273.

[94]   Parales RE and Ditty JL (2005) Laboratory evolution of catabolic enzymes and pathways. *Current Opinion of Biotechnology*, 16: 315-325.

[95]   Ang, E.L., Zhao, H., & Obbard, J.P. (2005). Recent advances in the bioremediation of persistent organic pollutants via biomolecular engineering. *Enzyme Microbial Technology,* 37: 487-496.

[96]   Shakeri, M., Sugano, Y., & Shoda, M. (2008). Stable repeated-batch production of recombinant dye-decolorizing peroxidase (rDyP) from *Aspergillus oryzae. Journal of Bioscience and Bioengineering*, 105: 683-686.

[97]   Shakeri M., & Shoda, M. (2010). Efficient decolorization of an anthraquinone dye by recombinant dye-decolorizing peroxidase (rDyP) immobilized in silica-based mesocellular foam. *J Mol Cat B: Enzymatic*, 62: 277-281.

[98]   Zhang, X., Wang, Y., Wang, L., Chen, G., Liu, W., & Gao, P. (2009). Site-directed mutagenesis of manganese peroxidase from Phanerochaete chrysosporium in an in vitro expression system. *Journal of Biotechnology*, 139: 176-178.

[99]   Ogola, H.J., Kamiike, T., Hashimoto, N., Ashida, H., Ishikawa, T., Shibata, H., & Sawa, Y. (2009). Molecular characterization of a novel peroxidase from the *Cyanobacterium anabaena sp.* strain PCC 7120. *Applied and Environmental Microbiology*, 75: 7509-7518.

[100] Ambrosio, S.T., & Campos-Takaki, G.M. (2004). Decolorization of reactive azo dyes by *Cunninghamella elegans* UCP 542 under co-metabolic conditions. *Bioresource Technology*, 91: 69-75.

[101] Cerniglia, C.E., Freeman, J.P., Franklin, W., & Pack, L.D. (1982). Metabolism of benzidine and benzidine-congener based dyes by human, monkey and rat intestinal bacteria. *Biochemical Biophysical Research Communication*, 107: 1224-1229.

[102] Merzouk, B., Gourich, B., Sekki, A., Madani, K., Vial, Ch., Barouki, M. (2009). Studies on decolorization of textile waswater by continuous electrocoagulation process. *Chemical Engineering Journal*, 149: 207-214.

[103] Sirinivasan, S.V., & Murthy, D.V. (2009) Statistical optimization for decolorization of textile dyes using *Trametes versicolor*. *Journal of Hazardous Material*, 65: 909-914.

[104] Jadhav, J.P., Kalyani, D.C., Telke, A.A., Phugare, S.S., & Govindwar, S.P. (2010). Evaluation of the efficacy of a bacterial consortium for the removal of color, reduction of heavy metals, and toxicity from textile dye effluent. *Bioresource Technology*, 101: 165-173.

[105] Ramalingam, Saraswathy, N., Shanmugapriya, S., Shakthipriyadarshini, S., Sadasivam, S., & Shanmugapraksh, M. (2010). Decolorization of textile dyes by *Aspergillus tamarii*, mixed fungal culture and *Penicillium purpurogenum*. *Journal of Scientific and Industrial Research*, 69: 151-153.

[106] Brosillon, S., Djelal, H., Merienne, N., & Amrane, A. (2008). Innovative integrated process for the treatment of azo dyes: coupling of phtotocatalysis and biological treatment. *Desalination*, 222: 331-339.

[107] Mathur, N., Bhatnagar, P., & Bakre, P. (2005). Assessing mutagenicity of textile dyes from Pali (Rajasthan) using Ames Bioassay. *Applied Ecology and Environmental Research*, 4: 111-118.

[108] Di Gregorio, S., Balestri, F., Basile, M., Matteini, V., Gini, F., Giansanti, S., Tozzi, M.G., Basosi, R., & Lorenzi, R. (2010). Sustainable discoloration of textile chromo-baths by spent mushroom substrate from the industrial cultivation of *Pleurotus ostreatus*. *Journal of Environmental Protection*, 1: 85-94.

[109] Chen, S.C., Kao, C.M., Huang, M.H., Shih, M.K., Chen, Y.L., Huang, S.P., & Liu, T.Z. (2003). Assessment of genotoxicity of benzidine and its structural analogues to human lymphocytes using comet assay. *Toxicological Science*, 71: 283-288.

[110] Grinevicius, V.M.A.S., Geremias, R., Laus, R., Bettega, K.F., Laranjeiras, M.C.M., Fávere, V.T., Filho, D.W., & Pedrosa, R.C. (2009). Textile effluents induce biomarkers of acute toxicity, oxidative stress and genotoxicity. *Archives of Environmental Contamination Toxicology*, 57: 307-314.

[111] Carita, R., & Marin-Morales, M.A. (2008). Induction of chromosome aberrations in the *Allium cepa* test system caused by the exposure of seeds to industrial effluents contaminated with azo dyes. *Chemosphere*, 18: 311-316.

[112] Vanhulle, S., Trovaslet, M., Enaud, E., Lucas, M., Sonveaux, M., Decock, C., Onderwater, R., Schnider, Y., & Corbisier, A. (2008). Cytotoxicity and genotoxicity evolution during decolorization of dyes by white rot fungi. *World Journal of Microbiology and Biotechnology*, 24: 337-344.

In: Non-Conventional Textile Waste Water Treatment   ISBN: 978-1-62100-079-2
Editor: Ahmed El Nemr   © 2012 Nova Science Publishers, Inc.

Chapter 5

ALGAE AS NON-CONVENTIONAL MATERIALS FOR TREATMENT OF TEXTILE WASTEWATER

Manal M. El Saadawy, Ahmed El Nemr[*]

Environmental Division, National Institute of Oceanography and Fisheries
Kayet Bey, El Anfoushy, Alexandria, Egypt

ABSTRACT

With the increased demand for textile products, the textile industry and its wastewaters have been increasing proportionally, making it one of the main sources of severe pollution problems worldwide. In particular, the release of colored effluents into the environment is undesirable, not only because of their color, but also because many dyes in textile wastewater and their breakdown products are toxic and/or mutagenic to life. This chapter shows the literatures examine of a wide variety of micro- and macro-algae species, which are capable of decolorizing textile wastewaters; discusses the effects of various parameters such as pH, temperature, concentrations of dye and biomass in solution, pretreatment method, etc. on the dyes removal process. Also, it discusses the equilibrium and kinetic models used in batch and continuous biosorption systems, which are important to determine the biosorption capacity of the sorbent and to design of treatment units.

1. INTRODUCTION

Wastewater from textile dyeing and finishing factories is a significant source of environmental pollution [1]. Reactive dyes are extensively used in textile industry, fundamentally due to the ability of their reactive groups to bind to textile fibers through covalent bonds [2], which facilitate the interaction of dyes with the fiber and reduce energy consumption [3]. The major environmental problem associated with the use of dyes is their loss during dyeing process since the fixation efficiency ranges from 60 to 90% [3].

---

[*] E-mail: ahmedmoustafaelnemr@yahoo.com; ahmed.m.elnemr@gmail.com.

Consequently, substantial amounts of unfixed dyes are released into the wastewater displaying a high organic load as indicated by high chemical oxygen demand (COD), low biodegradability and high-salt content of the textile effluents. The European Union (EU) directive 91/271 imposes limits on wastewater color, as it reduces light penetration in receiving water bodies [4]. Textile effluents are characterized by their strong color due to incomplete dye fixation on fibers [3, 5-7]. It is reported that over 100,000 commercially available dyes with a production of over 7×10^5 - 1×10^6 metric tons per year are used extensively in industry. The big consumers of dyes are textile, dyeing, paper and pulp, tannery and paint industries, and hence the effluents of these industries as well as those from plants manufacturing dyes tend to contain dyes in sufficient quantities [7, 8-13].

Mankind has used dyes for thousands of years [10] and the earliest known use of a colorant is believed to be by Neanderthal man about 1,80,000 years ago. However, the first known use of an organic colorant was much later, being nearly 4000 years ago, when the blue dye indigo was found in the wrappings of mummies in Egyptian tombs [14]. Till the late 19th century, all the dyes/colorants were more or less natural with main sources like plants, insects and mollusks, and were generally prepared on small scale. It was only after 1856 that with Perkin's historic discovery of the first synthetic dye, mauveine, which was manufactured synthetically on a large scale [11, 15].

Dyes are considered an objectionable type of pollutant because they are toxic [10, 16-18] generally due to oral ingestion and inhalation, skin and eye irritation, and skin sensitization leading to problems like skin irritation and skin sensitization and also due to carcinogenicity [10, 19, 20]. They impart color to water which is visible to human eye and therefore, highly objectionable on aesthetic grounds. Not only this, they also interfere with the transmission of light and upset the biological metabolism processes which cause the destruction of aquatic communities present in ecosystem [21, 22]. Further, the dyes have a tendency to sequester metal and may cause microtoxicity to fish and other organisms [22]. As such it is important to treat colored textile effluents to remove dyes. Also dyes may significantly affect photosynthetic activity in aquatic life reducing light penetration and may also be toxic to some aquatic life due to the presence of aromatics, metals, chlorides, etc., in them [8, 9, 23-25].

Table 1. Characterization of the cotton wet processing wastewaters

Process	COD (g l^{-1})	BOD (g l^{-1})	TS (g l^{-1})	TDS (g l^{-1})	pH	Color (ADMI)	Water usage (l kg^{-1})
Desizing	4.6-5.9	1.7-5.2	16-32	-	-	-	3-9
Scouring	8	0.1-2.9	7.6-17.4	-	10-13	694	26-43
Bleaching	6.7-13.5	0.1-1.7	2.3-14.4	4.8-19.5	8.5-9.6	153	3-124
Mercerizing	1.6	0.05-0.1	0.6-1.9	4.3-4.6	5.5-9.5	-	232-308
Dyeing	1.1-4.6	0.01-1.8	0.5-14.1	0.05*	5-10	1450-4750	8-300

COD, chemical oxygen demand; BOD, biochemical oxygen demand; TS, total solids; TDS, total dissolved solids; ADMI, American dye manufacturer institute. (*), case of some reactive dyes the salt concentration in the dye bath (dyeing process) can reach concentrations up to 60–100 g l^{-1}. Therefore, the values listed in the table can vary enormously depending on the type of the fiber and dye class.

Dyes usually have a synthetic origin and complex aromatic molecular structures which make them more stable and more difficult to biodegrade. Textile dyes are also designed to be resistant to fading by chemicals and light. They must also be resilient to both high temperatures and enzyme degradation resulting from detergent washing. For these reasons, biodegradation of dyes is typically a slow process [26]. These dyes show harmful effect on living organism on short period of exposure for example ingestion of methylene blue through the mouth produces a burning sensation and may cause nausea, vomiting, diarrhea and gastritis. Accidental large dose creates abdominal and chest pain, severe headache, profuse sweating, and mental confusion. Inhalation of crystal violet may cause irritation to the respiratory to the tracks, vomiting, diarrhea, pain, headache and dizziness. Long-term exposure may cause damage to the mucous membrane and gastrointestinal tract [27]. Therefore, the removal of dyes from aqueous effluent has received considerable attention by the environmental researchers [28]. Ozonation, photooxidation, electrocoagulation, adsorption, activated carbon, froth flotation, reverse osmosis, ion exchange, membrane filtration and flocculation processes, are general techniques applied for color removal from textile effluents and some of which have been shown to be effective, although they have some limitations [25, 29-31]. In recent years, a number of studies have been focused on some micro/macro-organisms, which are able to biodegrade or bioaccumulate the dyes in wastewaters [26, 32-37]. Textile wastewaters are characterized by extreme fluctuations in many parameters such as chemical oxygen demand (COD), biochemical oxygen demand (BOD), pH, color and salinity (Table 1). The wastewater composition will depend on the different organic-based compounds, chemicals and dyes used in the industrial dry and wet-processing steps [38-44].

The term "algae" refers to a large and diverse assemblage of organisms that contain chlorophyll and carry out oxygenic photosynthesis [45] and the algae contain polysaccharides, proteins and lipids, which play an important role in biosorption process due to their functional groups, such as carboxylate, hydroxyl, sulphate, phosphate and amino groups [45, 46].

Dye molecules comprise of two key components: the chromophores, which are responsible for producing the color, and the auxochromes, which can not only supplement the chromophore but also render the molecule soluble in water and give enhanced affinity to attach the fibers. Dyes exhibit considerable structural diversity and are classified in several ways. They can be classified both by their chemical structure and their application to the fiber type [11]. Dyes may also be classified on the basis of their solubility: soluble dyes which include acid, mordant, metal complex, direct, basic and reactive dyes; and insoluble dyes including azoic, sulfur, vat and disperse dyes. Besides this, either a major azo linkage or an anthraquinone unit also characterizes dyes chemically. It is worthwhile noting that the azo dyes are the one most widely used and accounts 65–70% of the total dyes produced. Though, the classification of dyes on basis of structure is an appropriate system and has many advantages, like it readily identifies dyes as belonging to a group and having characteristic properties, e.g., azo dyes (strong, good all-round properties, cost-effective) and anthraquinone dyes (weak, expensive), there are a manageable number of chemical groups (about a dozen). Besides these, both the synthetic dye chemist and the dye technologist use this classification most widely. However, the classification based on application is advantageous before considering chemical structures in detail because of the complexities of the dye nomenclature from this type of system. Some properties of dyes classified on their usage [10, 11] (See Chapter 1).

The aim of this chapter is to review the wide variety of algae, which are used for color removal from textile wastewater and discuss the effects of various parameters such as pH, temperature, dye concentrations, biomass, and pretreatment method, etc. on the color removal process. Also it discusses the equilibrium and kinetic models used in batch and continuous biosorption systems, which are important to determine the biosorption capacity of the algae.

2. TEXTILE PROCESSING

The most common textile processing set-up consists of sizing, desizing, scouring, bleaching, mercerising and dyeing processes [39, 47-49].

a. *Sizing* is the first preparation step, in which sizing agents such as starch, polyvinyl alcohol (PVA) and carboxymethyl cellulose are added to provide strength to the fibers and minimize breakage.
b. *Desizing* is the employed next to remove sizing materials prior to weaving.
c. *Scouring* then removes impurities from the fibers by using alkali solution (commonly sodium hydroxide) to breakdown natural oils, fats, waxes and surfactants, as well as to emulsify and suspend impurities in the scouring bath.
d. *Bleaching* is the step used to remove unwanted color from the fibers by using chemicals such as sodium hypochlorite and hydrogen peroxide.
e. *Mercerizing* is a continuous chemical process used to increase dye-ability, luster and fiber appearance. In this step a concentrated alkaline solution is applied and an acid solution washes the fibers before the dyeing step.
f. Finally, *Dyeing* is the process of adding color to the fibers, which normally requires large volumes of water not only in the dye-bath, but also during the rinsing step. Depending on the dyeing process, many chemicals like metals, salts, surfactants, organic processing assistants, sulphide and formaldehyde, may be added to improve dye

3. PREPARATION OF ALGAE FOR BIOSORPTION

Algae have been found to be potential biosorbents because of their availability in both fresh and saltwater. The biosorption capacity of algae is attributed to their relatively high surface area and high binding affinity [50, 51]. Cell wall properties of algae play a major role in biosorption; electrostatic attraction and complexation are known to take place during algal biosorption [52]. Functional groups such as hydroxyl, carboxylate, amino and phosphate found on the algal cell surface are considered to be responsible for sequestration of contaminants from wastewater [53]. The dye removal, especially by using algae, may be attributed to the accumulation of dye ions on the surface of algal biopolymers and further to the diffusion of the dye molecules from aqueous phase onto the solid phase of the biopolymer [54]. Extracellular polymers consist of surface functional groups, which enhance sorption of the dye molecules onto the surface of the polymer during dye removal process [55]. Mohan *et al.* [55] studied the released metabolic intermediates (long chain biopolymers), which have excellent coagulation capacity along with the dye remaining in the aqueous phase tend to adsorb onto the surface of the polymers and settle (biocoagulation). They also studied the removal of Reactive Yellow 22 dye by active *Spirogyra* sp., while, removal of Acid Red 274 dye using inactivated *Spirogyra rhizopus* system was tested by Ozer *et al.* [54] (Table 2). Dynamic batch experiments were carried out for the biosorption of basic yellow dye onto the green macroalgae *Caulerpa scalpelliformis* [56]. They collected the beach-dried seaweeds and they were washed with distilled water, shade dried and stored in an airtight pack at room temperature (28±2°C). The moisture content of the dried seaweed was 5±1% (w/w).

El-Sheekh *et al.* [57] collected different types of algae from different polluted sites in the industrial region in Quisna, and purified in axenic cultures (bacterial free) Bold's Basal medium [58] was used for growth of the green algae. The media were contained in Erlenmeyer conical flasks, sterilized and the pH was adjusted to 7.0. After inoculation they were kept in a culture room at 25±1°C under continuous light with intensity of 5000 and 3000 lux, respectively. Algae ($\sim$2 $\times$ 10^4 cells ml^{-1}) were introduced separately into Erlenmeyer conical flasks containing 150 ml medium and the azo dyes (20 ppm); cultures were maintained under sterile conditions on a rotary shaker. Samples were taken at different intervals times for measurements. The samples were centrifuged and the supernatant was evaluated via a light absorption method and percentage reduction rates were calculated after being compared with control (culture medium without algae).

Aksu and Tezer [26] examined the removal of three vinyl sulphone type reactive dyes (Remazol Black B (RB), Remazol Red RR (RR) and Remazol Golden Yellow RNL (RGY) onto dried green alga *Chlorella vulgaris,* using batch system. They grown the microorganism at 25°C in a liquid medium composed of glucose (5.0 g l^{-1}), yeast extract (0.5 g l^{-1}); peptone (0.5 g l^{-1}); tryptone (1.0 g l^{-1}); $FeSO_4.7H_2O$ (0.01 g l^{-1}), $MgSO_4.7H_2O$ (0.05 g l^{-1}). After the growth period, the algal cells were collected, washed twice with double-distilled water and dried at 60°C and used as dried biomass suspended in double-distilled water and homogenized and then stored in the refrigerator until used.

The biotreatment of triphenylmethane dye, Malachite Green (MG), by alga *Xanthophyta, Vaucheria* species, was investigated by Khataee *et al.* in the batch experiments [59]. Also, the biological treatment of Malachite Green (MG) solution using macroalgae *Cladophora* sp. has been reported Khataeea and Dehgha [60]. The algal species was collected and washed with distilled water to remove macro/microscopic contaminations Followed by autoclaving for 20 min to kill the algal cells (Table 2).

Batch sorption experiments were carried out by Kumar *et al.* [61] for the removal of MG from its aqueous solution using fresh water alga *Pithophora* sp, as biosorbent. The alga was collected and washed with deionized water until the wash-water contained no color and then dried in sunlight for 10 days and directly used as biosorbent without any pretreatment. Batch biosorption experiments were carried out for the removal of Methylene Blue (MB), a basic dye, from aqueous solution using raw and dried Mediterranean green alga *Enteromorpha* sp. [62]. They manually collected *Enteromorpha* spp., washed with distilled water to remove the surface-adhered particles and then dried for 48 h in an oven at 40°C. The dried biomass with an average particle size ranged between 1 and 2 mm was stored in desiccators for further use. Also, batch adsorption of MB, from aqueous solutions by using dried alga *Ulothrix* sp. was carried out by Doğar *et al.* [63]. They collected living algae filaments, rinsed with distilled water and then inactivated in an oven for 5–6 h at 100°C. The biomass sample was sieved to size fraction 125–150 μm.

The biosorptions of Acid red 88 (AR-88), Acid green 3 (AG-3), and Acid orange 7 (AO-7) using deactivated freshwater macroalga, *Azolla filiculoides* were investigated [64]. *A. filiculoides* was collected, sun dried, crushed and finally sieved to particle sizes in the range of 1–2 mm. The biomass was then treated with 0.1M HCl for 5 h followed by washing with distilled water and dried in shade.

The efficiency of *Pithophora* sp., was studied as biosorbent to remove MG from wastewaters [65]. Collected materials were washed with deionized water until the wash water contained no color and then sun dried for 48 h followed by activation at 300°C for 50 min in a muffle furnace. The powdered of activated material was then sieved and the particle size in the range of 0.3 to 1 mm was used for the biosorption process. Also, four types of sorbent materials were prepared by subjecting to thermal treatment at different activation temperatures and activation times. Initially, a number of thermally activated *Pithophora* sp. were prepared at 200, 300, 400°C at different activation times and used for biosorption study.

The macroalga *Caulerpa lentillifera* was found to have adsorption capacity for a basic dye, Astrazon Blue FGR, which a cationic dye consists of two main components: basic blue 159 and basic blue 3 with ratio of 5:1 w/w, respectively [66]. They collected algae and washed with deionized water, dried for 12 h at 80°C and stored in desiccators until used.

The green alga *Scenedesmus quadricauda* was used for the removal of Remazol Brilliant Blue R dye (RBBR), Reactive Blue 19 from aqueous solutions [67]. The alga was isolated from fresh water and the cell culture was grown in BG11 medium at pH 7.0 and 21°C with a 16:8 h light: dark cycle using 2400 lx light intensity [68]. The collected biomass was washed with distillated water. The potential of a green macroalga *Cladophora* species was investigated as available biomaterial for treatment of MG wastewater [69]. The algal species was acquired from Azna-lake in North of Iran and washed with distilled water, deride and used. The biodegradation of Direct Brown NM dye by the alga *Chlorella pyrenoidosa*, was assessed by Huang *et al.* [70]. The degradation of Direct Brown NM dye by calcium alginate immobilized algae was better than that of free algae. The mechanism of degradation of azo dyes by the algae *Chlorella pyrenoidosa*, *C. vulgaris, and Oscillateria tenuis* was investigated [71]. The sorption of three basic dyes, Astrazon Blue FGRL (AB), Astrazon Red GTLN (AR), and MB onto green macroalga *Caulerpa lentillifera* were investigated [72]. *Caulerpa lentillifera* after being washed with deionized water was dried for 12 h at 80°C. The dried alga was ground to the particle size range of less than 20 μm.

Freshwater green alga *Spirogyra* sp., was investigated as a biosorbents for removal of Synazol (reactive dye) from its multi component textile wastewater [73]. The algal biomass was washed with deionized water, dried for 20 h at 80°C and ground in a mortar, before used. The macroalga *Chara* sp., was used by Khataee *et al.* [74] to study the removal of MG from its solution. The removal of MB was studied by adsorption technique using Maine algae as adsorbents such as *Ulva lactuca* and *Sargassum* [75]. The algae were collected and washed thoroughly with distilled water and dried at 60±2°C for overnight and the dried constant was grind to obtain 100 μm mesh size and then used for adsorption studies.

The potential of green alga *Cosmarium* sp., was investigated as a viable biomaterial for biological treatment of triphenylmethane dye, MG [36]. Algal decolonization and degradation of monoazo Tatrazine and diazo (Ponceau ss) dyes was carried out using the green algal strains *Chlorella ellipsoidea*, *Chlorella kessleri*, *Chlorella vulgaris*, *Scenedesmus bijuga*,

Scenedesmus bijugatus and *Scenedesmus obliquus* [76], which were cultured in a sterile Tris-Acetone–Phosphate (TAP) medium [77]. The brown alga *Cystoseira barbatula Kützing*, which is widely distributed in the Mediterranean, was used to prepare an alternative low cost biosorbent to remove MB from aqueous solutions [78]. The wet alga samples were collected and taken into plastic bags filled with seawater to the laboratory immediately and then washed with tap water, distilled water and dried for 16 hours at 70°C. After being dried, the alga was grounded with mortar to 500 μm pore size and stored in desiccators.

Non-living dried biomass at 40°C of the alga *Chara aspera* is capable of binding two basic dyes, MB and basic blue 3 from their aqueous solution [79]. Dead marine alga, *Turbinaria conoides*, was washed with distilled water, sun-dried and then ground to particles with size less than 0.1 mm diameter, sieves and protonated by soaked in 0.1 mol HCl for 4 h followed by washing with distilled water and dried overnight at 60°C [80]

Meevasana and Pavasanta [81] used dried biomass of *Caulerpa lentillifera* for the removal of three binary dye mixtures prepared from the basic textile dyes Astrazon Blue FGRL, Astrazon Red GTLN, and Astrazon Golden Yellow GL-E. Brown marine algae *Turbinaria conoides* was washed with distilled water and sun-dried and protonated for 3 h using 0.1 M HCl and then washed with distilled water and dried overnight at 60°C followed by ground and sieved to different particle sizes and subsequently used for the removal of Acid Blue 9 [82]. The fresh water algae *Spirogyra* was used for the removal of Direct Brown Dye from aqueous solutions [83]. They collected alga and washed with ultra pure water and subjected to drying under diffused sunlight for 7 days and then crushed to particle size of 1-2 mm, followed protonation via treated with 0.1 M HCl for 12 h at room temperature and then washed with ultra pure water before drying and stored in airtight containers until used.

El Nemr *et al.* [84] tested the capacity of the green alga *Ulva lactuca* as viable biomaterials for removal of Direct Yellow 12 (DY-12) from aqueous solution. The Mediterranean green alga, *U. lactuca*, was collected from Alexandria coast, Egypt. The collected biomass was washed with sea water, tap water, and then distilled water, then dried in the sun for several days followed by oven dried for 24 h at 100°C. The dried alga was milled and sieved to give different particle sizes and stored in a sealed bottle until used. A preliminary study conducted to investigate Direct Brown 2-Diazo dye color removal using fresh marine alga, *Spirogyra* species [85]. The tested alga species is subjected to drying by blotting on a tissue paper weighed in required quantities and used for experimental studies. The Batch biological treatment of MB was carried out using green alga *Ulva lactuca* [86]. *Ulva lactuca* was washed with sea water, tap water, and then distilled water and the clean alga was exposed to sun dried for several days followed by oven drying for 24 h at 100°C, and then the dried algae were milled, sieved, and stored until used.

Green marine alga *Caulerpa racemosa* var. *cylindracea* (CRC) was used for the removal of a cationic dye, Malachite Green Oxalate (MGO) from aqueous solution [87]. Algal sample was collected, washed with seawater, distilled water and then dried in an oven for 12 h at 80°C followed by grinded with mortar and pestle and used in adsorption study without any treatment. Batch decolorization of solution containing synthetic MG dye was investigated using four algal genera (*Cosmarium, Chlorella, Chlamydomonas* and *Euglena*) [88]. The algal species was acquired from natural lake and used immediately. *Cosmarium* was grown in several glass jars containing growth medium (to obtain stock algal culture to be used during the experiments) using pH of the medium 7.5 and cultivated at 25°C under static incubation condition for a maximum 15 days exposure period. The jars were placed near the window and exposed to natural light. *Cosmarium* biomass was measured by counting the number of cells by optical microscopy using a Neubauer Hemocytometer. MB dye adsorption on *Sargassum muticum*, an invasive macroalga has been investigated [89]. The alga *Sargassum muticum*, collected and washed with distilled water, dried over night at 60°C, ground, and sieved in the size pore range from 0.5 to 1 mm followed by chemically modified by different treatments such as protonation and chemical cross-linking with $CaCl_2$ or H_2CO to improve the stability as well as the adsorption capacity of the algal biomass.

Table 2. Dyes removal using different algae species

Bisorbent	Name of Dye	pH	Temp. (°C)	C_0 (mg l^{-1})	Eq. time (hour)	Q_{max} (mg g^{-1})	Ref.
Chlorella vulgaris	Remazol Black B	2	35	80	4	86.3	[26]
Chlorella vulgaris	Remazol Red RR	2	25	80	4	55.2	[26]
Chlorella vulgaris	Remazol Golden Yellow RNL	2	25	80	4	35.0	[26]
Spirogyra species	Reactive Yellow (22)	4	27	250-1000	72	400	[55]
Spirogyra rhizopus	Acid Red 274	3	30				[54]
Im. Act. *Scenedesmus quadricauda*	Remazol Brilliant Blue R	2	30	150		68	[67]
H. Inact. *S. quadricauda*	Remazol Brilliant Blue R	2	30	150		95.2	[67]
Vaucheria sp.	Malachite Green	7.5	25	10	7	-	[59]
Pithophora sp.	Malachite Green	6	30	100	10	59.04	[61]
Row *Pithophora sp.*	Malachite Green	5		100	0.83	117.65	[65]
Cladophora sp.	Malachite Green	8		10	1.25		[60]
Ther. Act. *Pithophora sp.*	Malachite Green	5	30	100		117.65	[65]
Chlorella sp.	Malachite Green	10	25	0.005	2.5		[88]
Cladophora sp.	Malachite Green	8.5	25	10			[69]
Chara sp.	Malachite Green	8.5	25	10	7		[74]
Cosmarium sp.	Malachite Green	9	25	0.01		7.63	[36]
Turbinaria conoides	Malachite Green	8	30	100		66.6	[80]
Caulerpa racemosa var.	Malachite Green		45			25.67	[87]

cylindracea							
Enteromorpha sp.	Methylene blue	6	30	50	3	273.73	[62]
Sargassum muticum	Methylene blue		25			279.2	[89]
Ulothrix sp.	Methylene blue	7.9	20	100	12	86.1	[63]
Caulerpa lentillifera	Methylene blue	6.5	25			417	[72]
Ulva lactuca	Methylene blue	7	25				[75]
Sargassum	Methylene blue						[75]
Cystoseira barbatula Kützing	Methylene blue	6.4	35		3.5	38.6	[78]
Ulva lactuca	Methylene blue	10	25		2	40.2	[86]
Chara aspera	Methylene blue	11.2		0.1	2	139.4	[79]
Caulerpa scalpelliformis	Basic yellow dye	6	30	150	4	27	[56]
Chara aspera	Basic blue 3	4.3			2	17.8	[79]
Azolla filiculoides	Acid red 88	7			6	109	[64]
Azolla filiculoides	Acid green 3	3			6	133.5	[64]
Azolla filiculoides	Acid orange 7	3			6	109.6	[64]
Turbinaria conoides	Acid Blue 9	1	33	100	3.75	38.46	[82]
Caulerpa lentillifera	Astrazon Blue FGRL	6.5	25		0.16	38.9	[72]
Caulerpa lentillifera	Astrazon Red GTLN	6.5	25		0.5	47.6	[72]
Spirogyra sp.	Synazol	3	30		18	85	[73]
Spirogyra	Direct Brown	2	50	0.015	2	5.47	[83]
Ulva lactuca	Direct Yellow 12	10	25	100	2	10.99	[84]

Ther. Act.: Thermally activated; Im. Act.: Immobilized active; H. Inact.: Heat inactivated.

4. EFFECT OF pH ON DYE BIOSORPTION

Since pH is the most important parameter affecting not only the biosorption capacity, but also the color of the dye solution and the solubility of some dyes, various researchers have investigated the effect of pH on color removal. Aksu and Tezer [26] studied the effect of initial pH on sorption capacity of dried alga *C. vulgaris* for each dye (three vinyl sulphone type reactive dyes) in the pH range of 1.0–3.0 at 80 mg l^{-1} initial dye concentration. Biosorption of each of the dyes exhibited a similar variation with pH. Maximum uptake was at pH 2.0 in each case and then, the uptake was declined sharply with further increase in pH. Solution pH influences both the cell surface dye binding sites and the chemistry of dye in solution. The reactive dyes release colored dye anions into solution. The cell wall matrix of green algae contains different functional groups such as carboxyl, hydroxyl, sulphate and other charged groups which are created by their complex heteropolysaccharides and lipid components. Protein can constitute 10–70% of the green algal cell wall. At lower pH values (acidic) the biomass will have a net positive charge. It is expected that nitrogen containing functional groups such as amines or imidazoles in the biomass will also be protonated at the acidic pH values. Higher uptakes obtained at lower pH values may be due to the electrostatic attractions between these negatively charged dye anions and positively charged cell surface. Hydrogen ion also acts as a bridging ligand between the alga cell wall and the dye molecule. The reduction in adsorption capacity of dyes on alga with increasing pH can be attributed to change in surface characteristics and charge. As the pH of the system increases, the number of negatively charged sites increases and the number of positively charged sites decreases. A negatively charged surface site on the sorbent does not favor the adsorption of dye anions due to the electrostatic repulsion.

Khataee et al. [59, 74] also investigated the effect of pH on the removal of MG by Vaucheria sp.; they studied the pH in the range from 1.5 to 8.5 and observed that the amount of removed MG dye varied with pH, the decolorization efficiency was rapidly increased with increasing initial pH of the dye solution from 1.5 to 7.5. This can be explained on the basis of zero point of discharge for biomass. According to the zero point of charge of algae species, their surfaces are presumably positively charged in acidic solution and negatively charged in alkaline solution. Since MG is a cationic dye, the alkaline solution favors adsorption of it onto algae species surface, thus the decolorization efficiency increases. Dye removal was decreased after pH 7.5. A similar observation was also reported by Kumar et al. [65] for adsorption of MG onto Pithophora sp. They studied the effect of initial solution pH on the equilibrium uptake of MG over a pH range from 2 to 7 and observed that the amount the q_e value increased with increasing pH from 2 to 5 and with further increase in pH, the amount of dye adsorbed decreased slowly. The maximum amount of MG dye removal was 887.5 mg g^{-1} at pH 5, which can be explained on the basis of zero point of discharge for biomass. For algae sp., the isoelectric point would be at pH 3.0 [90, 91]. Above this pH the surface of algae may acquire a negative charge leading to increased dye cation uptake due to the electrostatic force of attraction. This can be visualized from the rapid increase in dye uptake rate for an increase in pH from 4 to 5. Previously, a number of studies have reported that there exist a linear relation between pH and the amount of basic dyes uptake, which was attributed to the negative surface charge of adsorbent, which might be increase with increasing initial solution pH and enhances the uptake of dye cations due to electrostatic force of attraction. The same results was obtained by Kumar et al. [61], when equilibrium uptake for the MG, a cationic dye, was found to be pH dependent and maximum uptake was observed at a pH of 6.

Ncibi et al. [62] examined the effect of initial pH on removal of MB by Enteromorpha spp., in pH ranged between 2 and 10 and found that the equilibrium sorption capacity reach the minimum at pH 2 (40.21 mg g^{-1}) and reach the maximum at pH 6, and then remained nearly constant (70.35 mg g^{-1}) over the initial pH ranges of 6–10. As a green alga, the cell wall matrix of Enteromorpha contains different functional groups such as carboxyl, hydroxyl, sulphate and other charged groups, which are created by their complex polysaccharides, protein and lipid components. Thus, at lower pH, the surface charge may get positively charged (i.e. protonation of the cell wall), thus making (H$^+$) ions compete effectively with dye cations toward actives sorption sites causing a decrease in the amount of adsorbed dye. In that case (lower pH), the biomass still able to adsorb MB, which could be attributed to the hydrogen ions acting as a bridging ligand between the alga cell wall and the dye molecule. Thereafter, at higher pH the alga polymeric components may get negatively charged (possible deprotonation), which enhances the positively charged dye cations through electrostatic forces of attraction. On the other hand, Dõgar et al. [63] studied the effect of pH on sorption capacity of biosorbent and the zeta potential of biosorbent particles in the pH range of 1.0–11.0 at 90 mg l^{-1} on the sorption of MB by a green algae species (Ulothrix sp.) and they reported that the adsorption onto biomass sharply increases at the pH range 1–6 while the adsorbed amount was not changed significantly in the range of pH 6–11. The zeta potential values negatively increase with increasing pH and the zero point of charge of the biomass was determined to be in the pH range of 1–2. For pH values higher than pH 7.9, due to structural changes in the intracellular components and cell membrane involving lipid and glycoprotein and so formation of more negatively charged sites as a result of basic hydrolysis. Similarly, Aravindhan et al. [56] observed that the uptake of basic yellow dye on to Caulerpa scalpelliformis increases from 17 to 27 mg g^{-1} for an increase in pH from 3.0 to 8.0. Several reasons may be attributed to the adsorption of dye by the seaweed relative to pH. The surface of the seaweed contains large number of reactive sites. At lower pH, the surface of the seaweed gets positively charged thus making the H^+ ions compete effectively with dye cations causing decrease in the amount of dye adsorbed (mg g^{-1}). At higher pH, the surface of the seaweed gets negatively charged, which enhances the interaction of positively charged dye cations with the surface of seaweed through the electrostatic forces of attraction [92].

The effect of pH on acid dyes uptake by a freshwater macroalga Azolla filiculoides in the batch process was studied by varying the pH from 2 to 7 [64]. For each pH value, the dye concentrations were varied from 10 to 1000 mg l^{-1} using biosorbent dosage 4 g l^{-1} and agitation speed 150 rpm was kept constant. Azolla biomass exhibited high AR88 dye uptakes in the pH range of 6–7, whereas it biosorbed more AG3 and AO7 dyes in the pH range of 2–3. Daneshvar et al. [88] demonstrated that the optimal pH for biosorption of MG by four algal species was at basic range. The effects of initial pH on dye sorption of IASq (The immobilized active Scenedesmus quadricauda) and IHISq (heat inactivated S. quadricauda) were studied in the pH range from 2-8 at an initial dye concentration of 150 mg l^{-1} [67]. The color removal efficiency of MG solution as a function of pH using a green macroalga Cladophora sp. was established [69].

The azo dyes release colored dye anions in the solution and at lower pH values, the biomass will have a net positive charge, which is expected that nitrogen containing functional groups such as amines or imidazoles in the biomass will also be protonated at acidic pH values [93-95]. The effect of initial pH on biodegradation efficiency was analyzed over a pH range from 1.5-8.5. The decolorization efficiency was rapidly increased with increasing initial pH of the dye solution from 1.5 to 7.5. Dye removal was decreased after pH of 7.5. Daneshvar et al. [36] reported the same result for the biodegradation efficiency of MG when they studied the effect of initial solution on the biodegradation efficiency of MG over a pH range from 2.0 to 11.0. It was observed that the amount of dye removed varies with pH and showed threefold increase in decolorization rate with increase in pH from 4.0 to 6.0, reached the maximum value of 92.4% at the pH of 9.0. On the other hand, Khalaf [73] studied the effect of initial pH (1–4) on dye biosorption from multi component textile effluent by autoclaved algal biomasses. He observed that the maximum percent of dye removal was obtained at pH 3, which may be explained in terms of electrostatic attraction between the positively charged surface of the biomass and the dye particles as mentioned above. Reactive dyes are also called anionic dyes because of the negative electrical structure of the chromophore group [96] and hence a negative surface charge does not favor the adsorption of dye anions due to the electrostatic repulsion [97].

Pavan *et al.* [98] have also found the best pH range between 7.0–10.0 for the MB removal due to the electrostatic interactions between adsorbent and MB. The effect of pH on the biosorption of two basic dyes, MB and BB3 by using of *Chara aspera* was also observed by Low *et al.* [79], in the pH range of 4-10 the sorption was fairly constant for both systems. However, the biosorption ability started to decrease when pH was lower than 4. The decrease could be attributed to the presence of excess H^+, making sorption less favorable. Also, the effect of pH on the removal of the biosorption of MG onto *Turbinaria conoides* was assessed, the equilibrium sorption capacity is minimum at pH 2 (11 mg g^{-1}) and increases monotonically up to pH 5. A further increase in pH leads to an appreciable increase in percentage adsorption. The absence of sorption at low pH can be explained by the fact that at this acidic pH, H^+ may compete with dye ions for the adsorption sites of adsorbent, thereby inhibiting the adsorption of dye. At higher solution pH, the *Turbinaria conoides* biomass may get negatively charged, which enhances the adsorption of positively charged dye cations through electrostatic forces of attraction. Moreover, a change of solution pH affects the adsorptive process through dissociation of functional groups on the adsorbent surface. Such behavior leads to a shift in the equilibrium characteristics of the adsorption process [80].

Rajeshkannan *et al.* [82] recorded the effect of pH on the bisorption of Acid Blue 9 onto *Turbinaria conoides*. The equilibrium sorption capacity was maximum at pH 1 (20.69 mg g^{-1}) and decreases up to pH 7, further increase in pH leads to drastic decrease in percentage adsorption. The ionic form of dye in solution and the electrical charge of the algal cell wall components depend on the solution pH [83, 99-101]. El-Nemr *et al.* [84] studied the equilibrium of DY-12 uptakes at various pH values by varying the suspension pH from 1.0 to 7.0. The uptake of dye was high at pH 7.0 and 1.0, but decreased with increasing suspension pH from 1.0–4.0. The lowest biosorption occurred at an initial pH of 4.0. The highest biosorption obtained at pH 7.0 may be attributed to the uncharged alga surface and the presence of DY-12 as sodium salt. The high percentage of removal observed at initial pH 1.0 can be attributed to the positive surface charge gained depending on the adsorption of H^+ ions on the algal surface, and also the hydrolysis of alga may occur, resulting in different dye removal mechanisms. On the other hand, the results observed at initial pH 4–6 may be attributed to the change on the dye and alga surface and on the large number of surface functional groups presented on the cell wall of *U. lactuca*. The pH dependence of DY-12 adsorption can largely be related to the type and ionic state of these functional groups and also on the chemistry of DY-12 in the solution. The uptake was high at neutral pH 7, thus making the experiment more environmentally friendly by not adding any other chemicals to the wastewater. Basic dye upon dissolution released colored dye cation in solution, and the adsorption of these charged dye groups onto the adsorbent surface was primarily influenced by the surface charge on the adsorbent, which in turn was influenced by the pH solution. The maximum affinity for this dye cation could be expected at alkaline pH values. At a low pH value, a fewer anionic adsorption sites on the dried *Ulva lactuca* were generated, and sorption was unfavorable, probably because of excess H^+ competing with dye molecule for sorption sites on the dried *Ulva lactuca* [86, 102-107].

5. EFFECT OF TEMPERATURE ON DYE BIOSORPTION

As various textile dye effluents are discharged at relatively high temperatures (50–60°C), therefore temperature will be an important as design parameter affecting the biosorption capacity in the real application of biosorption by biomass [23, 24]. Aksu and Tezer [26] investigated the effect of temperature on three vinyl sulphone type reactive dyes (Remazol Black B, Remazol Red and Remazol Golden Yellow RNL biosorption onto dried *Chlorella vulgaris,* in the temperature range of 25–55°C at an initial dye concentration of 80 mg l^{-1}. The biosorption of RB dye increased with increasing temperature up to 35°C (63.0 mg g^{-1}) due to higher affinity of sites for this dye and an increase of binding sites on the biomass, and decreased with further increasing in temperature, which may be attributed to the possible chemical sorption beside the physical sorption. The equilibrium uptake of RR dye decreased with increasing temperature suggesting that biosorption between *C. vulgaris* and RR dye was an exothermic process and the mechanism was mainly physical adsorption, dominant at lower temperatures. At 25°C, maximum equilibrium uptake of RR dye was 55.2 mg g^{-1}. The biosorption of RGY dye was also inversely proportional to the increase of temperature, i.e. increasing the temperature until 45°C lead to a decrease in the equilibrium uptakes from 35.0 mg g^{-1} (25°C) to 22.1 mg g^{-1} (45°C). No biosorption was observed at 55°C, which may be attributed to damage of certain surface sites of cell available for dye biosorption. The adsorption is favored by a decrease in temperature, a phenomenon which is also characteristic of physical adsorption.

Khataee *et al.* [59] studied the effect of temperature on the removal MG, by *Vaucheria* sp., and reported that within the temperature range between (5–45°C) the decolorization rate increased as the temperature rose. The results showed essentially no thermal deactivation of decolorization activity under operational temperatures, therefore, the used species could acclimatize in a broad range of temperatures. The same trend has been reported for biological decolorization of a Reactive dye by *Enterobacter sp.*, EC3 [108]. The same results were reached by the study of the removal of MG onto a green macroalgae *Cladophora* sp. and *Chara* sp. [60, 74]. The influence of temperature on the sorption of MG by the *Turbinaria conoides* biomass was studied [80] with a constant initial concentration of 100 mg l^{-1} and a temperature range of 20 to 50°C. The temperature profile indicated that as the temperature increases the sorption capacity increases to a maximum value and then decreases. This is because the biosorbent loses its properties at very high temperatures due to denaturation. The maximum sorption capacity was attained at 30°C. A similar result of temperature effect was also reported for the adsorption of Basic dye (Bismark brown) onto chitosan [109]. On the other hand; Sivarajasekar *et al.* [83] studied the effect of temperature in the removal of Direct Brown dye by *Spirogyra* sp. Increasing in operating temperature from 20 to 50°C showed a marked improvement in dye sorption capacity, this suggested that the dye-algal-sorption process may be attributed to endothermic nature [110].

Also, the temperature dependence of adsorption was studied by Dögar *et al.* [63] for the various initial dye concentrations at 20, 40, 50, and 60°C. This showed that the amount of adsorbed dye decreased with increasing temperature, indicating exothermic nature of sorption process. The effect of temperature on the sorption capacity of green seaweed was studied at 20-60°C [56]. The results showed that the sorption capacity decreased from 28 to 23 mg g^{-1} with temperature increase from 20 to 60°C. The equilibrium uptake of the cationic yellow dye decreased with increasing temperature suggesting that biosorption between *C. scalpelliformis* and cationic yellow dye was an exothermic process and the mechanism was mainly physical adsorption, dominant at lower temperatures. The effects of temperature on the equilibrium sorption capacities of immobilized active *Scenedesmus quadricauda* (IASq) and heat inactivated *S. quadricauda* (IHISq) for Remazol Brilliant Blue R (RBBR) were investigated in the temperature range of 20–45°C at the initial dye concentration of 150 mg l^{-1} [67]. The IHISq treatment has higher biosorption capacity compare to IASq. The biosorption capacities of the RBBR with IASq and IHISq were obtained at 30°C as 45.3 mg g^{-1} and 47.9 mg g^{-1}, respectively. The biosorption of the RBBR dye increases by increasing temperature up to 30°C. This temperature is suitable to bind with dye and cell wall matrix of *S. quadricauda*. The sorption decreased when the temperature was increased, the biosorption capacity was decreased due to the decreasing surface activity. Beyond 30°C the degrees in biosorption capacities were less significant in IHISq compared to IASq, implying that the biosorption capacity of active cells is affected more strongly by elevated temperatures than that of the heat activated cells.

The effect of temperature (15–45°C) on biosorption of Synazol, reactive dye, from multi component textile effluent by autoclaved biomass of *Spirogyra* sp. was investigated [73]. Over the examined range biosorption rate increased as the temperature rose. The maximum dye removal (44 and 36%) for alga biomasses was obtained at 30°C. An increase in the biosorbed dye amounts with increasing temperature from 15–30°C deals with an increase in the biosorption capacity of both biomasses. Further increase in temperature from 30 to 45°C may alter the surface activity of biomass result in a decrease in removal value, indicating that this process is exothermic in nature.

6. EFFECT OF INITIAL DYE CONCENTRATION ON DYE BIOSORPTION

A higher initial concentration provides an important driving force to overcome all mass transfer resistances of the dye between the aqueous and solid phases, thus increases the uptake. In addition, increasing initial dye concentration increases the number of collisions between dye anions and sorbent, which enhances the sorption process [26]. The effect of initial dye concentration on the sorption capacity was investigated between 20 and 800 mg l^{-1} for RB and RR dyes and between 10 and 200 mg l^{-1} for RGY dye at an initial pH value of 2.0 and at four different temperatures. The effect of initial dye concentration on the biosorption capacity was found to be of considerable significant for all dyes and temperatures studied. The RB dye uptake was enhanced notably as the initial concentration of dye increased. Uptake of the RR dye also increased with increasing the initial dye concentration tending to saturation at higher dye concentrations. Although uptake of the RGY dye increased with increasing dye concentration, there was no further uptake was observed above 200 mg l^{-1} dye concentration but reached the saturation capacity more quickly. When the initial dye concentration increased from 20 to 800 mg l^{-1}, the uptake capacity of dried *C. vulgaris* increased from 16 to 420 mg g^{-1} for RB dye at 35°C and from 14 to 182 mg g^{-1} for RR dye at 25°C. The uptake of the RGY dye increased from 6 to 53 mg g^{-1} with increasing initial dye concentration from 10 to 200 mg l^{-1}. For all dyes, increasing the initial dye concentration resulted in decreasing the color removal efficiency but increase the uptake capacities at all temperatures studied, which may be attributed to the saturation of the sorption sites on the biosorbent with increasing in dye concentration. However, higher adsorption yields were observed at lower concentrations of each dye.

The initial dye concentration can influence the efficiency of the biological treatment process through a combination of factors including the toxicity of the dye at higher concentrations, and the ability of the enzyme to recognize the substrate efficiently at the very low concentrations [108, 111]. The results obtained by Khataee et al. [59] showed that the increase of the initial dye concentration led to decrease in the biological decolorization efficiency. On the other hand Dögar et al. [63] reported that uptake of MB by dried Ulothrix sp., increased with increasing initial dye concentration. The surface of sorbent is bare in the initial stage; the sorption rapidly occurs and normally controlled by the diffusion process from the bulk to the surface. In the later stage, the sorption is likely an attachment-controlled process due to less available sorption sites. The increasing equilibrium uptake with increasing initial dye concentrations can be attributed to concentration gradient between bulk and sorbent surface and/or dimerization/aggregation process. Similar results were obtained by different researchers [36, 69, 74].

7. EFFECT OF INITIAL ALGAE WEIGHTT ON DYE BIOSORPTION

Khataee et al. [59] investigated the effect of different amounts of alga weight (0.5 – 6 g) on biological treatment of MG solution. Dye removal significantly increased with an increase in the amount of biomass until it reached the value of 89% with the biomass content of 6 g. The reason of this observation is thought to be the fact that increase of alga biomass gives more surface area for sorption of the dye molecule on the surface of alga [112]. The same trend has been reported for biological decolorization processes using different algal species [69, 74, 112, 113]. The effect of sorbent amount was studied by Ncibi et al. [62] using a range of 5 mg to 5 g of Enteromorpha sp. mixed with 50 ml of the MB dye. They showed that an increase in the biomass quantity causes a decrease in the residual MB concentration at equilibrium time and consequently an increase in the biosorption removal efficiency. Indeed, the biosorption removal efficiency values increased from 37 to 100%, as the biomass dose was increased from 0.1 to 5 g l^{-1}. Such a trend is mostly attributed to an increase in the sorptive surface area and the availability of more active adsorption sites. Similar results were obtained by El Nemr et al. [84] and El Sikaily et al. [86] for DY12 and MB, respectively.

The effect of Turbinaria conoides biomass dosage on the amount of color adsorbed was studied by agitating 200 ml of 100 mg l^{-1} of dye solution with different amounts of sorbent ranged from 0.25 to 0.55 g [80] and showed that the amount of dye adsorbed decreased from 42 to 29 mg g^{-1} and observed an increase in percentage color removal. The amount of solute adsorbed onto unit weight of adsorbent get split with increasing adsorbent dosage [61].

8. EQUILIBRIUM MODELING OF BIOSORPTION

8.1. Isotherm Models

Equilibrium data, commonly known as adsorption isotherms, are basic requirements for the design of adsorption systems used for the removal of pollutants. The Langmuir, Freundlich, Langmuir–Freundlich, Redlich–Peterson, Brunauer–Emmet–Teller (BET), Radke–Prausnitz, etc. are examples for isotherm models. El Nemr *et al.* [114] reported a comprehensive study concerning most known adsorption isotherm and kinetic models using removal of MB by rice husk activated carbon. Assuming the batch biosorption as a single-staged equilibrium operation, the separation process can be mathematically defined using these isotherm constants to estimate the residual concentration of dye or amount of biosorbent for the desired levels of purification. The isotherm constants obtained could also be used to find the stage number in multi-staged separation processes. Aksu and Tezer [26] estimated that equilibrium data of RB biosorption onto dried *Chlorella vulgaris* fitted very well to the Koble–Corrigan model while the Langmuir model described the biosorptions of RR and RGY dyes best in the studied concentration and temperature ranges. According to the Langmuir model, the maximum dye biosorption capacity of biomass was determined as 556 mg g^{-1} for RB dye at 35°C, and was determined as 196 and 72 mg g^{-1} for RR and RGY dyes at 25°C, respectively. Kumar *et al.* [61] stated that the equilibrium data for the removal of MG using *Pithophora sp.*, tend to fit Freundlich isotherm equation with higher correlation coefficient, which predicts that the coverage of MG onto *Pithophora sp.* particles may be multilayer (heterogeneous sorption). Ncibi *et al.* [62] showed that the experimental data were very well represented by the Langmuir model for the linear regression analysis and both the Langmuir and Redlich–Peterson isotherm models for the non-linear analysis. In both cases, such modeling behavior confirms the monolayer coverage of MB molecules onto energetically homogenous *Enteromopha* surface. On the removal of basic yellow dye onto the green macroalgae *Caulerpa scalpelliformis*, Aravindhan *et al.* [56] concluded that the Sorption equilibrium studies demonstrated that the biosorption followed Freundlich isotherm model, which implies a heterogeneous sorption phenomenon. On the Batch biosorption experiments carried out for the removal of MG using raw and thermally activated *Pithophora* sp., Kumar *et al.* [65] applied the different isotherms equations (Freundlich, Langmuir and Redlich-Peterson) and they found that the equilibrium data are very well represented by Redlich-Peterson isotherm model followed by Freundlich and Langmuir isotherm models with high correlation coefficient values.

The Langmuir, Freundlich, Temkin, Dubinin–Radushkevich and Flory–Huggins isotherm models were used to fit the equilibrium biosorption data for the removal of RBBR dye [67]. The Langmuir, Freundlich and Dubinin–Radushkevich equations have better coefficients than Temkin and Flory–Huggins equation describing the RBBR dye adsorption onto IASq and IHISq. From the Dubinin–Radushkevich model, the mean free energy was calculated as 6.42–7.15 kJ mol^{-1} for IASq and IHISq, indicating that the biosorption of dye was taken place by physical adsorption reactions. Marungrueng and Pavasant [72] suggested that the isotherm model for the removal of three basic dyes using green alga *Caulerpa lentillifera*, followed Langmuir model, which suggested that the sorption was monolayer coverage. Tahir *et al.* [75] suggested that the removal of MB using adsorbents such *Ulva lactuca* and *Sargassum* were fitted into the Langmuir and Freundlich adsorption isotherm equations. Dubinin-Radushkevich equation was used to analyze the adsorption behavior of the algae in aqueous MB solutions. Langmuir and Freundlich models were employed in the study by Kannan *et al.* [80] and they found that the Langmuir isotherm fits the data better than the Freundlich isotherm, which indicates that the adsorption of MG on *Turbinaria conoides* biomass takes place as monolayer adsorption on a surface that is homogenous in adsorption affinity. Also Rajeshkannan *et al.* [82] studied the equilibrium of the removal of Acid Blue 9 using brown marine algae *Turbinaria conoides*, and they found that the Freundlich and Redlich-Peterson isotherm fit the data well, while Langmuir isotherm is not applicable due to its low correlation coefficient. El-Nemr *et al.* [84] concluded that the adsorption isotherm followed only the Freundlich model with a correlation coefficient near unity for the bisorption of DY-12 onto green alga *Ulva lactuca*. The same algal sp. was used for the removal of basic blue 9 by El Sikaily *et al.* [86] and they found that the adsorption isotherm of basic blue 9 followed both the Langmuir and Freundlich models with a correlation coefficient near unity. Also, equilibrium data were analyzed by Bekçi *et al.* [87] using Freundlich, Langmuir and Dubinin–Radushkevich equations and they found Freundlich model gave the best fit, which indicates that the sorption of MG on *Caulerpa racemosa* var. *cylindracea* was a multilayer coverage (heterogeneous sorption).

8.2. Biosorption Kinetics

Aksu and Tezer [24] described the biosorption of three vinyl sulphone type reactive dyes by dried *Chlorella vulgaris*, in the batch adsorbed by pseudo first-order and pseudo second-order and saturation type kinetic models to the experimental data assuming that the external mass transfer can be neglected in the system. The results indicated that the dye uptake process followed the pseudo second-order and saturation type rate expressions for *C. vulgaris* system. The kinetic studies performed by Kumar *et al.* [61] for the biosorption MG by *Pithophora sp.*, indicated that equilibrium followed first order rate kinetics with an average rate constant of $0.9213 \, min^{-1}$.

Dögar *et al.* [63] applied three kinetic models, including the pseudo-first-order model, pseudo-second-order model, and intraparticle diffusion model on the sorption of MB onto dried *Ulothrix sp.* They found that the first-order and intraparticle diffusion models do not show good fitting with the experimental data due to their low correlation coefficients, while the data are in good agreement with the pseudo-second-order equation with correlation coefficient near the unity. This supporting the basic assumption in the model that chemisorptions or effective electrostatic interactions plays a major role in adsorption of MB onto dried *Ulothrix sp.* The absolute magnitude of ΔG^{o} may give an idea about the type of adsorption. While chemisorptions have an energy range 80–400 kJ mol^{-1}, physical sorption has a range $0 - (-20) \, kJ \, mol^{-1}$. The isosteric enthalpy ΔH^{o} and entropy ΔS^{o} values were calculated as $-11.8 \, kJ \, mol^{-1}$ and $37.5 \, J \, mol^{-1} \, K^{-1}$), respectively. This negative enthalpy value indicates that the adsorption process was exothermic; and the calculated entropy value small and positive. The positive adsorption entropy may be interrelated to the extent of hydration of cationic dye molecules. The thermodynamic results imply that the interactions between dye molecules and algae surface are highly electrostatic.

Aravindhan *et al.* [56] found that sorption data were found to follow pseudo-second order kinetics. They also calculated various thermodynamic parameters such as enthalpy of sorption ΔH^o, free energy change ΔG^o and entropy ΔS^o. The negative value of ΔH^o and negative values of ΔG^o showed that sorption process is exothermic and spontaneous. The negative value of entropy ΔS^o shows the decreased randomness at the solid–liquid interface during the sorption of dyes onto green seaweed.

Work carried out by Kumar *et al.* [65] indicated that by applying reversible first order kinetics, pseudo-first order, pseudo-second order models and they found that the sorption data fit very well to pseudo-second order model. The average pseudo-second order rate constant, and initial sorption rate were determined to be 3.46×10^{-3} and 7.97×10^2 mg g^{-1} h^{-1}, and the negative value of free energy change ($\Delta G^o = -8.585$ kJ mol^{-1}) indicate that sorption process is spontaneous and confirms affinity of biosorbent for the dye cations.

Lagergren's first order kinetic equation has been most widely used to describe the solute adsorption on various adsorbents, also the first-order and the pseudo second-order kinetic models were applied to the experimental data of removal of Astrazon Blue FGRL using *Caulerpa lentillifera* [66]. They found that the pseudo second-order model is more applicable than the first-order model. Also the Enthalpy of adsorption was calculated to give ΔH 14.87 kJ mol^{-1}. The positive enthalpy of adsorption indicated chemical adsorption, which suggested that the chemical bond between the *C. lentillifera* surface and the dye molecules could not be easily desorbed by physical means such as simply shaking or heating. Ergene *et al.* [67] analyzed the kinetic characteristics of the bisorption of RBBR onto *Scenedesmus quadricauda* and found that the biosorption process of dye was well explained with pseudo-second-order kinetics.

The values of ΔH^o and ΔS^o were calculated by Tahir *et al.* [75] for removal of MB by marine algae *Ulva lactuca* and *Sargassum*. The values of ΔG^o are negative, which showed that the adsorption process is spontaneous and the values of enthalpy were positive, which revealed the endothermic behavior of the system, whereas entropy values were negative. Also, Caparkaya and Cavas [78] was found that the pseudo-second order model was fitted better when compared to the linear regression correlation coefficient values obtained for biosorption of MB by a brown alga *Cystoseira barbatula*. The entropy ΔS^o, enthalpy ΔH^o and Gibbs free energy ΔG^o, and they found that ΔH^o were values were positive in all concentrations of dye, which indicated that the interactions between dye and alga are endothermic, while the negative values of ΔG^o showed that the adsorption was spontaneous. In a study carried by Kannan *et al.* [80], the kinetic studies on the bisorption of MG onto *Turbinaria conoides* showed that the pseudo-first-order model is better fit than the pseudo-second-order model. Rajeshkannan *et al.* [82] reported that the kinetic studies of the decolorization of Acid Blue 9 using brown marine algae *Turbinaria conoides* pseudo-second-order model fits the system well. Sivarajasekar *et al.* [83] studied the kinetic mechanism of the Direct Brown dye by *Spirogyra* using pseudo–first-order, pseudo-second-order, and intraparticle diffusion models. Pseudo-second-order fitted well the data. Intraparticle diffusion models revealed that the process was complex and followed both surface adsorption and particle diffusion. Kinetic of DY12 adsorption was investigated [84], and was found to fit well with the pseudo-second-order model. El Sikaily *et al.* [86] showed that the adsorption kinetics followed the pseudo-second order model ($R^2 = 1.0$) in the removal of MB from aqueous solution by *Ulva lactuca*. Bekçi *et al.* [87] reported that the biosorption process removal of MG by invasive marine alga *Caulerpa racemosa* var. *cylindracea* was followed the pseudo-second-order rate. The ΔG^o values are −7.1, −9.8 and −10.9 kJ mol^{-1} for 25, 35 and 45°C, respectively, demonstrated physisorption for the sorption of MG onto *Caulerpa racemosa* var. *cylindracea* (CRC) [87]. The physical interaction between the CRC surface and the dye molecules could be easily desorbed by physical means such as simply shaking or heating [50]. When the dye laden CRC was dried and then physical effects such as heating and shaking were applied, it observed that MG is desorbed by CRC. This observation could be an evident of the physisorption mechanism. The spontaneous nature of sorption appears due to negative values of ΔG^o, this also confirms affinity of CRC for the MG. The calculated ΔH^o value was found to be 49.6 kJ mol^{-1}. The positive ΔH^o values could lead to endothermic nature of interaction between MG dye and CRC sorbent. It was also observed that ΔS^o values 0.191 kJ mol^{-1} indicates an increase in degree of freedom of the sorbed dye molecules. In order to elucidate the mechanism of the adsorption of MB adsorption on *Sargassum muticum* [89], several models were tested such as the first order Lagergren model and pseudo-second order and they found that the experimental data were fitted to pseudo-first-order and pseudo-second-order equations. It was found that the adsorption of MB on *Sargassum* treated with CaCl$_2$ follows first order kinetics while those for HCl and H$_2$CO treatments show a better compliance with the pseudo-second order equation [89].

9. CONCLUSIONS

The usage of algae as biosorbents makes them selective and highly capable of biodegrading and biosorbing dyes from their solutions. The extensive research conducted on various biosorbents showed that they are emerging as a promising alternative to conventional treatment systems. Different species of algae have shown excellent color removal capabilities and they have been found to be potential suitable sorbents because of their cheap and availability, both in fresh or sea-water, as well as a relatively high surface area and high binding affinity. Biosorption on algae has mainly been attributed to the cell wall properties where both electrostatic attraction and complexation can play a role as well as the cell surfaces are naturally formed by various chemical groups such as hydroxyl, carboxylate, amino and phosphate, which are believed to be responsible for the sequestration of different materials from effluents. Moreover, most of the algal cells are often covered by mucilaginous layers characterized by a significant adsorption capacity due to the presence of alginate constituting 14–40% of the dry weight of the algae biomass. However, use of biosorbents to remove dyes color from wastewater is still in the research stage. Efforts are needed to commercialize this research through (*i*) selection of suitable biosorbents based on economic and market analysis, (*ii*) pilot-scale studies with actual wastewaters, and (*ii*) full-scale demonstration systems.

REFERENCES

[1]   Solozhenko, E.G., Soboleva N.M. & Goncharut, V.V. (1995). Decolorization of azo dye solutions by Fenton's oxidation. *Water Research*, 29: 2206–2210.

[2]   Weber, J., & Stickney, V.C. (1993). Hydrolysis kinetics of reactive Blue 19-vinyl sulfone. *Water Research*, 27: 63–67.

[3]   Camp, R., & Sturrock, P.E. (1990). The identification of the derivatives of CI reactive Blue 19 in textile wastewater. *Water Research*, 24: 1275–1278.

[4]   Hassana, S.S.M., Awwad, N.S., & Aboterika, A.H.A. (2009). Removal of synthetic reactive dyes from textile wastewater by Sorel's cement. *Journal of Hazardous Materials*, 162: 994–999.

[5]   O'Neill, C., Hawkes, F.R., Hawkes, D.L., Lourenço, N.D., Pinheiro, H.M. & Delée, W. (1999). Color in textile effluents – sources, measurements, discharge consents and simulation: a review. *Journal of Chemical Technology and Biotechnology*, 74: 1009–1018.

[6]   Hai, F.I., Yamamoto, K., & Fukushi, K. (2007). Hybrid treatment systems for dye wastewater. *Critical Review of Environmental Science and Technology*, 37: 315–377.

[7]   Husain, Q. (2006). Potential applications of the oxidoreductive enzymes in the decolorization and detoxification of textile and other synthetic dyes from polluted water: a review. *Critical Review of Biotechnology*, 26: 201–221.

[8]   Clarke, E.A., & Anliker, R. (1980). *Organic dyes and pigments: handbook of environmental chemistry, anthropogenic compounds*. New York: Springer-Verlag.

[9]   Mishra, G., & Tripathy, M. (1993). A critical review of the treatment for decolorization of textile effluent. *Colourage*, 40: 35–38.

[10]   Christie, R.M., (2007). *Environmental Aspects of Textile Dyeing*. Woodhead, Boca Raton, Cambridge.

[11]   Hunger, K. (2003). *Industrial Dyes: Chemistry, Properties, Applications*. Wiley-VCH, Weinheim; Cambridge.

[12]   Meyer, U. (1981). Biodegradation of synthetic organic colorants. In: Leisinger, T., Cook, A.M., Hunter, R., & Nuesch, J. (Eds.), *Microbial Degradation of Xenobiotic and Recalcitrant Compounds*. Academic Press, London, pp. 371–385.

[13]   Zollinger, H. (1987). *Color Chemistry – Synthesis, Properties of Organic Dyes and Pigments*. VCH Publishers, New York.

[14]   Gordon, P.F. & Gregory, P. (1983). *Organic Chemistry in Color*. Springer, Berlin.

[15]   Venkataraman. K. (1965). *The Chemistry of Synthetic Dyes*. Academic Press Inc., New York.

[16]   Bae, J.–S., & Freeman, H.S. (2007). Aquatic toxicity evaluation of new direct dyes to the *Daphnia magna*, *Dyes and Pigments*, 73: 81–85.

[17]   Combes, R.D., & Havelandsmith, R.B. (1982). A review of the genotoxicity of food, drug and cosmetic colors and other azo, triphenylmethane and xanthane dyes. *Mutation Research/Reviews in Genetic Toxicology,* 98: 101–243.

[18]   Nemerow, N.L., & Doby, T.A. (1958). Color removal in waste-water treatment plants. *Sewage and Industrial Wastes*, 30(9): 1160-1165

[19]   Hatch, K.L., & Maibach, H.I. (1999). Dyes as contact allergens: a comprehensive record. *Textile Chemistry Color AM Dyestuff Rep.* 1: 53–59.

[20]   Rai, H.S., Bhattacharyya, M.S., Singh, J., Bansal, T.K., Vats, P., & Banerjee, U.C. (2005). Removal of dyes from the effluent of textile and dyestuff manufacturing industry: a review of emerging techniques with reference to biological treatment. *Critical Review of Environmental Science and Technology*, 35: 219–238.

[21]   Kuo, W.G. (1992). Decolorizing dye waste-water with fenton reagent. *Water Research*, 26: 881–886.

[22]   Walsh, G.E., Bahner, L.H., & Horning, W.B. (1980). Toxicity of textile mill effluents to freshwater and estuarine algae, crustaceans and fishes. *Environmental Pollution*, A21:169–179.

[23]   Banat, I.M., Nigam, P., Singh, D. & Marchant, R. (1996). Microbial decolorization of textile-dye containing effluents: a review. *Bioresource Technology*, 58: 217–27.

[24]   Fu, Y., & Viraraghavan, T. (2001). Fungal decolorization of wastewaters: a review. *Bioresource Technology*, 79: 251–262.

[25]   Robinson, T., Mcmullan, G., Marchant, R., & Nigam, P. (2001). Remediation of dyes in textile effluent: a critical review on current treatment technologies with a proposed alternative. *Bioresource Technology*, 77: 247–255.

[26]   Aksu, Z., & Tezer, S. (2005). Biosorption of reactive dyes on the green alga *Chlorella vulgaris*. *Process Biochemistry*, 40: 1347–1361.

[27]   Ghosh, K., & Bhattacharyya, K.G. (2002). Adsorption of methylene blue on kaolinite. *Applied Clay Science*, 20: 295-300.

[28]   Khataee, A.R. (2009). Photocatalytic Removal of C.I. Basic Red 46 on Immobilized TiO_2 Nanoparticles: Artificial Neural Network Modeling. *Environmental Technology*, 30: 1155- 1168.

[29]   Daneshvar, N., Salari, D., & Khataee, A.R. (2004). Photocatalytic Degradation of Azo Dye Acid Red 14 in Water on ZnO as an Alternative Catalyst to TiO_2. *Journal of Photochemistry Photobiology A: Chemistry*, 162: 317-322.

[30]   Khataee, A.R., Pons, M.N., & Zahraa, O. (2009). Photocatalytic Degradation of Three Azo Dyes Using Immobilized TiO_2 Nanoparticles on Glass Plates Activated by UV Light Irradiation: Influence of Dye Molecular Structure. *Journal of Hazardous Materials*, 168: 451- 457.

[31]   Mittal, A., Kurup, L., & Gupta, V.K. (2005). Use of Waste Materials–Bottom Ash De-oiled Soya, as Potential Adsorbents for the Removal of Amaranth from Aqueous Solution. *Journal of Hazardous Materials*, 117: 171-178.

[32]   Adav, S.S., Lee, D.J. & Lai, J.Y. (2009). Treating chemical industries influent using aerobic granular sludge: Recent development. *Journal of Taiwan Institute of Chemical Engineers*, 40: 333-336.

[33]   Aksu, Z. (2005). Application of Biosorption for the Removal of Organic Pollutants: A Review. *Process Biochemistry*, 40: 997-1026.

[34]   Chang, J.S., & Kuo, T.S. (2000). Kinetics of Bacterial Decolorization of Azo Dye with Escherichia coli NO_3. *Bioresours Technology*, 75: 107 – 111.

[35]   Chang, J.S., Kuo, T.S., Choa, Y.P., Ho, J.Y., & Lin, P.J. (2000). Azo Dye Decolorization with a Mutant *Escherichia coli* Strain. *Biotechnology Letters*, 22: 807-812

[36]   Daneshvar, N., Ayazloo, M., Khataee, A.R., & Pourhassan, M. (2007). Biological decolorization of dye solution containing Malachite Green by microalgae *Cosmarium sp. Bioresours Technology*, 98: 1176-1182.

[37] You, S.J., & Teng, J.Y. (2009). Anaerobic decolorization bacteria for the treatment of azo dye in a sequential anaerobic and aerobic membrane bioreactor.' *Journal of Taiwan Institute of Chemical Engineers*, 40: 500-504

[38] Talarposhti, A.M., Donnelly, T., & Anderson, G.K. (2001). Color removal from a simulated dye wastewater using a two-phase anaerobic packed bed reactor. *Water Research*, 35: 425–432.

[39] Dos Santos, A.B., Bisschops, I.A.E., & Cervantes, F.J. (2006). Closing process water cycles and product recovery in textile industry: perspective for biological treatment. In: Cervantes, F.J., Van Haandel, A.C., Pavlostathis, S.G. (Eds.). Advanced Biological Treatment Processes for Industrial Wastewaters, *International Water Association, London*, 298–320.

[40] Correia, V.M., Stephenson, T., & Judd, S.J. (1994). Characterization of textile wastewaters: a review. Environmental Technology, 15: 917–929.

[41] Orhon, D., Babuna, F.G., & Insel, G. (2001). Characterization and modeling of denim-processing wastewaters for activated sludge. *Journal of Chemical Technology and Biotechnology*, 76: 919–931.

[42] Mattioli, D., Malpei, F., Bortone, G., & Rozzi, A. (2002). Water minimization and reuse in textile industry. Water Recycling and Resource Recovery in Industry: Analysis, Technologies and Implementation. *IWA Publishing, Cornwall, UK*, p. 677.

[43] Bisschops, & I.A.E., Spanjers, H. (2003). Literature review on textile wastewater characterization. *Environmental Technology*, 24: 1399–1411.

[44] Dos Santos, A.B., Francisco, J., Cervantes, J., & van Lier, B. (2007). Review paper on current technologies for decolorization of textile wastewaters: Perspectives for anaerobic biotechnology. *Bioresours Technology*, 98: 2369–2385.

[45] Davis, T.A., Volesky, B., & Mucci, A. (2003). A review of the biochemistry of heavy metal biosorption by brown algae. *Water Research*, 37: 4311-4330

[46] Veglio, F., & Beolchini, F. (1997). Removal of metals by biosorption: a review. *Hydrometallurgy*, 44 : 301-316

[47] EPA (1997). Environmental Protection Agency, *Profile of the Textile Industry*., Washington, USA.

[48] Dos Santos, A.B. (2001). Tratamento de àguas residuàrias têxteis pelo sistema de lodos ativados em batelada. Departamento de Engenharia Hidràulica e Ambiental, Universidade Federal do Cearà, Fortaleza, p. 111.

[49] Snowden-Swan, L.J. (1995). *Pollution prevention in textile industries. Industrial Pollution Prevention*. Handbook. McGraw-Hill, New York, USA.

[50] Donmez, G., & Aksu, Z. (2002). Removal of chromium (VI) from saline wastewaters by *Dunaliella* species. *Process Biochemistry*, 38: 751-762.

[51] Tien, C.-J. (2002). Biosorption of metal ions by freshwater algae with different surface characteristics. *Process Biochemistry*, 38: 605- 613.

[52] Satiroglu, N., Yalcınkaya, Y., Denizli, A., Arıca, M.Y., Bektas, S., & Genc, O. (2002). Application of NaOH treated *Polyporus versicolor* for removal of divalent ions of group IIB elements from synthetic wastewater. *Process Biochemistry*, 38: 65-72.

[53] Srinivasan, A., & Viraraghavan, T. (2010). Decolorization of dye wastewaters by biosorbents: A review. *Journal of Environmental Management*, 91: 1915-1929

[54] Ozer, A., Akkaya, G., & Turabik, M. (2006). The removal of Acid Red 274 from wastewater: combined biosorption and biocoagulation with *Spirogyra rhizopus*. *Dyes and Pigments*, 71: 83-89.

[55] Mohan, S.V., Rao, N.C., Prasad, K., & Karthikeyan, J. (2002). Treatment of simulated Reactive Yellow 22 (azo) dye effluents using *Spirogyra* species. *Waste Management*, 22: 575-582.

[56] Aravindhan, R., Roa, J.R., & Nair, B.U. (2007). Removal of basic dye from aqueous solution by sorption on green alga *Caulerpa scalpelliformis*. *Journal of Hazardous Materials*, 142: 68-76.

[57] El-Sheekh, M.M., Gharieb, M.M & Abou-El-Souod, G.W. (2009). Biodegradation of dyes by some green algae and cyanobacteria. *International Biodeterioration & Biodegradation,* 63(6): 699-704.

[58] Bischoff, H.W., & Bold, H.C. (1963). Phycological Studies. 4-Some Soil Algae from Enchanted Rock and Related Algal Species. Univ. Texas. N. 6318: 32–36.

[59] Khataee, A.R., Zarei, M., Dehghan, G., Ebadi, E. & Pourhassan, M. (2011). Biotreatment of a triphenylmethane dye solution using a *Xanthophyta* alga: Modeling of key factors by neural network. *Journal of Taiwan Institute of Chemical Engineers,* (Article in Press, Corrected Proof, doi:10.1016/j.jtice.2010.08.006)

[60] Khataeea, A.R., & Dehgha, G. (2011). Optimization of biological treatment of a dye solution by macroalgae *Cladophora* sp. using response surface methodology. *Journal of Taiwan Institute of Chemical Engineers*, 42: 26-33.

[61] Kumar, K.V., Ramamurthi, V., & Sivanesan, S. (2006). Biosorption of malachite green, a cationic dye onto *Pithophora* sp., fresh water algae. *Dyes and Pigments*, 69: 102-107.

[62] Ncibi, M.C., Ben Hamissa, A.M., Fathallah, A., Kortas, M.H., Baklouti, T., Mahjoub, B. & Seffen, M. (2009). Biosorptive uptake of methylene blue using Mediterranean green alga *Enteromorpha* sp. *Journal of Hazardous Materials*, 170: 1050–1055.

[63] Dõgar, Ç., Gürses, A., Açıkyıldız, M., & Özkan, E. (2010). Thermodynamics and kinetic studies of biosorption of a basic dye from aqueous solution using green algae *Ulothrix* sp. *Colloids and Surfaces B: Biointerfaces*, 76: 279–285.

[64] Padmesh, T.V.N., Vijayaraghavan, K., Sekaran, G. & Velan, M. (2005). Batch and column studies on biosorption of acid dyes on fresh water macro alga *Azolla filiculoides*. *Journal of Hazardous Materials*, B125: 121–129.

[65] Kumar, K.V., Sivanesan, S., & Ramamurthi, V. (2005). Adsorption of malachite green onto *Pithophora* sp., fresh water algae: Equilibrium and kinetic modeling. *Process Biochemistry*, 40: 2865–2872.

[66] Marungruenga, K., & Pavasant, P. (2006). Removal of basic dye (Astrazon Blue FGRL) using macroalga *Caulerpa lentillifera*. *Journal of Environmental Management*, 78: 268–274.

[67] Ergene, A., Ada, K., Tan, S., & Katırcıoğlu, H. (2009). Removal of Remazol Brilliant Blue R dye from aqueous solutions by adsorption onto immobilized *Scenedesmus quadricauda:* Equilibrium and kinetic modeling studies. *Desalination*, 249: 1308-1314.

[68] Rippka, R. (1989). *Methods in Enzymology*, vol. 167, Academic Press, New York, pp. 3-27.

[69]   Khataeea, A.R., Dehghanb, G., Zarei, M., Ebadia, E., & Pourhassan, M. (2011). Neural network modeling of biotreatment of triphenylmethane dye solution by a green macroalgae. *Chemical Engineering Research and Design*, 89(2): 172-178.

[70]   Huang, G.L., Sun, H.W., & Cong, L.L. (2000). Study on the physiology and degradation of dye with immobilized algae. Art Cells Blood Subst. *Immobilization Biotechnology*, 28: 347- 63.

[71]   Jinqi, L., & Houtian, L. (1992). Degradation of azo dyes by algae. *Environmental pollution*, 75: 273-278.

[72]   Marungruenga, K. & Pavasant, P. (2007). High performance biosorbent (*Caulerpa lentillifera*) for basic dye removal. *Bioresours Technology*, 98: 1567-1572.

[73]   Khalaf, M.A. (2008). Biosorption of reactive dye from textile wastewater by non-viable biomass of *Aspergillus niger* and *Spirogyra* sp. *Bioresours Technology*, 99: 6631-6634.

[74]   Khataee, A.R., Dehghan, G., Ebadi, A., Zarei, M. & Pourhassan, M. (2010). Biological treatment of a dye solution by Macroalgae *Chara* sp.: Effect of operational parameters, intermediates identification and artificial neural network modeling. *Bioresours Technology*, 101: 2252-2258.

[75]   Tahir, H., Sultan, M., & Jahanzeb, Q. (2008). Removal of basic dye methylene blue by using bioabsorbents *Ulva lactuca* and *Sargassum*. *African Journal of Biotechnology*, 7: 2649-2655.

[76]   Omar, H.H. (2008). Algal decolorization and degradation of monoazo and diazo dyes. *Pakistan Journal of Biological Science*, 11: 1310-1316.

[77]   Harris, E. (1989). The *Chlamydomonas* Source Book: A comprehensive guide to biology and laboratory use. Academic Press, San Diego, pp: 780.

[78]   Caparkaya, D., & Cavas, L. (2008). Biosorption of Methylene Blue by a Brown Alga *Cystoseira barbatula* Kützing. *Acta Chimical Slovacia*, 55: 547-553.

[79]   Low, K.S., Lee, C.K., & Toh, B.L. (1994). Binding of Basic Dyes by the Algae, *Chara aspera*. *Pertanika Journal of Science & Technology*, 2: 85-92.

[80]   Kannan, R.R., Rajasimman, M., Rajamohan, N. & Sivaprakash, B. (2010). Brown marine algae turbinaria conoides as biosorbent for Malachite green removal: Equilibrium and kinetic modeling. *Frontiers of Environmental Science & Engineering in China*, 4: 116-122.

[81]   Meevasanaa, K. & Pavasanta, P. (2008). Quantitative measurement techniques for binary dye mixtures: a case study in an adsorption system. *Science Asia*, 34: 390-394.

[82]   Rajeshkannan, R., Rajasimman, M., & Rajamohan, N. (2010). Optimization, equilibrium and kinetics studies on sorption of Acid Blue 9 using brown marine algae *Turbinaria conoides*. *Biodegradation*, 21: 713-727.

[83]   Sivarajasekar, N., Baskar, R., Balakrishnan, V. (2009). Bisorption of an azo dye from aqueous solutions onto *Spirogyra*. *Journal of the University of Chemical Technology and Metallurgy*, 44: 157-164.

[84]   El Nemr, A., Abdelwahab, O., Khaled A., & El Sikaily, A. (2006). Biosorption of Direct Yellow 12 from aqueous solution using green alga *Ulva lactuca*. *Chemistry & Ecology*, 22: 253-266.

[85]   Mohana, S.V., & Karthikeyana, J. (2000). Removal of Diazo dye from aqueous phase by algae *Spirogyra* species. Toxicology and *Environmental Chemistry* 74: 147-154.

[86] El Sikaily, A., Khaled, A., El Nemr, A., & Abdelwahab, O. (2006). Removal of Methylene Blue from aqueous solution by marine green alga *Ulva lactuca*. *Chemistry & Ecology*, 22: 149–157.

[87] Bekçi, Z., Sekiaş, & Y., Cavas, L. (2009). Removal of malachite green by using an invasive marine alga *Caulerpa racemosa* var. *cylindracea*. *Journal of Hazardous Materials*, 161: 1454-1460.

[88] Daneshvar, N., Khataee, A.R., Rasoulifard, M.H., & Pourhassan, M. (2007). Biodegradation of dye solution containing Malachite Green: Optimization of effective parameters using Taguchi method. *Journal of Hazardous Materials*, 143: 214-219.

[89] Rubin, E., Rodriguez, P., Herrero, R., Cremades, J., Barbara, I., & Sastre de Vicente, M.E. (2005). Removal of Methylene Blue from aqueous solutions using as biosorbent *Sargassum muticum*: an invasive macroalga in Europe. *Journal of Chemical Technology and Biotechology*, 80: 291–298.

[90] Crist, R.H., Oberholser, K., Shank, N., & Nguyen, M. (1981). Nature of bonding between metallic ions and algal cell walls. *Environmental Science and Technology*, 15: 1212-1217.

[91] Donmez, G.C., Aksu, Z., Ozturk, A., & Kutsal, T. (1999). A comparative study on heavy metal biosorption characteristics of some algae. *Process Biochemistry*, 34: 885-892.

[92] Akar, T., Tamir, T.A., Kiran, I., Ozcan, A., Ozcan, A.S., & Tunali, S. (2006). Biosorption potential of *Neurospora crassacells* for decolorization of Acid Red 57 (AR57) dye. *Journal of Chemical Technology and Biotechnology*, 81: 1100–1106.

[93] Aksu, Z., & Tezer, S. (2000). Equilibrium and kinetic modelling of biosorption of Remazol Black B by *Rhizopus arrhizus* in a batch system: effect of temperature. *Process Biochemistry*, 36: 431-439.

[94] Aksu, Z., & Iisiloglu, I.A. (2007). Use of dried sugar beet pulp for binary biosorption of Gemazol Turquoise Blue-G reactive dye and copper (II) ions: equilibrium modeling. *Chemical Engineering Journal*, 127: 177–188.

[95] Ergene, A., Tan, S., Katırcıoglu, H., & Oktem, Z. (2006). Biosorption of copper (II) on immobilized Synechocystis *aquatilis*. *Fresenius Environmental Bulletin*, 15: 283-288.

[96] Ozer, A., Akkaya, G., & Turabik, M. (2005). Biosorption of acid red 274 (AR 274) on *Enteromorpha prolifera* in a batch system. *Journal of Hazardous Materials*, B126: 119-127.

[97] Namasivayam, C., & Kavitha, D. (2002). Removal of congo red from water by adsorption onto activated carbon prepared from coir pith, an agricultural solid waste. *Dyes and Pigments*, 54: 47-58.

[98] Pavan, F.A., Lima, E.C., Dias, S.L.P., & Mazzocato, A.C. (2008). Methylene blue biosorption from aqueous solutions by yellow passion fruit waste. *Journal of Hazardous Materials*, 150: 703-712.

[99] Wilde, E.W., Benemann, J. R. (1993). Bioremoval of heavy metals by the use of microalgae. *Biotechnology Adsorption*, 11: 781-812.

[100] Mohan, S.V., & Karthikeyan, J. (1997). Removal of lignin and tannin colour from aqueous solution by adsorption onto activated charcoal. *Environmental Pollution*, 97: 183-187.

[101] Tüzün, I., Bayramoglu, G., Yalçın, E., Başaran, G., Çelik, G. & Arıca, M.Y. (2005). Equilibrium and kinetic studies on biosorption of Hg(II), Cd(II) and Pb(II) ions onto

microalgae *Chlamydomonas reinhardtii*. *Journal of Environmental Management*, 77: 85-92.

[102] Low, K.S., Lee, C.K., & Heng, L.L. (1993). Sorption of basic dyes by *Hydrilla Verticillata*. *Environmental Technology*, 14: 115-124.

[103] Low, K.S., & Lee, C.K. (1990). The removal of cationic dyes using Coco-nut husk as an adsorbent. *Pertanika*, 13: 221-228.

[104] Low, K.S., Lee, C.K., & Tan, K.K. (1995). Biosorption of basic dye by water hyacinth roots. *Bioresours Technology*, 52: 79-83.

[105] Mittal, A.K., & Gupta, S.K. (1996). Biosorsption of cationic dyes by dead macro fungus *Fonitopsis carnea*: batch studies. *Water Science and Technology*, 34: 81–87.

[106] Ramakrishna, K.R., & Viraraghavan, T. (1997). Dye removal using low cost adsorbents. *Water Science and Technology*, 36: 189-196.

[107] Schiewer, S., & Wong, M.H. (2000). Ionic strength effects in biosorption of metals by marine algae. *Chemosphere*, 41: 189-196.

[108] Wang, H., Zheng, X.W., Su, J.Q., Tian, Y., Xiong, X.J., & Zheng, T.L. (2009). Biological decolorization of the reactive dyes Reactive Black 5 by a novel isolated bacterial strain *Enterobacter* sp. EC3. *Journal of Hazardous Materials*, 171: 654-659.

[109] Chellababu, S., Sivarajan, M., Swaminathan, G., & Ramabrahman, B.V. (2008). Biosorption kinetics of Basic dye (Bismark Brown) in aqueous solutions by chitosan. *Pollution Research*, 27: 223-229.

[110] Mohan, S.V., Bhaskar, Y.V., & Karthikeyan, J. (2004). Biological decolourisation of simulated azo dye in aqueous phase by algae *Spirogyra* species. *International Journal of Environmental and Pollution*, 21: 211-222.

[111] Pearce, C.I., Lloyd, J.R., & Guthrie, J.T. (2003). The removal of color from textile wastewater using whole bacterial cells: a review. *Dyes and Pigments*, 58: 179-196.

[112] Khataee, A.R., Ayazloo, M., & Pourhassan, M. (2009). Biological Decolorization of C.I. Basic Green 4 solution by *Chlorella* sp.: Effect Operational Parameters. *Chinese Journal of Applied Environmental Biology*, 15: 110-114.

[113] Khataee, A.R., & Mirzajani, O. (2010). UV/Peroxydisulfate Oxidation of C.I. Basic Blue 3: Modeling of Key Factors by Artificial Neural Network. *Desalination*, 251: 64-69.

[114] El Nemr, A., El Sikaily, A. & Khaled, A. (2010). Modeling of adsorption isotherms of methylene blue onto rice husk activated carbon. *Egyptian Journal of Aquatic Research*, 36(3): 403-425.

In: Non-Conventional Textile Waste Water Treatment   ISBN: 978-1-62100-079-2
Editor: Ahmed El Nemr   © 2012 Nova Science Publishers, Inc.

Chapter 6

ROLE OF REDOX MEDIATORS IN ENHANCING DYE DECOLORIZATION BY USING OXIDOREDUCTIVE ENZYMES

Rukhsana Satar[1], Ahmed Bin Ali Jerah[2] and Qayyum Husain[2,*]
[1]Department of Biochemistry, Faculty of Life Sciences,
Aligarh Muslim University, Aligarh-202002, India
[2]Department of Clinical Biochemistry, Faculty of Applied Medical Sciences,
Jazan University, Jazan, Kingdom of Saudi Arabia

ABSTRACT

Due to the indiscriminate and frequent release of hazardous and harmful substances, environmental pollution is increasing day-by-day. Decolorization of textile wastewaters containing high concentration of colored effluents has attracted the attention of environmentalists concerning their toxicity to aquatic life and mutagenicity to humans. Presently, enzyme based procedures have attracted attention of the researchers for targeting aromatic pollutants as a new, simple, cost effective, potential and viable eco-friendly alternative to conventional methods which are associated with harsh side effects. The inhibition by toxic substances in enzymatic treatment is minimum and the process can be operated over a broad range of aromatic concentrations with low retention time. Majority of dyes are recalcitrant to the action of enzymes, however, the presence of redox mediators facilitates decolorization of such dyes to a great extent. These redox mediators enhance the range of substrates and efficiency of degradation of the recalcitrant dyes by several folds. Enzymes whose potential has been exploited for this purpose are laccases, lignin peroxidase, manganese peroxidase, horseradish peroxidase, turnip peroxidase, tomato peroxidase, bitter gourd peroxidases, white radish peroxidase, bilirubin oxidase, tyrosinase, quinone reductase and others. Among several redox mediators reported in the literature very few are frequently used, for example, 1-hydroxybenzotriazole, veratryl alcohol, violuric acid, 2-methoxyphenothiazone, 3-hydroxyanthranilic acid, anthraquinone 2,6-disulfonic acid, 2,2-azino-bis(3-ethylbenzothiazoline-6-sulfonic acid), *N*-hydroxyacetanilide, phenol, phenol red, 3,3',5,5'-tetramethyl benzidine;

---

* Email: qayyumbiochem@gmail.com, Mobile: 00966-595021577.

dichlorophenol red, 2,2',6,6'-tetramethylpiperidine-*N*-oxyl radical, syringaldehyde, acetosyringone, acetovanillone, *p*-coumaric acid, ferulic acid, sinapic acid, vanillin, lawsone, menadione, phloroglucinol and thymol. Use of the enzyme-redox mediator system seems to be a promosing tool to enhance the chances of remediation of a wide spectrum of textile dyes present in various industrial effluents/wastewaters.

ABBREVIATIONS

AS	acetosyringone;
AV	acetovanillone;
ABTS	2,2-azino-bis-(3-ethylbenzthiazoline-6-sulfonic acid;
AP	aminopyrine;
AQDS	anthraquinone 26-disulfonic acid;
AQS	anthraquinone-2-sulfonate;
AS	acetosyringone;
BGP	bitter gourd peroxidase;
BOD	biological oxygen demand;
BOX	bilirubin oxidase;
CI	Color index;
CLF	commercial laccase formulation;
COD	chemical oxygen demand;
CPZ	Chlorpromazine;
DyP	dye decolorizing peroxidase;
DR 17	Disperse Red 17;
DB 1	Disperse Brown 1;
EDTA	ethylenediamine tetraacetic acid;
FSP	fenugreek seed peroxidase;
HOBT	1-hydroxybenzotriazole;
HAA	3-hydroxyanthranilic acid;
HRP	horseradish peroxidase;
LiP	lignin peroxidase;
LME	lignin-modifying enzymes;
LPO	lactoperoxidase;
MMA	4-methoxymandelic acid;
MnP	manganese peroxidase;
MPL	myeloperoxidase;
M_r	molecular weight;
NHP	N-hydroxyphthalimide;
PAH	polycyclic aromatic hydrocarbons;
PHBS	4-hydroxybenzenesulfonic acid;
PTPA	phenothiazine-10-propionic acid;
RBBR	Remazol Brilliant Blue R;
rDyP	recombinant dye decolorizing peroxidase;
SA	syringaldehyde;
SBP	soybean peroxidase;

SS	suspended solid;
TEMPO	2,2,6,6-tetramethylpiperidin-1-yloxy;
TMP	tomato peroxidase;
TOC	total organic carbon;
TP	turnip peroxidase;
VA	veratryl alcohol;
VLA	violuric acid;
VN	vanillin;
WRF	white rot fungi;
WRP	white radish peroxidase.

1. INTRODUCTION

Environmental pollution implies any alternation in the surroundings, but the term is restricted in use especially to mean any deterioration in the physical, chemical, and biological quality of the environment. All types of pollution directly or indirectly affect living organizms and particularly human health. The pollutants fall under the broad category of xenobiotic compounds and are released into the environment by the action of human and occur at concentrations higher than "natural levels". The use of sophistication in the production of synthetic compounds and their applications is essential with the undesirable discharge of hard-to-biodegrade waste xenobiotic compounds. However, prior to their final discharge of such types of compounds into envirnment it becmoes necessary to detoxify and remove them from polluted water. Among the various types of environmental pollution, water pollution is an age-old serious problem, but it has gained an alarming dimension lately due to population increase, sewage disposal, industrial waste, radioactive waste, etc. These factors have contributed so much to the pollution of water resources that nearly 70–80% rivers and streams all over the world carry polluted water [1, 2]. Continuation of this trend may have catastrophic impact on human health and environment. Therefore, effective means of solving this problem must be developed to preserve the quality of life on this planet for future generations.

The production of synthetic compounds and their application is essential but there is an undesirable discharge of poorly biodegradable wastes from various manufacturing operations, e.g. coal conversion, petroleum refining, resin, dye and other organic compound manufacturing, dyeing and textile, mining, pulp and paper [2, 3]. Dyes are the most important classes of synthetic industrial chemicals that are often present in the industrial effluents from various manufacturing operations [4-6]. Synthetic dyes are extensively used as coloring material for textiles, paper, leather, hair, fur, plastics, wax, cosmetic bases and foodstuff [7]. However, inefficiencies in dyeing processes have resulted into loss of the large amounts of dyestuff in effluent, which posed serious threat to the environment [8, 9]. Wastewater from textile and dyestuff industries contains synthetic and complex molecular compounds, which make them more stable and difficult to degrade [6, 10, 11]. Moreover, dye effluent usually contains chemicals that may be toxic, carcinogenic and mutagenic to various microbes, aquatic animals and human beings [12-14]. The seriousness of the problem is apparent from the magnitude of research that has been done in the field in last decade [8, 15-18].

1.1. Toxicity of Dyestuffs

Interest in the remediation of synthetic dyes has primarily been prompted by concern over their possible toxicity and carcinogenicity [19-21]. Roughly 60-70% of the dyes used in textile industries are azo compounds, i.e. molecules with one or more azo (N=N) bridges [8, 22]. The azo dyes have already been divided into two groups according to their water solubility. Water soluble azo dyes are anionic (acidic dyes) or cationic (basic dyes) while the water insoluble dyes are non-ionic (neutral). Dyes are highly visible; some of them can be detected at a concentration range <1 mg l^{-1} and are synthesized to be chemically and photolytically stable thus persist in natural environments [23]. However, most of the azo dyes are not toxic by themselves but after releasing into the aquatic environment, these compounds might be converted into potentially carcinogenic amines and other aromatic compounds [22, 24-28]. Consequently, the release of potentially hazardous dyes in the environment can be an ecotoxic risk and can affect human beings through the food chain [29-31]. The risk, which dyes represent in wastewaters, depends on their chemical structure, physical properties, concentration and exposure time [8, 13]. The investigations have been carried out to evaluate the effects of dyestuffs and dye containing effluents on the activity of both aerobic and anaerobic bacteria in wastewater treatment systems. The acute toxicity of azo dyes is rather low. Algal growth and fish mortality is not affected by dye concentrations below 1 mg l^{-1}. The most acutely toxic dyes for fish and algae are acid and basic dyes, especially those with a triphenylmethane structure [32]. Mortality tests with rats showed that only 1% out of 4461 commercial dyestuffs tested had LD_{50} values below 250 mg kg^{-1} body weight whereas a majority of dyes showed LD_{50} values between 250 and 2000 mg kg^{-1} body weight. Therefore, the chances of human mortality due to acute dyestuff toxicity are probably very low. However, in humans some azo dyestuffs have been reported to cause allergic reactions, i.e. eczema or contact dermatitis [33, 34]. The majority of sensitizing dyes present in clothes practically all belong to the group of disperse dyes [35, 36]. Disperse dyes are the most heavily used textile dyes. These are structurally classified as mainly an azo and anthraquinone chromophoric system with small molecular size and low aqueous solubility [13]. Anthraquinone based dyes are most resistant to degradation by bacteria due to their fused aromatic structures [23]. Reactive azo dyes are problematic due to their excessive consumption and high water solubility [37]. Metal-based complex dyes such as chromium-based dyes can lead to the release of chromium, which is carcinogenic [38, 39].

Chronic effects of dyestuffs, especially of azo dyes, have been studied for several decades. Some azo dyes in purified form showed mutagenic or carcinogenic property [26]. Intestinal cancers are common in highly industrialized societies and possible connection between these tumours and the use of azo dyes has been investigated [37]. Numerous dyes were found to cause cerebral and skeletal abnormalities in foetus [40]. Textile dyeing, paper printing and leather finishing industry workers exposed to benzidine based dyes had a higher than normal incidence of urinary bladder cancer [41]. Benzidine based dyes when administered to various experimental animals undergo reduction of azo bonds with appearance of human bladder carcinogen, benzidine and benzidine metabolites in the urine [40, 42]. The carcinogenicity mechanism probably includes the formation of acyloxy amines through *N*-hydroxylation and *N*-acetylation of the aromatic amines followed by *O*-acylation.

These acyloxy amines can be converted to nitrenium and carbonium ions that bind to DNA and RNA thus inducing mutations and tumour formation [43].

Generally described, genotoxicity is related to all aromatic amines containing benzidine moieties as well as with some aromatic amines with toluene, aniline and naphthalene moieties [44]. The toxicity and carcinogenicity of aromatic amines depends on the three-dimensional structure of the molecule and on the location of amino group(s). 2-Naphthylamine is a known carcinogen while 1-naphthylamine is much less toxic. Moreover, the nature and the position of other substituents could increase (nitro, methyl or methoxy) or decrease (carboxyl or sulphonate) toxicity [45]. Sulphonated aromatic amines in contrast to some of their unsulphonated analogs have either no or very low genotoxic and tumorigenic potential. Dyes are toxic to some aquatic life due to the presence of metals and chlorides [46-49]. These concerns have led to new and strict regulations concerning colored wastewater discharges, compelling the dye manufacturers and users to adopt "cleaner technology" approaches. Therefore, effective means for solving this problem by the development of new lines of ecologically safe dyeing auxiliaries and improvement of exhaustion of dyes on to fiber must be adopted in order to maitain the quality of life for coming generations on this planet [50-52].

1.2. Classification of Dyes

Aromatic compounds that absorb light/electromagnetic energy with wavelengths in the visible range (350-700 nm) are colored. Dyes contain chromophores, delocalized electron systems with conjugated double bonds and auxochromes, electron-withdrawing or electron donating substituents that intensify the color of the chromophore by altering the overall energy of the electron system. Usual chromophores are -C=C-, -C=N-, -C=O, -N=N-, $-NO_2$ and quinoid rings whereas usual auxochromes are $-NH_3$, -COOH, $-SO_3H$ and –OH [53]. The Color Index (CI) number, developed by the Society of Dyers and Colorists, is used for dye classification [54]. Once the chemical structure of a dye is known, a five digit CI number is assigned to it. The first word is the dye classification and the second word is the hue or shade of the dye. For example, CI Acid Yellow 36 (CI 13065) is a yellow dye of the acid type. Further dyes are classified either according to their constitution or method of application.

Chemical structures determine the colors, properties and uses of dyes and provided the only rational basis for the classification of such type of compounds. There are numerous groups of dyes based on the presence of different structural units/chemical structures/chromophores. The most important group of dyes includes azo (monoazo, disazo, triazo, polyazo), anthraquinone, naphthoquinone, arylmethane (diarylmethane, triarylmethane) phthalocyanine and polymethine dyes. Various other groups present in dyes are indigoid, azine, oxazine, thiazine, xanthene, nitro, nitroso, thiazole, indamine, indophenol, lactone, aminoketone and hydroxyketone and dyes of undetermined structures such as stilbene and sulphur dyes are also in use [54].

A wide spectrum group of dyes/colorants has been classified depending on application characteristics. These include acid dyes, basic dyes, direct dyes, disperse dyes, fiber reactive dyes, insoluble azo dyes, vat dyes and mordant dyes [50]. Dyestuffs give colored wastewaters that have high chemical oxygen demand (COD) and total organic carbon (TOC) values and low biological oxygen demand (BOD) values. Several physical, chemical and biological techniques have been employed to treat colored effluents.

The choice of the most suitable treatment procedure or their combinations depends on the type of dyestuffs and the method of dyeing used in the textile manufacturing. Physico-chemical processes have been employed to remove high molecular weight (M_r) organic compounds; their color, toxicity, suspended solids (SS) and COD but BOD and compounds of low M_r are not effectively removed. Currently available methods include chemical oxidation, reverse osmosis, adsorption, membrane filtration, coagulation/flocculation, sorption, electrolysis, advanced oxidation processes (chlorination, bleaching, ozonation, Fenton oxidation and photocatalytic oxidation) and chemical reduction. These methods have faced some serious drawbacks such as high cost and salt content in the effluent, problems related to disposal of concentrate and excessive use of chemicals and energy [55-57]. The procedures like ozonation, flocculation, photocatalytic oxidation and electrochemical have resulted in low color removal and formation of more toxic compounds. Moreover, chemical coagulation, membrane techniques and reverse osmosis have successfully been applied for the treatment of major portion of the colored pollutants but these techniques have been found highly expensive [7, 8].

Several investigators have used living organisms as potential tool to combat with the pollution problem in an ecoefficient manner which involved the use of bacteria or fungi, often in combination with physicochemical processes [58-61]. Numerous types of microorganisms have been identified and isolated those are capable of degrading persistant non-degradable dyes [62-66]. However, the analysis of contaminated soil have shown that such types of toxic compounds can sometimes persist even for longer duration in the presence of microorganisms that are capable of completely mineralizing the such contaminants. Another problem of using microorganisms is that often the environment of the surrounding is not suitable for the optimum working of microorganisms [2, 23, 67].

In the early 1980s, enzymologists for the first time explored an idea of using oxidoreductive enzymes for the remediation of wastewater contaminated with aromatic pollutants [3, 23, 68, 69]. This approach of treating pollutants is highly advantageous due to enzymes can act a broad range of substrates and are less sensitive to operational upsets than the microbial populations [1]. The variety of chemical transformations catalyzed by enzymes has made these catalysts a prime target for exploitation by the emerging biotechnological industries. Recent advances in this direction, through better isolation and purification procedures have allowed the production of cheaper and more readily available enzymes that can be used in many remediation processes to target specific recalcitrant pollutants present in wastewaters [70-72]. Enzymes isolated from their parent organisms have been often preferred over intact organisms containing the enzyme because the isolated enzymes act with greater specificity, their activity could be better standardized, are easy to handle and store and enzyme concentration is not dependent on the growth rate of microorganisms [73]. Moreover, unlike chemical catalysts, the enzymatic systems have the potential of accomplishing complex chemical conversions under mild environmental conditions with high efficiency and greater reaction velocity [74, 75]. Due to their high specificity to individual species, enzymatic processes have been developed to specifically target selected compounds that cannot be treated effectively or reliably using traditional techniques [76-78]. Alternatively, enzymatic treatment has been employed as a pretreatment step to remove one or more compounds that interfere with subsequent downstream treatment processes. If inhibitory or toxic compounds can be removed selectively, the bulk of the organic material could be treated biologically, thereby minimizing the cost of treatment [79]. Thus, the potential advantages of enzymatic treatment as compared to conventional treatments can be summed up as; application to recalcitrant materials, operation at low and high contaminant concentrations over a wide range of pH, temperature and salinity, absence of shock loading effects, delays associated with the acclimatization of biomass, reduction in sludge volume, the ease and simplicity of controlling the process, need of bio-acclimatization and remediation of various aromatic compounds under dilute conditions. [70, 80]. Enzymes catalyze detoxification/ decolorization of dyes quite fast, i.e. within minutes to few hours as compared to algae and fungi which take several days or even months to show the same results [58, 81]. Oxidoreductive enzymes; laccases peroxidases and other polyphenol oxidases have shown their great potential in the remediation and conversion of a wide spectrum of aromatic pollutants such as phenols, aromatic amines, biphenyls, bisphenols and dyes to less toxic insoluble compounds, which could be easily removed out of wastewater [2-4, 70, 78, 82-84].

These enzymes can act on a broad range of substrates and convert them into less toxic insoluble compounds, which can be easily removed from waste [82, 85-88]. However, sometimes these enzymes cannot act on organic pollutants due to recalcitrant nature of such compounds. These recalcitrant substrates get converted into less toxic forms in the presence of certain low-molecular weight compounds that are known as redox mediators. A redox mediator enhanced the rate of enzyme-catalyzed reaction and increased the range of selection of their substrates [70, 89, 90].

In this chapter an effort has been made to review the role of various redox mediators in enzyme-catalyzed decolorization and removal of aromatic colored pollutants from textile industrial effluents. Oxidoreductive enzymes like laccases, lignin peroxidases, manganese peroxidases and various plant peroxidases have been selected here because the range for their substrates was significantly enhanced in the presence of redox mediators.

2. REDOX MEDIATORS

Redox mediators are compounds that speed up the rate of reaction by shuttling electrons from the biological oxidation of primary electron donors or from bulk electron donors to the electron-accepting aromatic compounds [91, 92]. Redox mediators provide high redox potentials (>900 mV) to attack recalcitrant structural analogs and are able to migrate into aromatic structure of the compounds and accelerate reactions by lowering the activation energy of the total reaction. In some cases, the presence of these mediators might even be a prerequisite for the reaction to take place [93]. It has been found that these small molecules are capable of acting as electron transfer mediators and they help in oxidizing non-phenolic compounds, thus expanding the range of compounds that can be oxidized by enzymes [94]. The catalytic effect of such organic molecules with redox mediating properties on the bio-transformation of a wide variety of organic and inorganic compounds has been extensively investigated [74, 90, 95, 96]. The need and nature of redox mediator for the degradation of a specific dye depends on the source of enzyme [97]. The role and mechanism of action of laccase-mediator system is well characterized and can also be applied for other enzymes [98-102]. 3-Hydroxyanthranilic acid was the first natural mediator which was described for laccases. When a substrate is oxidized by laccase, the redox mediator forms cation radicals; short-lived intermediates that co-oxidize non-substrates. These cation radicals can be formed by two mechanisms: the redox mediator can perform either by one-electron oxidation of the substrate to a radical cation [103] or the redox mediator can abstract a proton from the substrate, converting it into a radical [92]. For example, 2,2-azino-bis-(3-ethylbenzthiazoline-6-sulfonic acid) (ABTS) acts by the first mechanism [104].

A correlation between the enzyme redox potential and its activity toward substrates has been described. The driving force for the redox reaction catalyzed by oxidoreductive enzymes is expected to be proportional to the difference between the redox potentials of the oxidizing enzyme and the reducing substrate/dye [106, 107]. Among the mediators, those presenting the >N-OH moiety; HOBT, N-hydroxyphthalimide (NHP) and violuric acid (VLA) proved very efficient towards benzylic substrates, through a radical H-abstraction route of oxidation involving an aminoxyl radical (>N-O˙) intermediate [108].

The presence of oxidizing mediators enhanced the decolorization of those dyes which were slowly decolorized in the absence of a redox mediator [109, 110]. Enzyme cofactors like FAD are known as effective redox mediators for azo dye reduction [111], and in addition, artificial quinones can also act as redox mediators. In abiotic systems, quinones have been shown to accelerate chemical azo dye reduction by sulfide [112] as well as electrochemical azo dye reduction [113], and in biological systems they were shown to accelerate azo dye reduction by an anaerobically incubated aerobic biomass [114], as well as azo dye reduction by anaerobic granular sludge [112]. The effect of anthraquinone 2,6-disulfonic acid (AQDS), a redox mediator, on the continuous treatment of a synthetic wastewater containing the slowly reducible reactive azo dye Reactive Red 2 was investigated [112]. Batch experiments demonstrated that AQDS could increase the firstorder rate constant of Reactive Red 2 reductive cleavage by one order of magnitude. In the continuous experiment, addition of AQDS to the reactor resulted in higher Reactive Red 2 removal (up to 98% at 155 µM AQDS).

Anthraquinone has been reported to really accelerate the decolorization of X-3B under optimal conditions [115]. It exhibited that decolorization process proceeded primarily by enzymatic reduction associated with a minor portion of bio-adsorption on the surface of inactivated microbial cells. A salt-tolerant bacterium was isolated from the surface soil of a pharmaceutical factory, which could efficiently decolorize azo dyes. The strain was identified as Exiguobacterium sp. according to its morphological characteristics and 16S rRNA gene sequence analysis. For color removal and cells growth, the optimal inoculation amount, pH, temperature, salinity, and metal ions were 6% (v/v), 5.4-7.0, 30-40 °C, 15% (w/v) NaCl, and 1.0 mmol l^{-1} $Mg^{(2+)}$ or $Ca^{(2+)}$, respectively. In another study, the effects of various quinone compounds on the decolorization rates of sulfonated azo dyes by *Sphingomonas xenophaga* QYY were investigated [116]. The results showed that anthraquinone-2-sulfonate (AQS) was the most effective redox mediator and AQS reduction was the rate-limited step of AQS-mediated decolorization of sulfonated azo dyes. Based on AQS biological toxicity tests, it was assumed that AQS might enter the cells and kill them. In the cytoplasmic extracts from strain QYY, AQS more effectively increased decolorization rates of sulfonated azo dyes than other quinone compounds. In addition, a NADH/FMN-dependent AQS reductase was involved in this process and it was confirmed by using nondenaturing polyacrylamide gel electrophoresis. Anthraquinone acting as a redox mediator could significantly accelerate the reduction process of azo dye, Acid Red GR, by a newly isolated biphenyl-degrading bacterium [117]. Yet in another study, a packed-bed reactor with silica-gel-bound laccase beads appeared to be exceptionally potential in the continuous decolorization of indigo carmine for 18 d without loss in activity [118]. This system offered perfect ability to degrade recalcitrant dyes with ABTS acting as a mediator.

The mediated effects of reduction products of some ortho-hydroxyl substituted azo dyes on biodecolorization were investigated by [119]. The results indicated that the addition of reduction products such as 1-naphthol-2-amino-4-sulfonic acid acting as redox mediator could effectively accelerate dye decolorization by Shigella sp. QRZ-1. The best accelerating effect was obtained with the addition of reduction products of Acid Red 14 (AR14), resulting in an over 3-fold increase in decolorization efficiency of many azo dyes. In sequencing batch reactor experiments, the accelerating effect of reduction products of this dye was more obvious (1.5-fold) during the startup of the system. When the dye concentration was increased to 500 mg l^{-1}, the accelerated decolorization efficiency was still maintained around 95%. The presence of Acid Red 14 in the feed enhanced the decolorization performance of anaerobic sludge, indicating that the strategy may be beneficial for practical application.

Veratryl alcohol (VA, 3,4-dimethoxy benzyl alcohol), a secondary metabolite of several white rot fungi (WRF), after its oxidation to the VA cation radical (VA$^+$) by lignin peroxidase (LiP), acted as a mediator for the degradation of lignin [120]. Mediating properties of VA could be enhanced if the radical is somehow complexed to the LiP. Nevertheless, VA stimulates LiP, probably by protecting the enzyme against the damaging effect of H_2O_2 [121, 122]. It has been reported that VA might enhance the dye decolorization catalyzed by LiP [123].

The presence of redox mediators VA, acetosyringone (AS) or TEMPO as oxidizing mediators generally enhanced the rate of dye decolorization by (versatile peroxidise) VP from *Bjerkandera Adusta* [110]. The decolorization of industrial dyes using extracellular enzymes produced by 21 basidiomycetes, mainly edible mushrooms has already been investigated [124]. Among the 27 dyes used in this study, nine were decolorized by over 40%. Most fungi decolorized Acid Orange 20, but they showed different specificities in the case of the other dyes. Determination of activity staining by native polyacrylamide gel electrophoresis revealed that all the decolorization activities corresponded to ABTS oxidation activities.

Decolorization of 21 different reactive textile and other industrially important dyes by BGP has been evaluated [89]. The decolorization of dyes and their mixtures was drastically increased in the presence of 1.0 mM HOBT. Textile effluent was also significantly decolorized by BGP in the presence of 1.0 mM HOBT [125]. The decolorization of acid dyes by TP was significantly enhanced in the presence of 2.0 mM HOBT [126]. Redox mediated decolorization of direct dyes by TP has been extensively studied [83, 127]. Dyes were recalcitrant to the action of enzyme without a redox mediator and were decolorized to different extents in the presence of a number of redox mediators (2.0 mM); vanillin (VN), L-histidine and VLA. However, 0.6 mM HOBT emerged as a potential redox mediator for TP catalyzed decolorization of direct dyes and their mixtures. A comparative study was performed for the decolorization and removal of two textile carpet industrial effluents by TP and TMP [28]. The decolorization of effluents was enhanced in the presence of 2.0 mM HOBT. Matto and Husain [129] investigated decolorization of Direct Red 23 and Direct Blue 80 by TP in the presence of HOBT, phenol, VN, VLA, VA and syringaldehyde (SA). HOBT decolorized the direct dyes significantly. Decolorization of Acid Red 27 by azoreductase was enhanced effectively by quinone redox mediators; lawsone and menadione [130]. The role of six redox mediators for the decolorization of a textile effluent by fenugreek seeds peroxidase (FSP) has been investigated [131]. However, the effluent was decolorized maximally in the presence of 1.0 mM HOBT. The decolorization of textile effluent in batch process by FSP was 85% in 5 h whereas the complete decolorization of textile effluent by membrane-entrapped FSP was observed within 11 h of its operation.

3. ENZYME-MEDIATOR APPROACH FOR DYE/WASTEWATER TREATMENT

3.1. Laccases

Decolorization of different dyes by laccase in the presence of redox mediators has been shown in Table 1. Laccases (EC 1.10.3.2) are multi-Cu oxidases that can catalyze the oxidation of a range of reducing substrates with concomitant reduction of O_2. Because of their capability of catalyzing the oxidation of aromatic compounds, laccases are attracting increasing attention as potential industrial enzymes in various applications, such as pulp delignification, wood fiber modification, dye or stain bleaching, chemical or medicinal synthesis, and decontamination of water or soil [132-133]. Laccases contain one type 1 (T1) Cu center, one type 2 (T2) Cu center, and one type 3 (T3) Cu center. The T2 and T3 sites form a trinuclear Cu cluster onto which O_2 is reduced. The T1 Cu oxidizes the reducing substrate and transfers electrons to the T2 and T3 Cu. Laccase is able to oxidize certain phenols with E_0 values higher than its own (0.5 to 0.8 V versus the normal hydrogen electrode). However, many inorganic and organic compounds with comparable E_0 values such as 1,2,3,5-tetramethoxybenzene are not laccase substrates due to unfavorable kinetics [134]. Under certain conditions, however, these compounds can be indirectly oxidized by laccase through the mediation of small, redox-active laccase substrates. ABTS was the first compound found capable of efficiently mediating the laccase oxidation of high-E_0, nonsubstrate lignin model compounds such as VA and nonphenolic lignin model dimers [91]. Based on product structure analysis, it has been proposed that laccase-oxidized ABTS can abstract an H atom from the lignin model compounds, leading to indirect laccase catalysis upon the oxidation of the compounds [135]. Several other types of mediators, particularly phenoxazines and N-OH compounds, have been recognized for their mediation function in laccase catalysis [132, 136-138].

Detailed, comparative information on the interaction between mediator and laccase remains to be reported [139], although various physical and chemical characterizations have been performed on several well-known laccase mediators [140-143]. For N-OH-type mediators, it has not been clear whether their oxidation by laccase involves H abstraction or electron transfer, similar to that found with the oxidation of phenol [144]. Several investigators have compared fungal laccases in combination of variety of redox mediator and found that the redox potential of the laccases varied depending on the source of the laccase. This would dictate the need and nature of redox mediator for the degradation of a particular dye to occur [139]. It has been reported that the laccases from the lignin-degrading basidiomycetes, *Trametes versicolor* and *Polyporus pinisitus* and the ascomycete *Myceliophthora thermophila* were capable to decolorize synthetic dyes to different extents. In the presence of low-molecular-weight redox mediators, the broad substrate specificity of laccases can be extended even more [145]. The oxidation of indigo carmine dye by a laccase from *Trametes versicolor* has been described [146]. Indigo degradation was also observed with purified laccases from *Trametes hirsuta* and *Sclerotium rolfsii*. The degradation of indigo both in effluent and in fabrics using purified laccases from *Trametes hirsute* and *Sclerotium rolfsii* in combination with redox mediator has been reported.

Table 1. Laccase catalyzed decolorization of dyes in presence of various redox mediators

Redox mediator	Dyes	References
HOBT, VLA, PTPA	RBBR	[150, 151]
AS	Indigo	[149]
ABTS	Alizarin Red	[148]
	Decolorization of reactive azo and acid dyes	[208]
	stilbene dye, Direct Yellow 11, Basazol 46L	[168]
ABTS, HOBT	Sella Solid Red, Luganil Green	[102]
	Four azo, three anthraquinone, one indigoid dye and their mixtures	[153]
HOBT	Acid Blue 225, Acid Violet 17, Reactive Black 5	[155]
	Decolorization of several dyes	[156]
	azo sulfonated dyes	[106]
	Reactive Black 5	[162]
	RBBR	[151]
HOBT, 2-methoxy-phenothiazine	Rhodamine 6 G, Erioglaucine, Trypan Blue	[107]
Syringaldazine, AS	Decolorization of Reactive Black/azure	[160, 209]
HOBT, PZ, *p*-HBA, NNDS	Indigo Carmine, Phenol Red	[163]
VA, HOBT	Reactive Blue 114, Reactive Yellow 15, Reactive Red 239, Reactive Black 5	[165]
ABTS, HOBT, NHA, POM, VLA, TEMPO	Six reactive textile dyes	[166]
VLA, PG, thymol	RBBR, Indigo, CBB, Acid Red, Azure A	[167]
p-coumaric acid, ferulic acid & sinapic acid	Industrial dyes	[169]
AV, AS	RBBR, carminic acid	[170]
Natural/synthetic mediators	Reactive & acidic dyes	[172]
SA, HOBT	Reactive dye effluent	[158]
Phenolic compounds	MG	[174]

Low molecular mass redox mediators like ABTS have been found necessary for laccase-catalyzed decolorization of most of the dyes [147, 148]. The effect of known redox mediators AS, HOBT, and 4-hydroxybenzenesulfonic acid (PHBS) was compared in terms of the laccase catalyzed degradation of indigo. The maximum about 30% increase in oxidation rate of indigo with *Sclerotium rolfsii* (SR) 1 and AS was observed [149]. Like wise, a laccase plus redox mediator formulation was used in the textile industry in the finishing process for indigo stained material (Novo Nordisk Product Sheet B917 and Application Sheet B 919). The decolorization of Remazol Brilliant Blue R (RBBR) by a commercial laccase formulation (CLF) containing laccase, a redox mediator, and a nonionic surfactant has been described [150]. These low-molecular weight components were removed from the CLF by gel filtration, which made it possible to compare the effect of laccase alone. Apart from slightly better thermostability of the CLF as compared to the laccase alone, the pH and temperature profiles were similar, regardless of the presence of the low molecular-weight components. The laccase alone did not decolorize RBBR: SA and low-molecular-weight redox mediator, HOBT, was necessary to initiate decolorization. Here, a comparison of the kinetics of RBBR decolorization using the CLF and laccase alone has been described. Provided that a redox mediator was included, it was suggested that laccase might be suitable for the wastewater treatment of similar anthraquinone dyes. These investigators have further shown that a pure fungal laccase obtained from a commercial formulation used in the textile industry did not decolorize RBBR. Decolorization was only observed when a redox mediator was added together with the laccase. Under the conditions specified, 5.7 mM VLA was the most effective mediator studied and almost complete decolorization was observed within 20 min. In contrast, 11 mM HOBT decolorized RBBR at about a two-fold slower rate and to a lesser extent. However, the higher concentrations of HOBT were inhibitory, which could be due to inactivation of laccase by the toxic effect of HOBT radical. The CLF that contained phenothiazine-10-propionic acid (PTPA) as the mediator was least effective, giving 30% decolorization under identical experimental conditions. Thus the investigators suggested that similar laccase plus mediator systems could be used for the detoxification of related anthraquinone textile dyes [151]. HOBT was found to be the most effective mediator and it showed decolorization of Sella Solid Red to 88% in 10 min and Luganil Green to 49% in 20 min by laccase [102]. Some investigators found identical results, which showed that the use of redox mediators was important for the decolorization of reactive dyes with soluble and immobilized laccase preparations [152]. In another study it has been reported that the laccases from the lignin-degrading basidiomycetes *Trametes versicolor* and *Polyporus pinisitus* and the ascomycete *Myceliophthora thermophila* were capable to decolorize synthetic dyes to different extents. The addition of 2.0 mM of the redox mediator HOBT further improved and facilitated the decolorization of all nine investigated dyes [153]. A laccase has been isolated from the culture filtrate of *Lentinula edodes* [154]. This enzyme was effective in the decolorization of chemically different dyes without any mediators, but the decolorization of two dyes, Red Poly (vinyl amine) sulfonate-anthrapyridone dye and Reactive Orange 16, did require some redox mediators. The decolorization efficiency of *Trametes modesta* laccase was improved remarkably in the presence of mediators like HOBT and 2-methoxyphenothiazine [155]. The addition of HOBT to the ligninolytic fluids from the cultures of *Trametes trogii* increased both the range and rate of decolorization of different dyes [156].

Two biological approaches for decolorization of azo sulfonated dyes have been compared: reductive decolorization with the ascomycete yeast *Issatchenkia occidentalis* and enzymatic oxidative decolorization with *Trametes villosa* laccase alone or in the presence of the mediator HOBT. The redox potential difference between the biological cofactor involved in the reductive activity of growing cells and the azo dye was a reliable indication for the decolorization ability of the biocatalyst. A linear relationship was observed between the redox potential of the azo dyes and the decolorization efficiency of enzyme, enzyme/mediator and yeast [106].

Some workers have reported a combined effect of the redox mediators and metal ions on the laccase-catalyzed decolorization of synthetic acid dyes. Decolorization of dyes was significantly high on combination of both the procedures [157, 158]. Laccase catalyzed decolorization of different industrial dyes was mediated by various new natural mediators. An enzyme showing alkaliphilic laccase activity was purified from the culture supernatant of *Myrothecium verrucaria* 24G-4. The enzyme was highly stable under alkaline conditions, showed an optimum reaction at pH of 9.0 for 4-aminoantipyrine/phenol coupling, and decolorized synthetic dyes under alkaline conditions [159].

Ten phenols were selected as natural laccase mediators after screening 44 different compounds with Reactive Black 5 as a substrate. Their performances were monitored at different mediator/dye ratios and incubation times (up to 6 h) by the use of *Pycnoporus cinnabarinus* and *Trametes villosa* laccases and were compared with those of eight known synthetic mediators, including -NOH- compounds. Among the six types of dyes assayed, only Reactive Blue 38 (phthalocyanine) was resistant to laccase–mediator system under the conditions used. Acid Blue 74 (indigoid dye), Reactive Blue 19 (anthraquinoid dye), and Aniline Blue (triarylmethane-type dye) were partially decolorized by laccases alone, although decolorization was much more efficient and rapid in the presence of mediators, whereas Reactive Black 5 and Azure B could be decolorized only in the presence of mediators. The efficiency of each natural mediator depended on the type of dye to be treated but, with the only exception being Azure B (<50% decolorization), nearly complete decolorization (80–100%) was attained in all cases. Similar results were also obtained with the best synthetic mediators but the reactions were significantly slower. Phenolic aldehydes, ketones, acids, and esters related to the three lignin units were among the best mediators, including *p*-coumaric acid, VN, acetovanillone (AV), methyl vanillate, and above all, SA and AS. The last two compounds were found especially promising, ecofriendly and potentially cheap mediators for industrial applications since they provided the highest decolorization rates, in only 5-30 min, depending on the type of dye to be treated [160]. The decolorization of a number of recalcitrant reactive azo and acid dyes using the culture filtrate and purified laccase from the fungus *Cyathus bulleri* was investigated. Decolorization of such dyes was seen with the culture filtrate of the fungus containing predominantly laccase. In spite of no observable effect of purified laccase on other dyes, the ability to decolorize these was achieved in the presence of the redox mediator ABTS, with 50% decolorization in 0.5–5.4 d [161].

The addition of 2.0 mM HOBT improved the rate of laccase catalyzed decolorization of Direct Red 28, Reactive Black 5, Acid Blue 25 and Azure B by 17, 63, 12 and 56%, respectively [153]. Decolorization of Acid Blue 225, Acid Violet 17 and Reactive Black 5 by laccase was increased 2-6 folds in the presence of HOBT [155]. The presence of HOBT was found to be essential for the decolorization of Reactive Black 5 by purified laccase from *Pleurotus sajor-caju* [162]. The potential of crude and partially purified WL1 laccase from *Trichoderma harzianum* for the decolorization of synthetic dyes, Rhodamine 6G, Erioglaucine and Trypan Blue has been evaluated in the presence of HOBT [107, 163] have studied the effect of redox mediators on dye decolorization by laccase isoenzymes from *Trametes versicolor*. All the tested redox mediators; HOBT, promazine, *p*-hydroxybenzoic acid and 1-nitroso-2-naphthol-3,6-disulfonic acid led to higher dye decolorization than that obtained without mediator addition. Promazine was the most effective mediator while *p*-hydroxybenzoic acid did not significantly improve the degree of decolorization.

A CLF containing laccase, a redox mediator and a non-ionic surfactant has been used [164]. Small molecular weight components were removed from the CLF by gel filtration, which made it possible to compare the effect of its laccase alone. Apart from slightly better thermostability of the CLF as compared with the laccase alone, the pH and temperature profiles were similar regardless of the presence of the small molecular weight components. The laccase alone did not decolorize RBBR. HOBT was necessary for decolorization to occur. Sequential decolorization of reactive dyes was carried out by a laccase mediator system using VA and HOBT as mediators [165]. VA resulted in a high level of decolorization on the first and second cycles for Reactive Blue 114 (≥95%), Reactive Yellow 15 and Reactive Red 239 (≥80%) while for Reactive Black 5 a slightly lower value (70%) was observed on the second cycle. The degree of Reactive Blue 114 decolorization remained 90% after the third cycle and about 60% after seven cycles. When HOBT was used as mediator a slight decrease in decolorization efficiency was observed. Tavares *et al.* [166] performed a screening on the degradation of six reactive textile dyes using several laccase mediators; ABTS, HOBT, N-hydroxyacetanilide (NHA), polioxometalates, VLA and 2,2,6,6-tetramethylpiperidin-1-yloxy (TEMPO). ABTS was found to be the most effective mediator. The efficiency of ABTS depended on the type of dye, pH, temperature and dye concentration. The optimum temperature and pH values were 35°C and 5.0, respectively, for maximum decolorisation (above 70%) of Reactive Black 5, Reactive Blue 114 and Reactive Yellow 15. For Reactive Red 239 the optimum conditions were found at 40°C and pH of 4.5 (above 56% decolorization). ABTS has no effect at low concentrations, except for Reactive Blue 114, where it resulted in the best decolorization (93%). A comparison of decolorization based on the percentage absorbance reduction at the maximum absorbance wavelength of each dye and throughout the visible spectrum was made. The decolorization capability of laccase/mediator system was related to the types of mediator, the dye structure and expeimental conditions [167]. After screening 14 different compounds with Indigo Carmine (indigoid dye) as a substrate, phloroglucinol, thymol, and VLA were selected as laccase mediators resulting in 90-100% decolorization of this dye in 1 h. Thus, these three compounds were used as mediators for the decolorization of other four dyes. VLA was quite effective in decolorizing RBBR, Coomassie Brilliant Blue G-250, and Acid Red. Thymol was able to mediate decolorization of RBBR and Azure A. Phloroglucinol had no mediating capability in decolorization of these dyes. Two recalcitrant dyes; stilbene dye, Direct Yellow 11 and methine dye, Basazol 46L were effectively decolorized by HRP, SBP and laccase in the presence of ABTS as a mediator [168]. The stilbene dye, Direct Yellow 11 responded to both SBP and laccase/ABTS. SBP was more effective in the oxidative removal of methine dye, Basazol 46L as compared to the other peroxidases.

The capabilities of *p*-coumaric acid, ferulic acid and sinapic acid as laccase mediators in oxidation of industrial dyes have been investigated [169]. Sinapic acid behaved as highly efficient mediator in decolorization of dyes, including the recalcitrant Reactive Black 5. This mediating capacity was related to the specificity constant of the enzyme oxidizing this *p*-hydroxycinnamic acid, which was 16 times higher than for the typical substrate ABTS. The kinetics of ABTS oxidation by laccase in the presence of *p*-hydroxycinnamic acids suggested that the stable phenoxyl radical of a sinapic acid transformation product acts as laccase mediator.

Laccase activity of wood rotting fungi was studied for the decolorization of RBBR and carminic acid [170]. The addition of AV or AS intensified these processes: decolorization was more effective as compared to the experiment performed without these compounds. In the presence of AS, decolorization was more extensive than AV. However, the level of destaining was relatively low in comparison to laccase activity on syringaldazine. The highly purified constitutive form of *Cerrena unicolor* and inducible form of *Trametes versicolor* laccases also decolorized both dyes. The fungus, *Lentinus lepideus*, which has no laccase activity did not decolorize at all. This fact indicates laccase not solely responsible for decolorization and probably decolorization of dyes involves more than one mechanism.

Laccase from basidiomycete fungus *Cyathus bulleri* has been evaluated for its ability to decolorize a number of reactive and acidic dyes in the presence of natural and synthetic mediators [171]. The extent of decolorization was examined at different mediator/dye concentrations and incubation time. Among the synthetic mediators, ABTS was effective at low mediator/dye ratios and resulted in 80–95% decolorization at rates that varied from 226 ± 4 nmol min^{-1} mg^{-1} for Reactive Orange 1 to $1,333\pm15$ nmol min^{-1} mg^{-1} for Reactive Red 198. Other synthetic mediators like HOBT and VA showed both concentration and time dependent increases in percent decolorization. Natural mediators like VN, on the other hand, were found to be less effective on all the dyes except Reactive Orange 1. Computed rates of decolorization were about two-fold lower than that with ABTS. The laccase–ABTS system also led to nearly 80% decolorization for the simulated dye mixture. No clear correlation between laccase activity on the mediator and its ability to decolorize dyes was found, but pH had a significant effect: optimum pH for decolorization coincided with the optimum pH for mediator oxidation. The treated samples were also evaluated for toxicity in model microbial systems. The laccase–mediator system appears promising for treatment of textile wastewaters. Laccase-ABTS system has been reported to be a promising tool for the treatment of waters containing Rhodamine B [172]. Seven redox mediators were investigated in the mediatiator-assisted laccase catalyzed oxidation reactions. Among the mediators tested, ABTS was found to be the best one showing 80% decolorization of Rhodamine B within 48 h while only 20% decolorization was achieved with no mediator. The best molar ratio of dye/mediator in this system was 1:10 and dye/enzyme ratio was 0.5 µmol/U. The optimum conditions for Rhodamine B decolorization were at pH 4.0-5.0 and temperature 35-40°C.

It has been shown that the redox mediator system is necessary for the decolorization of simulated reactive dye effluent by laccase [158]. SA, a natural redox mediator, was very effective than the synthetic mediator, HOBT. The initial rate of effluent decolorization in the presence of SA (0.0831/h) was 5.6 times higher than HOBT (0.0152/h). Although the rate of decolorization was markedly decreased in the effluent containing mixed metal ions, presence of SA showed effective decolorization. This study indicates that *G. lucidum* laccase and natural redox mediator system could be a potential candidate for color removal from reactive dye effluent. In a further study thes workers investigated the efficacy of phenolic extract of wheat bran and lignin-related phenolic compounds as natural redox mediators on laccase-mediated transformation of Malachite Green (MG) using purified laccase from the white-rot fungus *Ganoderma lucidum*. *G. lucidum* laccase was able to decolorize 40.7% MG dye (at 25 mg l^{-1} after 24 h of incubation. Whereas, the addition of phenolic extract of wheat bran enhanced the decolorization significantly (p <0.001) by two to three-fold than that of purified laccase alone. Among various natural phenolic compounds, AV, *p*-coumaric acid, ferulic acid, SA, and VN were the most efficient mediators, as effective as the synthetic mediator HOBT. Characterization of MG transformation products by HPLC, ultraviolet-visible (UV-VIS) and liquid chromatography-mass spectrometry-electrospray ionization analysis revealed that *N*-demethylation was the key mechanism of decolorization of MG by laccase. Growth inhibition test based on mycelial growth inhibition of white rot fungus *Phanerochaete chrysosporium* revealed that treatment with laccase plus natural mediators effectively reduced the growth inhibitory levels of MG than that of untreated one. Among all the tested compounds, SA showed the highest enhanced decolorization, as a consequence reduced growth inhibition was observed in SA-treated samples. The results of the present study revealed that the natural phenolic compounds could alternatively be used as potential redox mediators for effective laccase-mediated decolorization of MG [173].

Decolorization of Reactive Red 198, Rem Blue RR, Dylon Navy 17, Rem Red RR, and Rem Yellow RR by using laccase and laccase-mediated system has been studied [174]. Among these dyestuffs, decolorization of Rem Blue RR and Dylon Navy 17 was performed with crude laccase under optimized conditions. VN was selected as laccase mediator after screening six different compounds with Rem Yellow RR, Reactive Red 198 and Rem Red RR as substrates. However, Rem Yellow RR was not decolorized by either laccase or laccase-mediated system. It is observed that the culture supernatant contained high laccase activity after treatment with catalase that was responsible for the decolorization. Besides, culture supernatant with high laccase activity as enzyme source was treated with catalase. In this way, the hypothesis that laccase was the enzyme responsible for decolorization was supported. The Rem Blue RR was decolorized to 64.84% under the optimum conditions and Dylon Navy 17 to 75.43% with crude laccase. However, using the laccase and VN, the decolorization of Reactive Red 198 and Rem Red RR was found to be 62 and 68%, respectively. These results demonstrated that the decolorization abilities of laccase and/or laccase mediator systems were based on the types of mediator, the dye structure, and the standard experimental conditions.

3.2. Peroxidases

Applications of different redox mediators in dye removal by various types of microbial and plant peroxidases have been shown in Table 2 and 3. The heme-containing peroxidases are known to catalyze the one-electron oxidation of a wide range of structurally diverse aromatic compounds. This was usually accomplished through the catalytic cycle first described for horseradish peroxidase (HRP) and later refined by Dunford and other investigators [175, 176]. H_2O_2 oxidized ferric peroxidase by two electrons to the enzyme intermediate compound I, described as an oxyferryl porphyrin δ cation radical (reaction 1). The porphyrin radical (P^+) accepts one electron from an organic substrate, yielding the corresponding substrate free radical and an oxyferryl heme intermediate, known as compound II (reaction 2). A subsequent one-electron reduction of compound II by a second substrate molecule yields ferric peroxidase (reaction 3). This catalytic cycle differs slightly for substrates that donate electrons rather than a hydrogen atom when oxidized by peroxidises [177]. In this case, the protons for liberation of the ferryl oxygen atom as water do not come from the substrate and compound II, but instead were likely to be obtained from bulk solution. A unique feature of peroxidase-catalyzed reactions was the oxidation of substrates to diffusible free radical intermediates. These substrate radicals are known to participate in a variety of non-enzymatic reactions including disproportionation, polymerization and electron transfer (oxidative or reductive). One particularly important reaction of radicals (especially cation radicals) derived from peroxidases was that of redox mediation or mediation by electron transfer [178-180]. This mechanism proposes that radicals (A^+) generated by a peroxidase may act as diffusible oxidants to oxidize secondary molecules (B) (reaction 4). This type of reaction could have several consequences for the kinetics of peroxidase-catalyzed oxidation reactions. Foremost was that the rate of generation of secondary radicals (B^+) can be dramatically stimulated in the presence of a redox mediator (A). This type of mechanism may have toxicological implications if B^+ or a subsequent metabolite is toxic. Under these circumstances, the presence of A may stimulate the production of toxic metabolites produced by peroxidases.

Moreover, the accumulation of A can be completely inhibited in the presence of B. This may have a range of consequences desirable or undesirable depending on the destructive and/or beneficial properties of A^+. If, for example, A^+ had some therapeutic role, the presence of B would interfere with that function. One reaction catalyzed by peroxidases that may be affected by redox mediation was the oxidation of aminopyrine (AP) to its radical (AP^+). While the exact mechanism of toxicity of this compound was not known, it has been proposed that it must first be oxidized before it can exert its toxic effects [181]. Cytochromes P-450, prostaglandin synthase and a variety of peroxidases have been shown to oxidize AP to a number of potentially toxic metabolites, including AP^+. Oxidation of AP by cytochromes P-450, however, was a relatively slow reaction, and it has been shown that the rates for HRP oxidation of this chemical are 2-3 orders of magnitude faster. Myeloperoxidase (MPO) has also been shown to oxidize AP through the production of HOCl. For these reasons, the rate of oxidation of AP by peroxidases became important in examining the toxicity of AP and other similar chemicals with toxic side effects. It was proposed that the rate of oxidation of AP catalyzed by HRP, MPO, and other peroxidases may be stimulated in the presence of other peroxidase substrates acting as redox mediators. In order to examine this hypothesis, chlorpromazine (CPZ), a common peroxidase substrate, was used as a redox mediator. Using HRP, AP, and CPZ in a model system, these investigators demonstrated that CPZ^+, generated by HRP, can oxidize AP to AP^+ and that CPZ stimulates the rate of AP oxidation by two orders of magnitude. Furthermore, a similar effect was observed with the MPO mimic HOCl and the mammalian peroxidases lactoperoxidase (LPO) and MPO. The implication of the kinetics of this mechanism in the toxicity of AP and other similar compounds was discussed. Peroxidases in particular have been extensively studied for the treatment of dyes as these show many attractive properties such as wide specificity, high stability in solution and easy accessibility from plant materials and fungal sources [48, 182-184].

3.2.1. Lignin Peroxidases

LiP from the white rot fungus *Phanerochaete chrysosporium* catalyzed the reduction of cytochrome c, nitro blue tetrazolium, ferric iron, molecular oxygen, and triiodide in a reaction mixture containing $LiPH_2$, H_2O_2, ethylenediamine tetraacetic acid (EDTA), and iodide [185]. Activity followed first order kinetics with respect to EDTA concentration. The reductive activity observed with $LiPH_2$ using iodide as the mediator was comparable to that obtained using a variety of other free radical mediators such as VA, 1,4-dimethoxybenzene, and 1,2,3-

and 1,2,4-trimethoxybenzene. EDTA-derived radicals were detected by electron spin resonance (ESR) spin trapping upon incubation of $LiPH_2$ with H_2O_2, iodide, and EDTA. Reduction activity was also observed using other peroxidases such as LPO, horseradish peroxidase (HRP), and MPO. For the reduction activity of $LiPH_2$, it was proposed that the oxidation of EDTA was mediated by the iodide radical, and EDTA radicals mediate the reduction of various electron acceptors. The role of VA in lignin peroxidase-catalyzed oxidation of anisyl alcohol with pre-steady-state and steady-state kinetic methods has been investigated [186]. VA has been proposed to act as a redox mediator for substrates that are not directly oxidized by the enzyme. Alternatively, its mediation activity has also been attributed to its ability to protect the enzyme from H_2O_2-dependent inactivation. LiP from *P. chrysosporium* was able to catalyze reductive reactions using VA as a mediator and either oxalate or EDTA as electron donors [187]. Reduction of oxygen to superoxide, monitored by oxygen consumption, was used as a measure of the reductive activity of LiP. In the presence of EDTA, the rate of O_2 reduction catalyzed by LiP decreased with time and increasing concentrations of H_2O_2. When oxalate replaced EDTA, LiP-catalyzed O_2 reduction did not decrease with time, and increasing concentrations of H_2O_2 increased the duration and extent of O_2 reduction. LiP was converted to the compound III state in the presence of EDTA, H_2O_2, and VA. When oxalate replaced EDTA, compound II was observed. The importance of the VA cation radical (VA^+) in the conversion of LiP compound III to active enzyme has been previously examined [188]. Further they proposed that rapid reduction of VA^+ by EDTA results in accumulation of LiP compound III and the loss of activity, resulting in a decrease in LiP-catalyzed reduction reactions. Oxalate was less effective in reducing the VA^+; therefore, some VA^+ remains to convle 1ert compound III to active enzyme and maintain LiP catalyzed reduction reactions. Thus it was reported that the oxalate, a normal secondary metabolite of *P. chrysosporium*, was a suitable candidate for mediating reduction reactions by LiP *in vivo*.

It has been demonstrated that the oxidation of 4-methoxymandelic acid (MMA) was mediated by VA. Increasing VA concentration in the presence of 2 mM MMA resulted in increased oxidation of MMA yielding anisaldehyde [189]. It was discovered that LiP isozyme H_2 ($LiPH_2$) has the ability to oxidize Mn_2^+. Furthermore, at pH 4.5, the physiological pH of *Phanerochaete chrysosporium*, $LiPH_2$ oxidizes Mn_2^+ at a much faster rate (25 times faster) than VA. The ability of Mn_2^+ to act as a redox mediator for indirect oxidations catalyzed by $LiPH_2$ was therefore investigated. In the presence of physiologically relevant levels of oxalate and Mn^{2+}, the rate of $LiPH_2$-catalyzed oxidation of all substrates studied was dramatically increased. Up to 10-fold stimulations were observed compared to the rates of oxidation of substrate in either the presence or absence of VA. They proposed that the stimulation was due to the ability of $LiPH_2$ to oxidize Mn^{2+}, producing the strong oxidant Mn^{3+}, at a high rate. The rates of oxidation of the substrates showed a hyperbolic dependence on Mn_2^+ in the presence of oxalate, a chelator, which was required for maximal activity. The oxalate dependence of the oxidation rates correlated well with the concentration of the 1:1 complex of Mn^{2+}-oxalate. The importance of the ability of Mn_2^+-oxalate to stimulate the oxidation of chemicals by $LiPH_2$ was discussed. LiP-catalyzed oxidation of guaiacol and the role of VA in this reaction have been investigated by steady-state and pre-steady-state methods [190]. Pre-steady-state kinetic analyses demonstrated that guaiacol was a good substrate for both compounds I and II, the two- and one-electron oxidized enzyme intermediates, respectively, of LiP. The rate constant for the reaction with compound I was $1.2 \times 10^{(6)}/M$/sec. The reaction of guaiacol with compound II exhibited a K_d of 64 µM and a first-order rate constant of 17/sec. Oxidation of guaiacol led to tetraguaiacol formation. This reaction exhibited classical Michaelis–Menten kinetics with a K_m of 160 μM and a k_{cat} of 7.7/sec. VA was capable of mediating the oxidation of guaiacol. These results demonstrated that VA can serve as a mediator for phenolic substrates like dyes in the LiP reaction.

Table 2. Applications of redox mediators in dye removal by microbial peroxidases

Enzyme	Redox Mediator/s	Dyes	References
LiP	VA	Six industrial azo, phthalocyanine dyes	[191]
		Procian Brilliant Blue HGR, Ranocid Fast Blue, Acid Red 119, Navidol Fast Black MSRL	[193]
		RBBR	[5]
		Reactive Brilliant Red K-2BP	[194]
MnP	VLA, HOBT	Reactive Black 5, Reactive Blue 19, Reactive Red 22, Reactive Yellow 15	[21]
MnP	Tween-80	Direct Blue 15, Direct Green 6, Congo Red	[196]
VP	VA, AS, TEMPO	Direct Yellow 58, Disperse Red 60, Vat Blue 7, Reactive Yellow 2	[110]

Table 3. Applications of redox mediators in dye removal by plant peroxidases

Source of Enzyme	Redox Mediator/s	Dyes	References
Horseradish/ Soybean	ABTS	Direct Yellow 11, Basazol 46L	[168]
Bitter gourd	HOBT	21 reactive textile, other industrially important dyes	[89]
		Textile industrial effluent	[125]
		Textile industrial effluent	[201]
		DR 17, DB1	[202]
	Phenol	DR 17, DB1	[203]
White radish	HOBT	Reactive Red 120, Reactive Blue 171	[204]
Turnip	HOBT	Acid dyes	[126]
		Direct dyes	[83,127]
		Textile carpet effluent	[28]
Tomato	HOBT, VN, phenol, VLA, VA, SA	Direct Red 23, Direct Blue 80	[129]
	HOBT	Textile carpet effluent	[28]
Fenugreek seeds	HOBT	Textile industrial effluent	[131]

LiP produced by *Trametes versicolor* decolorized RBBR in the presence as well as in the absence of VA. VA enhances and stabilizes the RBBR-decolorization rates by lignin peroxidase. RBBR has better substrate reactivity than VA for LiP. RBBR is also decolorized directly by LiP and competitively inhibits VA oxidation by LiP. In the presence of higher concentrations of RBBR (i) RBBR decolorization rates improve, (ii) veratryl aldehyde appears after a lag and (iii) VA oxidation rates decrease. The lag is due to consumption of VA cation radical $(VA^{\cdot+})$ generated upon LiP-catalyzed VA oxidation, during RBBR oxidation. That may result in the formation of compound III in the absence of $VA^{\cdot+}$ and contributes to the inhibitory influence of RBBR on LiP activity [5]. LiP from *Bjerkandera adusta* showed low activity with most of the azo and phthalocyanine dyes. However, the specific activity increased 8-100 folds when VA was included in the reaction mixture [191]. Maximum decolorization achieved by partially purified LiP from *Phanerochaete chrysosporum* was 80% for Procion Brilliant Blue HGR, 83% for Ranocid Fast Blue, 70% for Acid Red 119 and 61% for Navidol Fast Black MSRL [192]. This decolorization efficiency was observed at 0.2 and 0.4 mM l^{-1} H_2O_2, 2.5 mM l^{-1} VA and pH 5.0 after 1 h. LiP produced by *Trametes versicolor* decolorized RBBR in the presence as well as in the absence of VA [5]. Decolorization of Reactive Brilliant Red K-2BP by LiP with higher addition of H_2O_2 and VA was enhanced to 89%, whereas decolorization by MnP was optimized only with a suitable dose of H_2O_2 (0.1 mM) and decreased by the addition of Mn^{2+} [193].

3.2.2. Manganese Peroxidase

MnP oxidizes its natural substrate, i.e. lignin as well as textile dyes [22, 191]. MnP has been reported as the main enzyme involved in dye decolorization by *Phanerochaete chrysosporium* [194]. Purified MnP decolorized Reactive Black 5, Reactive Blue 19, Reactive Red 22 and Reactive Yellow 15 whereas laccase was ineffective to decolorize Reactive Black 5 and Reactive Red 22. However, all these dyes were decolorized after addition of redox mediators; VLA and HOBT [21]. Decolorization of azo dyes; Direct Blue 15, Direct Green 6, and Congo Red catalyzed by MnP from *Phanerochaete chrysosporium* was enhanced by the addition of Tween-80 [195].

3.2.3. Horseradish Peroxidase (HRP)

HRP has been found an effective enzyme in the degradation of industrially important textile dyes [196-198]. These investigators have evaluated specificity of HRP toward different dyes, such as Remazol Blue, Cibacron Red, Acid Black 10 BX and Direct Yellow 10. The enzyme activity for Remazol Blue was found to be far better at pH 2.5 than at neutral pH whereas Remazol Blue worked as a strong competitive inhibitor of HRP at neutral pH [196]. The importance of HRP catalyzed reaction in the treatment of an acid azo dye, Acid Black 10 BX has been investigated [197]. HRP catalyzed reaction was found to be dependent upon the aqueous phase pH, contact time, H_2O_2, dye and HRP concentrations. The effective degradation of Direct Yellow 12 by HRP in the presence of H_2O_2 was found a viable approach for the degradation of azo dyes from aqueous solutions [198]. The potential of HRP in the decolorization of textile dyes and industrial effluents has been studied [199]. The obtained decolorization of Remazol Turquoise Blue G 133%, Lanaset Blue 2R and the textile effluent was 59, 94 and 52%, respectively.

3.2.4. Bitter Gourd Peroxidase (BGP)

The significance of peroxidases from bitter gourd in decolorizing industrially important dyes has been described by many workers. BGP had decolorized 21 dyes used in textile and other important industries in sodium acetate buffer, pH 5.6, in the presence of 0.75 mM H_2O_2 and 1.0 mM HOBT. Decolorization rate was drastically increased when dyes were treated by BGP in the presence of 1.0 mM HOBT [86, 89]. The greater fraction of the color was removed when the textile dyes were treated with increasing concentrations of enzyme but four out of eight reactive dyes were recalcitrant to the decolorization by BGP. The rate of decolorization was enhanced when the dyes were incubated with fixed quantity of enzyme for increasing times. Decolorization of non-textile dyes resulted in the degradation and removal of dyes from the solution without any precipitate formation. Thus it indicated that BGP-HOBT system was an effective biocatalyst for the treatment of effluents containing recalcitrant dyes from textiles, dye manufacturing and printing industries. Recently, it has been reported that BGP could be used in the detoxification and biotransformation of several aromatic amines, phenols and dyes present in wastewater/industrial effluents [87, 126]. Catalytic efficiency of BGP has been enhanced in presence of redox mediators. Complex mixtures of dyes were also significantly decolorized by BGP in the presence of 1.0 mM HOBT [89, 125].

Calcium alginate-starch gel entrapped BGP has been employed for the treatment of a textile industrial effluent in batch as well as in continuous reactor [200]. The textile effluent was recalcitrant to decolorization by BGP; thus, its decolorization was evaluated in the presence of 1.0 mM HOBT, a redox mediator. Immobilized enzyme exhibited same pH and temperature optima for effluent decolorization as attained by free enzyme. Immobilized enzyme was capable of removing more than 70% of effluent color in a stirred batch process after 3 h of incubation. Entrapped BGP retained 59% effluent decolorization reusability after its tenth repeated use. The two-reactor system containing calcium alginate-starch entrapped enzyme retained more than 50% textile effluent decolorization efficiency even after 2 months of its operation. The absorption spectra of the treated effluent exhibited a marked difference in the absorption at various wavelengths as compared to untreated effluent. The use of a two-reactor system containing enzyme-mediator system and an adsorbent will be significantly successful for treating industrial effluents at large scale, and it will help in getting water free from aromatic pollutants.

Salt fractionated bitter gourd proteins have been used in the presence of H_2O_2 for the decolorization of water insoluble disperse dyes; Disperse Red 17 (DR 17) and Disperse Brown 1 (DB 1) [201]. The role of nine different redox mediators; bromophenol, 2,4-dichlorophenol, guaiacol, HOBT, SA, VLA, and VN on decolorization of disperse dyes by BGP has been reported. Among these redox mediators, HOBT was found to be most effective in enhancing the decolorization of both dyes by peroxidase. BGP (0.36 U ml^{-1}) decolorized DR 17 maximally 90% in the presence of 0.1 mM HOBT while DB 1 was decolorized to 65% in the presence of 0.2 mM HOBT. Maximum decolorization of the dyes was obtained at pH 3.0 and 40°C within 1 h of incubation. Phenol has also been used as a redox mediator for the decolorization of these dyes [202]. BGP (0.215 U ml^{-1}) could decolorize about 60% of DR 17 in the presence of 0.2 mM phenol, whereas DB 1 was decolorized by only 40% even in the presence of 0.4 mM phenol. Maximum decolorization of dyes was described in the presence of 0.75 mM H_2O_2 in a buffer of pH 3.0 and 40 °C within 30 min. The K_m values obtained were 0.625 mg l^{-1} h^{-1} and 2.5 mg l^{-1} h^{-1} for DR 17 and DB 1, respectively. In all the experiments,

DB 1 was found to be more recalcitrant to decolorization catalyzed by BGP, as compared to DR 17. The application of such enzyme plus redox mediator systems may be extendable to other recalcitrant and water insoluble synthetic dyes using novel redox mediators and peroxidases from other new and cheaper sources.

3.2.5. White Radish Peroxidase (WRP)

In another study, WRP immobilized on Celite 545 has been employed for the treatment of reactive dyes: Reactive Red 120 and Reactive Blue 171 [203]. Effect of different redox mediators: HOBT, SA, VA and VLA on the decolorization of reactive dyes by WRP has been demonstrated. The used dyes were decolorized to different levels in the presence of these mediators. However, HOBT was found to be the most effective mediator for decolorization of Reactive Red 120 and Reactive Blue 171 by WRP. Maximum decolorization of the dyes was observed at pH 5.0 and 40°C in 1 h. Among the reported dyes, WRP exhibited significantly higher affinity for Reactive Red 120. Toxicity of the dyes was tested by *Allium cepa* test. Absorption spectra of treated and untreated dye solutions were found to show a marked difference. Efficiency of immobilized peroxidise was checked in a continuous reactor where the immobilized enzyme exhibited 73% decolorization of Reactive Red 120 even after 1 month of operation of the reactor.

3.2.6. Turnip Peroxidase (TP)

The wastewater containing acid dyes was remarkably decolorized by TP in the presence of HOBT, in a buffer of pH 5.6 and at 40°C. Various complex mixtures of acid dyes were also successfully decolorized by TP in the presence of HOBT [126]. Matto and Husain [83] demonstrated the effect of various redox mediators on the salt-fractionated turnip (*Brassica rapa*) proteins mediated decolorization of direct dyes, used in textile industry. The rate and extent of decolorization of dyes were significantly enhanced by the presence of different types of redox mediators. Six out of 10 employed compounds have proved their potential in enhancing the decolorization of direct dyes. The performance of TP was studied in presence of H_2O_2 at different concentrations of mediator and enzyme. The effectiveness of each mediator depends on the type of dye treated. The decolorization of all tested direct dyes was maximum in the presence of 0.6 mM redox mediator at pH 5.5 and 30°C. Complex dye mixtures were also maximally decolorized in the presence of 0.6 mM redox mediator (HOBT/VLA).

In order to examine the operational stability of the enzyme preparation, the enzyme was exploited for the decolorization of mixtures of dyes for different times in a stirred batch process. There was more than 80% decolorization of all dyes and their mixtures in the presence of HOBT/VLA after 60 min. Total organic carbon analysis of treated dyes or their mixtures showed that these results were quite comparable to the loss of color from solutions. However, the treatment of such polluted water in the presence of a redox mediator caused the formation of insoluble precipitate, which could be removed by the process of centrifugation. The decolorization and decontamination of two textile carpet industrial effluents using concanavalin A-cellulose immobilized plant peroxidases have been investigated [28]. Both effluents were recalcitrant for the action of plant peroxidases. However, the decolorization was enhanced in the presence of 2.0 mM HOBT. Textile carpet effluent red and textile carpet effluent blue respectively were decolorized 75 and 81% by soluble TP (0.423 U ml^{-1}) and 69 and 60% by soluble tomato peroxidase (0.705 U ml^{-1}). After 15 min of reaction time, textile carpet effluent red and textile carpet effluent blue respectively were decolorized 65 and 56% by TP and 63 and 51% by tomato peroxidase. Both of the effluents were maximally decolorized at pH 5.0 by using soluble and immobilized turnip peroxidase, whereas the maximum decolorization by soluble and immobilized tomato peroxidase (TMP) was observed at pH 6.0. It was observed that both effluents were decolorized by soluble and immobilized peroxidases maximally at 40°C. However, the immobilized TP-treated effluent exhibited significant loss of TOC from the solution. These observations suggested that major toxic compounds get easily removed out of the TP/TMP treated samples.

3.2.7. Tomato Peroxidase

The role of partially purified TMP in decolorizing direct dyes; Direct Red 23 and Direct Blue 80 has been described [129]. These dyes were maximally decolorized by TMP at pH 6.0 and 40°C. The absorption spectra of the treated dyes exhibited marked differences in the absorbance at various wavelengths as compared to untreated dyes. Decolorization and remediation of two textile carpet industrial effluents by TMP has been investigated [28]. Textile carpet effluent red and blue were decolorized by 0.705 U ml^{-1} TMP at pH 6.0 and 40°C to 69 and 59%, respectively. The TMP treated effluents exhibited significant loss of TOC.

3.2.8. Bilirubin Oxidase

The dye-decolorizing potential of bilirubin oxidase (BOX) has been demonstrated for an anthraquinone dye, RBBR. Zhang *et al.* [205] have reported that the optimal pH and temperature for maximum decolorization of this dye was at pH 7.0 and 28°C using a nonligninolytic fungus, strain Myrothecium sp. IMER1. A decolorization efficiency of approximately 90% was achieved by cultivation for 7 d at an initial dye concentration of 80 mg l^{-1}). The adsorption of the dye by cells was observed at the beginning of the decolorization, then the color became faint and finally disappeared when BOX was released by the strain. Additionally, the visual observation and UV-VIS spectral analysis demonstrated that decolorization involved biosorption and biodegradation. Native polyacrylamide gel electrophoresis of crude enzyme and purified BOX confirmed that BOX, which is an important extracellular oxidoreductase, played an important role in decolorization. Furthermore, purified BOX was demonstrated to degrade RBBR and other dyes by *in vitro* enzymatic experiments. However, the dye was decolorized 40% within 4 h by the BOX alone, whereas it was more efficiently decolorized to 91.5% in the presence of ABTS within 25 min [205]. The effects of operational parameters on decolorization were examined. The results showed that the decolorization efficiency decreased with increasing RBBR concentration and a marked inhibition effect was noticed when the dye concentrations were above 100 mg l^{-1}. The optimum temperature for enzymatic decolorization was 40°C. BOX showed efficient decolorization of the dye with a wide pH range of 5.0-8.5. The maximum decolorization activity occurred at pH 8.0 with ABTS and at pH 5.0 without ABTS. Analysis of RBBR UV-VIS spectra after BOX treatment indicated that the decolorization of RBBR was due to biodegradation. The authors suggested that ABTS serves as an electron mediator to facilitate the oxidation of RBBR and the BOX–ABTS mediator-involved dye decolorization mechanism was similar to that of laccase. Operation over a wide range of pH and efficient decolorization suggested that the BOX can be used to decolorize synthetic dyes from effluents, especially for anthraquinonic dyes. Reports are available where ABTS has earlier been used as electron transfer mediator of BOX [206].

3.2.9. Quinone Reductase

Zhou *et al.* [207] investigated the decolorization ability of gene-engineered strain *Escherichia coli* YB and the effects of methylhydroquinone (MHQ) pretreatement on decolorization performance of *E. coli* JM109 and anaerobic sludge using quinoid redox mediator and bacterial cellular quinone reductase. The results indicate that lawsone is an effective accelerator for azo dye decolorization by *E. coli* YB overexpressing cellular quinone reductase AZR. In the presence of 0.2 mmol l^{-1} lawsone, 75% Amaranth (1.0 mmol l^{-1}) can be decolorized in 2 h. *E. coli* YB can also decolorize high concentration of azo dye in the presence of lawsone. Around 50% Amaranth (5.0 mmol l^{-1}) is decolorized in 8 h. Compared to lawsone; menadione is a less effective mediator. *E. coli* YB takes 12 h to reach 70% decolorization in the presence of 2.5 mmol l^{-1} menadione. Repeated decolorization studies showed that *E. coli* YB had stable decolorizing ability in the presence of lawsone. Four rounds of repeated decolorization can be completed in 12 h. Lawsone can also accelerate the decolorization of azo dyes with complex structures such as Acid Scarlet GR and Reactive Brilliant Red K-2BP. With the optimal LQ concentrations, 70% Acid Scarlet GR and Reactive Brilliant Red K-2BP are decolorized in 9 h and 30 h, respectively. Decolorization performances of *E. coli* JM109 and anaerobic sludge pretreated with MHQ are improved. After MHQ pretreatment,in the presence of lawsone, 80% Amaranth (1.0 mmol l^{-1} can be decolorized in 5 h by *E. coli* JM109, while more than 75% Amaranth can be removed in 11 h by sludge.

4. CONCLUSION

From this chapter it appeared that the use of redox mediators along with oxidoreductive enzymes will definitely solve a complex problem of degradation and remediation of recalcitrant colored pollutants which are entering into the environment every day from various manufacturing operations. Moreover, the redox mediator-enzyme system will be highly suitable for the transformation of recalcitrant dyes into less toxic compounds.

ACKNOWLEDGEMENTS

The authors are thankful to the department of Biochemistry, Faculty of Life Sciences, Aligarh Muslim University, Aligarh, India and Department of Clinical Biochemistry, Faculty of Applied Medical Sciences, Jazan University, Jazan, Kingdom of Saudi Arabia for providing all the necessary facilities to compile this chapter.

REFERENCES

[1]   Karam, J., & Nicell, J.A. (1997). Potential applications of enzymes in waste treatment. *Journal of Chemical Technology and Biotechnology*, 69: 141-147/153.

[2]   Duran, N., & Esposito, E. (2000). Potential applications of oxidative enzymes and phenoloxidase-like compounds in wastewater and soil treatment: A review. *Applied Catalysis B: Environmental*, 28: 83-99.

[3]   Husain, Q., & Jan, U. (2000). Detoxification of phenols and aromatic amines from polluted wastewater by using phenol oxidases. A review. *Journal of Scientific and Industrial Research*, 59: 286-293.

[4]   Torres, E., Bustos-Jaimes, I., & Le Borgne, S. (2003). Potential use of oxidative enzymes for the detoxification of organic pollutants. *Applied Catalysis B: Environmental*, 46: 1-15.

[5]   Christian, V., Shrivastava, R., Shukla, D., Modi, H., Rajiv, B., & Vyas, M. (2005). Mediator role of veratryl alcohol in the lignin peroxidase-catalyzed oxidative decolorization of Remazol Brilliant Blue R. *Enzyme and Microbial Technology*, 36: 426-431.

[6]   Palmieri, G., Cennamo, G., & Sannia, G. (2005). Remazol Brilliant Blue R decolorization by fugus *Pleurotus ostreatus* and its oxidative enzymatic system. *Enzyme Microb. Technol.*, *36*, 17-24.

[7]   O'Neill, C., Lopez, A., Esteves, S.R., Hawkes, F.R., Hawkes, D.L., Wilcox, S.J. (2000). Azo-dye degradation in an anaerobic-aerobic treatment system operating on simulated textile effluent. *Applied Microbiology and Biotechnology*, 53: 249-254.

[8]   Robinson, T., McMullan, G., Marchant, R., & Nigam, P. (2001). Remediation of dyes in textile effluent: A critical review on current treatment technologies with a proposed alternative. *Bioresource Technology*, 77: 247-255.

[9]   Keharia, H., & Madamvar, D. (2003). Bioremediation concept for treatment of dye containing wastewater: A review. *Indian Journal of Experimental Biology*, 41: 1068-1075.

[10]   Padmesh, T. V. N., Vijayaraghavan, K., Sekaran, G. and Velan, M. (2005). Batch and column studies on biosorption of acid dyes on fresh water macro alga *Azolla filiculoides*. *Journal of Hazardous Materials*, 125: 121-129.

[11]   Al-Aseeri, M., Bu-Ali, Q., Haji, S., & Al-Bastaki, N. (2007). Removal of Acid Red and sodium chloride mixtures from aqueous solutions using nanofiltration, *Desalination*, 206: 407-413.

[12]   Verma, P., Baldrian, P., & Nerud, F. (2003). Decolorization of structurally different synthetic dyes using cobalt(II)/ascorbic acid/hydrogen peroxide system. *Chemosphere*, 50: 975-979.

[13]   Golob, V., & Ojstrsek, A. (2005). Removal of vat and disperse dyes from residual pad liquors. *Dyes and Pigments*, 64: 57-61.

[14]   Beak, M.H., Ijagbemi, C.O., & Kim, D.S. (2009). Treatment of Malachite Green-containing wastewater using poultry feathers as adsorbent. *Journal of Environmental Science and Health*, 44: 536-542.

[15] Robinson, T., Chandran, B., & Nigam, P. (2001). Studies on the production of enzyme by white-rot fungi for decolourisation of textile dyes. *Enzyme and Microbial Technology*, 29: 575-579.

[16] Jager, I., Hafner, C., & Schneider, K. (2004). Mutagenicity of different textile dye products in *Salmonella typhimurium* and mouse lymphoma cells. *Mutation Research*, 561: 35-44.

[17] Pricelius, S., Held, C., Sollner, S., Deller, S., Murkovic, M., Ullrich, R., Hofrichter, M., Cavaco-Paulo, A., Macheroux, P., & Guebitz, G.M. (2007). Enzymatic reduction and oxidation of fibre-bound azo-dyes. *Enzyme and Microbial Technology*, 40: 1732-1738.

[18] Ghodake, G.S., Kalme, S.D., Jadhav, J.P., & Govindwar, S.P. (2009). Purification and partial characterization of lignin peroxidase from *Acinetobacter calcoaceticus* NCIM 2890 and its application in decolorization of textile dyes. *Applied Biochemistry and Biotechnology*, 152: 6-14.

[19] Koyuncu, I. (2002). Reactive dye removal in dye/salt mixtures by nano filtration membranes containing vinyl sulphone dyes: Effect of feed concentration and cross flow velocity. *Desalination*, 143: 243-253.

[20] Novotny, C., Dias, C., Kapanen, A., Malachova, K. Vandrovcova, M., Itavaara, M., & Lima, N. (2006). Comparative use of bacterial, algal and protozoan tests to study toxicity of azo and anthraquinone dyes. *Chemosphere*, 63: 1436-1442.

[21] Kokol, V., Doliska, A., Eichlerova, I., Baldrain, P., & Nerud, F. (2007). Decolorization of textile dyes by whole cultures of *Ischnoderma resinosum* and by purified laccase and Mn-peroxidase. *Enzyme and Microbial Technology*, 40: 1673-1677.

[22] Stolz, A. (2001). Basic and applied aspects in the microbial degradation of azo dyes. *Applied Microbiology and Biotechnology*, 56: 69-80.

[23] Nigam, P., Armour, G., Banat, I.M., Singh, D., & Marchant, R. (2000). Physical removal of textile dyes from effluents and solid state fermentation by dye-adsorbed agricultural residues. *Bioresource Technology*, 72: 219-226.

[24] Neamtu, M., Yediler, A., Siminiceanu, I., Macoveanu, M., & Kettrup, A. (2004). Decolorization of Disperse Red 354 azo dye in water by several oxidation processes-A comparative study. *Dyes and Pigments*, 60: 61-68.

[25] Umbuzeiro, G.A., Freeman, H., Warren, S.H., Kummrow, F., & Claxton, L.D. (2005). Mutagenicity evaluation of the commercial product CI Disperse Blue 291 using different protocols of the Salmonella assay. *Food and Chemical Toxicology*, 43: 49-56.

[26] Umbuzeiro, G.A., Freeman, H.S., Warren, S.H., Oliveira, D.P., Terao, Y., Watanabe, T., & Claxton, L.D. (2005). The contribution of azo dyes to the mutagenic activity of the Cristais River. *Chemosphere*, 60: 55-64.

[27] Ozturk, A., & Abdullah, M.I. (2006). Toxicological effect of indole and its azo dye derivatives on some microorganisms under aerobic conditions. *Science of the Total Environment*, 358: 137-142.

[28] Lima, R.O.A., Bazo, A.P., Salvadori, D.M.F., Rech, C.M., Oliveira, D.P., & Umbuzeiro, G.A. (2007). Mutagenic and carcinogenic potential of a textile azo dye processing plant effluent that impacts a drinking water source. *Mutation Research*, 626: 53-60.

[29] Cicek, F., Ozer, D., & Ozer A. (2007). Low cost removal of reactive dyes using wheat bran. *Journal of Hazardous Materials*, 146: 408-416.

[30] Khenifi, A., Bouberka, Z., Sekrane, F., Kameche, M., & Derriche, Z. (2007). Adsorption study of an industrial dye by an organic clay. *Adsorption*, 13: 149-158.

[31] Mondal, S. (2008) Methods of dye removal from dye house effluent: An overview. *Environmental Engineering and Science*, 25: 383-396.

[32] Greene, J.C., & Baughman, G.I. (1996). Effects of 46 dyes on population growth of freshwater green alga *Selenastrum capricornutum*. *Textile Chemist Colorist*, 28: 23-30.

[33] Giusti, F., Mantovani, L., Martella, A., & Seidenari, S. (2002). Hand dermatitis as an unsuspected presentation of textile dye contact sensitivity. *Contact Dermatitis*, 47: 91-95.

[34] Giusti, F., & Seidenari, S. (2003). Disperse dye dermatitis: Clinical aspects and sensitizing agents. *Exogenous Dermatology*, 2: 6-10.

[35] Pratt, M., & Taraska, V. (2000). Disperse blue dyes 106 and 124 are common causes of textile dermatitis and should serve as screening allergens for this condition. *American Journal of Contact Dermatitis*, 11: 30-41.

[36] Ryberg, K., Goossens, A., Isaksson, M., Gruvberger, B., Zimerson, E., Nilsson, F., Bjork, J., Hindsen, M., & Bruze, M. (2009). Is contact allergy to disperse dyes and related substances associated with textile dermatitis? *British Journal Dermatology*, 160: 107-115.

[37] Keharia, H., & Madamvar, D. (2003). Bioremediation concept for treatment of dye containing wastewater: A review. *Indian Journal of Experimental Biology*, 41: 1068-1075.

[38] Banat, I.M., Nigam, P., Singh, D., & Marchant, R. (1996). Microbial decolorization of textile-dye-containing effluents: A review, *Bioresource Technology*, 58: 217-227.

[39] Capar, G., & Yetis, U. (2006). Effect of color and surfactants on nanofiltration for the recovery of carpet printing wastewaters. *Separation Science and Technology*, 41: 2771-2784.

[40] Murugesan, K., Kalaichelvan, P.T. (2003). Synthetic dye decolourization by white rot fungi. *Indian Journal of Experimental Biology*, 41: 1076-1087.

[41] Rothman, N., Talaska, G., Hayes, R., Bhatnagar, V., Bell, D., Lakshmi, V., Kashyap, S., Dosemeci, M., Kashyap, R., Hsu, F., Jaeger, M., Hirvonen, A., Parikh, D., Davis, B., & Zenser, T. (1997). Acidic urine pH is associated with elevated levels of free urinary benzidine and N-acetylbenzidine and urothelial cell DNA adducts in exposed workers. Cancer Epidemiol. Biomark. Prev. 6: 1039-1042.

[42] Platzek, T., Lang, C., Grohmann, G., Gi, U.S., & Baltes, W. (1999). Formation of a carcinogenic aromatic amine from an azo dye by human skin bacteria *in vitro*. *Human and Experimental Toxicology*, 18: 552-559.

[43] Hathway, D.E., & Kolar, G.F. (1980). Mechanisms of reaction between ultimate chemical carcinogens and nucleic acid. *Chemical Society Reviews*, 9: 241-264.

[44] Pavanello, S., & Clonfero, E. (2000). Biological indicators of genotoxic risk and metabolic polymorphisms. *Mutation Research*, 463: 285-308.

[45] Chung, K.T., & Cerniglia, C.E. (1992). Mutagenicity of azo dyes: Structure-activity relationships. *Mutation Research*, 277: 201-220.

[46] Arslan, I. (2001). Treatability of a simulated disperse dye-bath by ferrous iron coagulation, ozonation, and ferrous iron-catalyzed ozonation, *Journal of Hazardous Materials*, 85: 229-241.

[47]   Daneshvar, N., Ayazloo, M., Khatae, A.R., & Pourhassan, M. (2007). Biological decolourization of dye solution containing Malachite Green by microalgae *Cosmarium* sp. *Bioresource Technology*, 98: 1176-1182.

[48]   Husseiny, S.M. (2008). Biodegradation of the reactive and direct dyes using Egyptian isolates. *Journal of Applied Sciences Research*, 4: 599-606.

[49]   Rezaee, A., Ghaneian, M.T., Hashemian, S.J., Moussavi, G. Khavanin, A., & Ghanizadeh, G. (2008). Decolorization of Reactive Blue 19 dye from textile wastewater by the UV/H$_2$O$_2$ process. *Journal of Applied Sciences*, 8: 1108-1112.

[50]   Hao, O. J., Kim, H., & Chiang, P.C. (2000). Decolorization of wastewater. *Critical Reviews in Environmental Science Technology*, 30: 449-505.

[51]   Rott, U. (2003). Multiple use of water in industry-the textile industry case. *Journal of Environmental Sciences and Health*, 38: 1629-1639.

[52]   Hai, F.I., Yamamoto, K., & Fukushi, K. (2007). Hybrid treatment systems for dye wastewaters. *Critical Reviews in Environmental Science and Technology*, 37: 315-377.

[53]   van der Zee, F. P., Bisschops, I. A. E., Lettinga, G. and Field, J. A. (2003). Activated carbon as an electron acceptor and redox mediator during the anaerobic biotransformation of azo dyes. *Environ. Sci. Technol.*, 37, 402-408.

[54]   Kiernan, J.A. (2001). Classification and naming of dyes, stains and fluorochromes. *Biotechnic and Histochemistry*, 76: 261-277.

[55]   Ghoreishi, M., & Haghighi, R. (2003). Chemical catalytic reaction and biological oxidation for treatment of non-biodegradable textile effluent. *Chemical Engineering Journal*, 95: 163-169.

[56]   Mielgo, I., Lopez, C., Moreira, M.T., Feijoo, G., & Lema, J.M. (2003). Oxidative degradation of azo dyes by manganese peroxidase under optimized conditions. *Biotechnology Progress*, 19: 325-331.

[57]   Anjaneyulu, Y., Chary, N.S., & Raj, D.S.S. (2005). Decolorization of industrial effluents-available methods and emerging technologies: A review, *Reviews in Environmental Science and Biotechnology*, 4: 245-273.

[58]   Borchert, M., & Libra, J.A. (2001). Decolorization of reactive dyes by the white rot fungus *Trametes versicolor* in sequencing batch reactors. *Biotechnology and Bioengineering*, 75: 313-321.

[59]   McMullan, G., Meehan, C., Conneely, A., Kirby, N., Robinson, T., Nigam, P., Banat, I.M., Marchant, R., & Smyth, W.F. (2001). Microbial decolourisation and degradation of textiles dyes. *Applied Microbiology and Biotechnology*, 56: 81-87.

[60]   Zissi, U., & Lyberatos, G. (2001). Partial degradation of *p*-aminoazobenzene by a defined mixed culture of *Bacillus subtilis* and *Stenotrophomonas maltophilia*. *Biotechnology and Bioengineering*, 72: 49-54.

[61]   Asses, N., Ayed, L., Bouallagui, H., Ben Rejeb, I., Gargouri, M., & Hamdi, M. (2009). Use of *Geotrichum candidum* for olive mill wastewater treatment in submerged and static culture, *Bioresource Technology*, 100: 2182-2188.

[62]   Fu, Y., & Viraraghavan, T. (2001). Fungal decolorization of dye wastewaters: A review. *Bioresource Technology*, 79: 251-262.

[63]   Hao, J.J., Song, F.Q., Huang, F., Yang, C.L., Zhang, Z.J., Zheng, Y., & Tian, X.J. (2007). Production of laccase by a newly isolated deuteromycete fungus *Pestalotiopsis* sp. and its decolorization of azo dye. *Journal of Industrial and Microbial Biotechnology*, 34: 233-240.

[64] Pandey, A., Singh, P., & Iyengar, L. (2007). Bacterial decolorization and degradation of azo dyes. *International Biodeterioration and Biodegradation*, 59: 73-84.

[65] Shimokawa, T., Hirai, M., Shoda, M., & Sugano, Y. (2008). Efficient dye decolorization and production of dye decolorizing enzymes by the basidiomycete *Thanatephorus cucumeris* Dec 1 in a liquid and solid hybrid culture. *Journal of Biosciences and Bioengineering*, 106: 481-487.

[66] Pereira, L., Coelho, A.V., Viegas, C.A., dos Santos, M.M.C., Robalo, M.P., & Martins, L.O. (2009). Enzymatic biotransformation of the azo dye Sudan Orange G with bacterial Cot A-laccase. *Journal of Biotechnology*, 139: 68-77.

[67] Bhatt, N., Patel, K.C., Keharia, H., & Mdamvar, V. (2005). Decolorization of diazo-dye Reactive Blue 172 by *Pseudomonas aeruginosa* NBAR12. *Journal of Basic Microbiology*, 45: 407-418.

[68] Duran, N., Rosa, M.A, D'Annibale, A., & Gianfreda, L. (2002). Applications of laccase and tyrosinases (phenoloxidases) immobilized on different supports: A review. *Enzyme and Microbial Technology*, 31: 907-931.

[69] Rodriguez-Couto, S. (2009). Enzymatic biotransformation of synthetic dyes. *Current Drug Metabolism*, 10: 1048-1054.

[70] Husain, Q. (2006). Potential applications of the oxidoreductive enzymes in the decolorization and detoxification of textile and other synthetic dyes from polluted water: A review. *Critical Reviews in Biotechnology*, 60: 201-221.

[71] Xu, F., & Salmon, S. (2008). Potential applications of oxidoreductases for the re-oxidation of Leuco Vat or sulfur dyes in textile dyeing. *Engineering in Life Sciences*, 8: 331-337.

[72] Hamid, M., & Rehman, K. (2009). Potential applications of peroxidases. *Food Chemistry*, 115: 1177-1186.

[73] Wagner, M., & Nicell, J.A. (2003). Impact of the presence of solids on peroxidase-catalyzed treatment of aqueous phenol. *Journal of Chemical Technology and Biotechnology*, 78: 694-702.

[74] Husain, M., & Husain, Q. (2008). Applications of redox mediators in the treatment of organic pollutants by using oxidoreductive enzymes: A review. *Critical Reviews in Environmental Science and Technology*, 38: 1-42.

[75] Michniewicz, A., Ledakowicz, S., Ullrich, R., & Hofrichter, M. (2008). Kinetics of the enzymatic decolorization of textile dyes by laccase from *Cerrena unicolor*. *Dyes and Pigments*, 77: 295-302.

[76] Ryan, S., Schnitzhofer, W., Tzanov, T., Cavaco-Paulo, A., & Gubitz, G. M. (2003). An acid-stable laccase from *Sclerotium rolfsii* with potential for wool dye decolourization. *Enzyme and Microbial Technology*, 33: 766-774.

[77] Couto, S.R., Rosales, E., & Sanroman, M.A. (2005). Decolourization of synthetic dyes by *Trametes hirsute* in expanded-bed reactors. *Chemosphere*, 62: 1558-1563.

[78] Husain, Q. Husain, M., & Kulshrestha, Y. (2009). Remediation and treatment of organopollutants mediated by peroxidases: A review. *Critical Reviews in Biotehnology*, 24: 94-119.

[79] Gianfreda, L., & Rao, M.A. (2004). Potential of extra cellular enzymes in remediation of polluted soils: A review. *Enzyme and Microbial Technology*, 35: 339-354.

[80] Held, C., Kandelbauer, A., Schroeder, M., Cavaco-Paulo, A., & Guebitz, G.M. (2005). Biotransformation of phenolics with laccase containing bacterial spores. *Environmental Chemistry Letters*, 3: 74-77.

[81] Sumathi, S., & Manju, B.S. (2000). Uptake of reactive textile dyes by *Aspergillus foetidus*. *Enzyme and Microbial Technology*, 27: 347-355.

[82] Khan, A.A., & Husain, Q. (2007). Decolorization and removal of textile and non-textile dyes from polluted wastewater and dyeing effluent by using potato (*Solanum tuberosum*) soluble and immobilized polyphenol oxidase. *Bioresource Technology*, 98: 1012-1019.

[83] Matto, M., & Husain, Q. (2007). Decolorization of direct dyes by salt fractionated turnip proteins enhanced in the presence of hydrogen peroxide and redox mediators. *Chemosphere*, 69: 338-345.

[84] Wang, P., Fan, X., Cui, L., Wang, Q., & Zhou, A. (2008). Decolorization of reactive dyes by laccase immobilized in alginate/gelatin blent with PEG. *Journal of Environmental Sciences*, 20: 1519-1522.

[85] Kandelbauer, A., Erlacher, A., Cavaco-Paulo, A., & Guebitz, G.M. (2004). Laccase catalyzed decolorization of the synthetic dye Diamond Black PV 200 and some structurally related derivatives. *Biocatalysis and Biotransformation*, 22: 331-339.

[86] Akhtar, S, Khan, A.A., & Husain, Q. (2005). Potential of immobilized bitter gourd (*Momordica charantia*) peroxidases in the decolorization and removal of textile dyes from polluted wastewater and dyeing effluent. *Chemosphere*, 60: 291-301.

[87] Akhtar, S., & Husain, Q. (2006). Potential applications of immobilized bitter gourd (*Momordica charantia*) peroxidase in the removal of phenols from polluted water. *Chemosphere*, 65: 1228-1235.

[88] Rao, M.A., Scelza, R., Scotti, R., & Gianfreda, L. (2010). Role of enzymes in the remediation of polluted environments. *Journal of Soil Science and Plant Nutrition*, 10: 333-353.

[89] Akhtar, S., Khan, A.A., & Husain, Q. (2005). Partially purified bitter gourd (*Momordica charantia*) peroxidase catalyzed decolorization of textile and other industrially important dyes, *Bioresource Technology*, 96: 1804-1811.

[90] dos Santos., A.B., Bisschops, L.A.E., Cervantes, F.J., & Van Lier, J.B. (2004). Effect of different redox mediators during thermophilic azo dye reduction by anaerobic granular sludge and comparative study between mesophilic (30 °C) and thermophilic (55 °C) treatments for decolourisation of textile wastewaters. *Chemosphere*, 55: 1149-1157.

[91] Bourbonnais, R., & Paice, M.G. (1990). Oxidation of non-phenolic substrates. An expanded role for laccase in lignin biodegradation. *FEBS Letters*, 267: 99-102.

[92] Fabbrini, M., Galli, C., & Gentili, P. (2002). Comparing the catalytic efficiency of some mediators of laccase. *Journal of Molecular Catalysis B: Enzymatic*, 16: 231-240.

[93] van der Zee, F.P., Cervantes, F.J. (2009). Impact and application of electron shuttles on the redox (bio)transformation of contaminants: A review. *Biotechnology Advances*, 27: 256-277.

[94] Crestini, C., Jurasek, L., & Argyropoulos, D.S. (2003). On the mechanism of the laccase-mediator system in the oxidation of lignin. *Chemistry*, 9: 5371-5378.

[95] Guo, J., Zhou, J., Wang, D., Yang, J., & Li, Z. (2008). The new incorporation bio-treatment technology of bromoamine acid and azo dyes wastewaters under high-salt conditions. *Biodegradation*, 19: 93-98.

[96] Jing, W., Lihua, L., Jiti, Z., Hong, L., Guangfei, L., Ruo fei, J., & Fenglin, Y. (2009). Enhanced biodecolorization of azo dyes by electropolymerization-immobilized redox mediator. *Journal of Hazardous Materials*, 168: 1098-1104.

[97] Xu, F., Juozas J., Kulys, J.J., Duke, K., Li, K., Krikstopaitis, K., Heinz-Josef, W., Deussen, H.J. W., Abbate, E., Vilija Galinyte, V., & Schneider, P. (2000). Redox chemistry in laccase-catalyzed oxidation of *N*-hydroxy compounds. *Applied and Environmental Microbiolog*, 66: 2052-2056.

[98] Bourbonnais, R., Paice, M.G., Reidm, I.D., Lanthier, P., & Yaguchi, M. (1995). Ligninolytic oxidation by laccase from *Trametes versicolor* and role of the mediator 2,2`-azino-bis-(3 ethyl benzothiozoline-6-sulfonate) in kraft deploymerization. *Applied Environmental Microbiology*, 61: 11876-11880.

[99] Xu, F. (1996). Oxidation of phenols, anilines and benzinothiols by fungal laccases: Correlation between activity and redox potential as well as halide inhibition. *Biochemistry*, 35: 7608-7614.

[100] Call, H.P., & Muecke, I. (1997). History, overview and applications of mediated lignolytic systems, especially laccase–mediator-systems (Lignozy [®] process). *Journal of Biotechnology*, 53: 163-202.

[101] Johannes, C., & Majcherczyk, A. (2000). Natural mediators in the oxidation of polycyclic hydrocarbons by laccase mediator system. *Applied and Environmental Microbiology*, 66: 524-528.

[102] Couto, S.R., Sanroman, M., & Gubitz, G.M. (2005). Influence of redox mediators and metal ions on synthetic acid dye decolourization by crude laccase from *Trametes hirsute*. *Chemosphere*, 58: 417-422.

[103] Xu, F., Deussen, H.J., Lopez, B., Lam, L., & Li, K. (2001). Enzymatic and electrochemical oxidation of N-hydroxy compounds. Redox potential, electron transfer kinetics, and radical stability. *European Journal of Biochemistry*, 268: 4169-4176.

[104] Potthast, A., Rosenau, T., & Fischer, K. (2001). Oxidation of benzyl alcohols by the laccase-mediator system (LMS)-A comprehensive kinetic description. *Holzforschung*, 55: 47-56.

[105] Hirai, H., Shibata, H., Kawai, S., & Nishida, T. (2006). Role of 1-hydroxybenzotriazole in oxidation by laccase from *Trametes versicolor*: Kinetic analysis of the laccase-1-hydroxybenzotriazole couple. *FEMS Microbiology Letters*, 265: 56-59.

[106] Zille, A., Ramalho, P., Tzanov, T., Millward, R., Aires, V., Cardoso, M.H., Ramalho, M.T., Gubitz, G.M., & Cavaco-Paulo, A. (2004). Predicting dye biodegradation from redox potentials. *Biotechnology Progress*, 20: 1588-1592.

[107] Sadhasivam, S., Savitha, S., & Swaminathan, K. (2009). Redox-mediated decolorization of recalcitrant textile dyes by *Trichoderma harzianum* WL1 laccase. *World Journal of Microbiology and Biotechnology*, 25: 1733-1741.

[108] d'Acunzo, F., Galli, C., Gentili, P., & Sergi, F. (2006). Mechanistic and steric issues in the oxidation of phenolic and non-phenolic compounds by laccase or laccase-mediator systems. The case of bifunctional substrates. *New Journal of Chemistry*, 30: 583-591.

[109] Astolfi, P., Brandi, P., Galli, C., Gentili, P., Gerini, M.A., Greci, L., & Lanzalunga, O. (2005). New mediators for the enzyme laccase: Mechanistic features and selectivity in the oxidation of non-phenolic substrates, *New Journal of Chemistry*, 29: 1308-1317.

[110] Tinoco, R., Verdin, J., & Vazquez-Duhalt, R. (2007). Role of oxidizing mediators and tryptophan 172 in the decoloration of industrial dyes by the versatile peroxidase from *Bjerkandera adusta*. *Journal of Molecular Catalysis B: Enzymatic*, 46: 1-7.

[111] Russ, R., Rau, J., & Stolz, A. (2000). The function of cytoplasmic flavin reductases in the reduction of azo dyes by bacteria. *Applied and Environmental Microbiology*, 66: 1429-1434.

[112] van der Zee, F.P., Lettinga, G., & Field, J.A. (2001). Azo dye decolourisation by anaerobic granular sludge. *Chemosphere*, 44: 1169-1176.

[113] Bechtold, T., Burtscher, E., & Turcanu, A. (1999). Anthraquinones as mediators for the indirect cathodic reduction of dispersed organic dyestuffs, *Journal of Electroanalytical Chemistry*, 465: 80-87.

[114] Keck, A., Klein, J., Kudlich, K., Stolz, A., Kuackmuss, H.J., & Mattes, R. (1997). Reduction of azo dyes by redox mediators originating in the naphthalenesulfonic acid degradation pathway of *Sphingomonas* sp. strain BN 6. *Applied and Environmental Microbiology*, 63: 3684-3690.

[115] Tan, L., Qu, Y.Y., Zhou, J.T., Li, A., & Gou, M. (2009). Identification and characteristics of a novel salt-tolerant Exiguobacterium sp. for azo dyes decolorization. *Applied Biochemistry and Biotechnology*, 159: 728-738.

[116] Jiao, L., Lu, H., Zhou, J., & Wang J. (2009). Quinone-mediated decolorization of sulfonated azo dyes by cells and cell extracts from Sphingomonas xenophaga. *Journal of Environmental Science*, 21: 503-508.

[117] Zhao, L., Zhou, J., Jia, Y., & Chen, J. (2010). Biodecolorization of Acid Red GR by a newly isolated Dyella ginsengisoli LA-4 using response surface methodology. *Journal of Hazardous Materials*, 181: 602-608.

[118] Rekuc, A., Bryjak, J., Szymanska, K., & Jarzebski, A.B. (2010). Very stable silica-gel-bound laccase biocatalysts for the selective oxidation in continuous systems. *Bioresource Technology*, 101: 2076-2083.

[119] Liu, G., Wang, J., Lu, H., Jin, R., Zhou, J., & Zhang, L. (2009). Effects of reduction products of ortho-hydroxyl substituted azo dyes on biodecolorization of azo dyes. *Journal of Hazardous Materials*, 171: 222-229.

[120] Farrell, R.L., Murtagh, K.E., Tien, M., Mozuch, M.D., & Kirk, T.K. (1989). Physical and enzymatic properties of lignin peroxidase isoenzymes from *Phanerochaete chrysosporium*. *Enzyme and Microbial Technology*, 11: 322-328.

[121] Akhtar, M., Blanchette, R.A., & Kirk, T.K. (1997). Fungal delignification and biochemical pulping of wood. *Advances in Biochemical Engineering and Biotechnology*, 57: 159-195.

[122] Heinfling, A., Martinez, M.J., Martinez, A.T., Bergbauer, M., & Szewzyk, U. (1998). Transformation of industrial dyes by manganese peroxidases from *Bjerkandera adusta* and *Pleurotus eryngii* in a manganese-independent reaction. *Applied and Environmental Microbiology*, 64: 2788-2793.

[123] Ollikka, P., Alhoumaki, K., Leppanen, V.M., Glumoff, T., Raijola, T., & Suominen, Y. (1993). Decolorization of azo, triphenyl methane, heterocyclic and polymeric dyes by

lignin peroxidase isoenzymes from *Phenerochaete chrysosporium*. *Applied and Environmental Microbiology*, 59: 4010-4016.

[124] Nozaki, K., Beh, C.H., Mizuno, M., Isobe, T., Shiroishi, M., Kanda, T., & Amano Y. (2007). Screening and investigation of dye decolorization activities of basidiomycetes. *Applied Microbiology and Biotechnology*, 74: 1232-1239.

[125] Matto, M. and Husain, Q. (2009). Decolorization of textile effluent by bitter gourd peroxidase immobilized on concanavalin A layered calcium alginate–starch beads. *Journal of Hazardous Materials*, 164: 1540-1546.

[126] Kulshrestha, Y., & Husain, Q. (2007). Decolorization and degradation of acid dyes mediated by salt fractionated turnip (*Brassica rapa*) peroxidases. *Toxicology and Environmental Chemistry*, 89: 255-267.

[127] Matto, M., & Husain, Q. (2009b). Decolorization of direct dyes by immobilized turnip peroxidase in batch and continuous processes. *Ecotoxicology and Environmental Safety*, 72: 965-971.

[128] Husain, Q., & Kulshrestha, Y. (2011). Removal of colored compounds from textile carpet industrial effluents by using immobilized turnip (*Brassica rapa*) and tomato (*Lycopersicon esculentum*) peroxidases. *Water Science and Technology*, (in press).

[129] Matto, M., & Husain, Q. (2008). Redox mediated decolorization of Direct Red 23 and Direct Blue 80 catalyzed by bioaffinity based immobilized tomato (*Lycopersicon esculentum*) peroxidase. *Biotechnology Journal*, 3: 1224-1231.

[130] Liu, G., Jiti, Z., Zhou, Wang, J., Zhou, M., Lu, H., & Jin R. (2009a). Acceleration of azo dye decolorization by using quinone reductase activity of azoreductase and quinone redox mediator. *Bioresource Technology*, 100: 2791-2795.

[131] Husain, Q., Karim, Z., & Banday, Z.Z. (2010). Decolorization of textile effluent by soluble fenugreek (*Trigonella foenum-graecum L*) seeds peroxidase. *Water, Air and Soil Pollution*, 212: 319-332.

[132] Kawai, S., Umezawa, T., & Higuchi. T. (1989). Oxidation of methoxylated benzyl alcohols by laccase of *Coriolus versicolor* in the presence of syringaldehyde. *Wood Research*, 76: 10-16.

[133] Johannes, C., Majcherczyk, A., & Huttermann, A. (1998). Oxidation of acenaphthene and acenaphthylene by laccase of *Trametes versicolor* in a laccase mediator system. *Journal of Biotechnology*, 61: 151-157.

[134] Kersten, P.J., Kalyanaraman, B., Hammel, K., Reinhammar, B., & Kirk, T.K. (1990). Comparison of lignin peroxidase, horseradish peroxidase and laccase in the oxidation of methoxybenzenes. *Biochemistry Journal*, 268: 475-480.

[135] Muheim, A., Fiechter, A., Harvey, P.J., & Schoemaker H.E. (1992). On the mechanism of oxidation of non-phenolic lignin model compounds by the laccase–ABTS couple. *Holzforschung*, 46: 121-126.

[136] Sariaslani, F.S., Beale, J.M., and Rosazza, P. (2006). Oxidation of rotenone by *Polyporus anceps* laccase. *Journal of Natural Products*, 47: 692–697.

[137] Amitai, G.R., Adani, G., Sod-Moriah, I., Rabinovitz, A., Vincze, H., Leader, B., Chefetz, L., Leibovitz-Persky, D., Friesem, D., & Hadar, Y. (1998). Oxidative biodegradation of phosphorothiolates by laccase. *FEBS Letters*, 438: 195-200.

[138] Bohmer, S., Messner, K. & Srebotnik, E. (1998). Oxidation of phenanthrene by a fungal laccase in the presence of 1-hydroxybenzotriazole and unsaturated lipids. *Biochemical and Biophysical Research Communications*, 244: 233-238.

[139] Li, K., Xu, F., & Erickson, K.E.L. (1999). Comparision of fungal laccases and redox mediators in the oxidation of a non-phenolic lignin model compound. *Applied and Environmental Microbiology*, 65: 2654-2660.

[140] Ander, P., & Messner, K. (1998). Oxidation of 1-hydroxybenzotriazole by laccase and lignin peroxidase. *Biotechnology Techniques*, 12: 191-195.

[141] Bourbonnais, R., Leech, D., & Paice, M.G. (1998). Electrochemical analysis of the interactions of laccase mediators with lignin model compounds. *Biochimica et Biophysica Acta*, 1379: 381-390.

[142] Collins, P.J., Dobson, A.D.W., & Field, J.A. (1998). Reduction of the 2,2-azinobis(3-ethylbenzthiazoline-6-sulfonate) cation radical by physiological organic acids in the absence and presence of manganese. *Applied and Environmental Microbiology*, 64: 2026-2031.

[143] Li, K., Helm, R.F., & Erikssen, K.E.L. (1998). Mechanistic studies of the oxidation of a non-phenolic lignin model compound by the laccase/1-hydroxybenzotriazole redox system. *Biotechnology and Applied Biochemistry*, 27: 239-243.

[144] Xu, F. (1997). Effects of redox potential and hydroxide inhibition on the pH activity profile of fungal laccases. *Journal of Biological Chemisty*, 272: 924-928.

[145] Reyes, P., Pickard, M.A., & Vazquez-Duhalt, R. (1999). Hydroxybenzotrizole increases the range of textile dyes decolorized by immobilized laccase. *Biotechnology Letters*, 21: 875-880.

[146] Wong, Y., & Yu, J. (1999). Laccase-catalyzed decolorization of synthetic dyes. *Water Research*, 33: 3512-3520.

[147] Lu, R., Shen, X.L., & Xia, L.M. (2005). Studies on laccase production by *Coriolus versicolor* and enzymatic decoloration of dye. *Chem. Ind. Forest Prod.*, 25: 73-76.

[148] Lu, L., Zhao, M., & Wang, Y. (2007). Immobilization of laccase by alginate-chitosan microcapsules and its use in dye decolorization. *World Journal of Microbiology and Biotechnology*, 23: 159-166.

[149] Campos, R., Kandelbauer, A., Robra, K.H., Cavaco-Paulo, A., & Guebitz, G.M. (2001). Indigo degradation with purified laccase from *Trametes hirsuta* and *Sclerotium rolfsii*. *Journal of Biotechnol*ogy, 89: 131-139.

[150] Soares, G.M., Costa-Ferreira, M., & Pessoa de Amorim, M.T., (2001). Decolorization of an anthraquinone-type dye using a laccase formulation. *Bioresource Technology*, 9: 171-177.

[151] Soares, G.M., de Amorim, M.T., & Costa-Ferreira, M. (2001). Use of laccase together with redox mediators to decolorize Remazol Brilliant Blue R. *Journal of Biotechnology*, 89: 123-129.

[152] Peralta-Zamora, P., Pereira, C.M., Tiburtius, E.R., Moraes, S.G., Rosa, M.A., & Minussi, R.C. (2002). Decolorization of reactive dyes by immobilized laccase. *Applied Catalysis*, 1295: 1-14.

[153] Claus, H., Faber, G., & Koenig, H. (2002). Redox-mediated decolorization of synthetic dyes by fungal laccases. *Applied Microbiology and Biotechnology*, 59: 672-678.

[154] Nagai, M., Sato, T., Watanabe, H., Saito, K., Kawata, M., & Enei, H. (2002). Purification and characterization of an extracellular laccase from the edible mushroom *Lentinula edodes*, and decolorization of chemically different dyes. *Applied Microbiology and Biotechnology*, 60: 327-335.

[155] Nyanhongo, G.S., Gomesa, J., Gubitz, G.M., Zvauya, R., Read, J., & Steiner, W. (2002). Decolorization of textile dyes by laccases from a newly isolated strain of *Trametes modesta*. *Water Research*, 36: 1449-1456.

[156] Trupkin, S., Levin, L., Forchiassin, F., & Viale, A. (2003). Optimization of a culture medium for ligninolytic enzyme production and synthetic dye decolorization using response surface methodology. *Journal of Industrial Microbiology and Biotechnology*, 30: 682-690.

[157] Rodriguez-Couto, S., Sanroman, M., & Guebitz, G.M. (2005). Influence of redox mediators and metal ions on synthetic acid dye decolorization by crude laccase from *T. hirsuta*. *Chemosphere*, 58: 417-422.

[158] Murugesan, K., Kim, Y.M., Jeon, J.R., & Chang, Y.S. (2009). Effect of metal ions on reactive dye decolorization by laccase from *Ganoderma lucidum*. *Journal of Hazardous Materials*, 168: 523-529.

[159] Sulistyaningdyah, W.T., Ogawa, J., Tanaka, H., Maeda, C., & Shimizu, S. (2004) Characterization of alkaliphilic laccase activity in the culture supernatant of *Myrothecium verrucaria* 24G-4 in comparison with bilirubin oxidase. *FEMS Microbiology Letters*, 230: 209-214.

[160] Camarero, S., Ibarra, D., Martinez, M.J., & Martinez, A.J. (2005). Lignin-derived compounds as efficient laccase mediators for decolorization of different types of recalcitrant dyes. *Applied Environmental Microbiology*, 71: 1775-1784.

[161] Salony, Mishra, S., & Bisaria, V.S. (2006). Production and characterization of laccase from *Cyathus bulleri* and its use in decolourization of recalcitrant textile dyes. *Applied and Microbiology Biotechnology*, 71: 646-653.

[162] Murugesan, K., Dhamija, A., Nam, I.H., Kim, Y.M., & Chang. Y.S. (2007). Decolourization of Reactive Black 5 by laccase: Optimization by response surface methodology. *Dyes and Pigments*, 75: 176-184.

[163] Moldes, D., & Sanroman, M.A. (2006). Amelioration of the ability to decolorize dyes by laccase: Relationship between redox mediators and laccase isoenzymes in *Trametes versicolor*. *World Journal of Microbiology and Biotechnology*, 22: 1197-1204.

[164] Soares, G.M., Costa-Ferreira, M., & Pessoa de Amorim, M.T. (2008). Decolorization of an anthraquinone-type dye using a laccase formulation. *Bioresource Technology*, 99: 463-471.

[165] Tavares, A.P.M., Cristovao, R.O., Gamelas, J.A.F., Loureiro, J.M., Boaventuraa, R.A.R., & Macedo, E.A. (2008) Sequential decolourization of reactive textile dyes by laccase mediator system. *Journal of Chemical Technology and Biotechnology*, 84: 442-446.

[166] Tavares, A.P.M., Cristovao, R.O., Loureiro, J.M., Boaventuraa, R.A.R., & Macedo, E.A. (2008). Optimisation of reactive textile dyes degradation by laccase-mediator system. *Journal of Chemical Technology and Biotechnology*, 83: 1609-1615.

[167] Hu, M.R., Chao, Y.P., Zhang, G.Q., Xue, Z.Q., & Qian, S. (2009). Laccase-mediator system in the decolorization of different types of recalcitrant dyes. *Journal of Industrial and Microbial Biotechnology*, 36: 45-51.

[168] Knutson, K., Kirzan, S., & Ragauskas, A. (2005). Enzymatic biobleaching of two recalcitrant paper dyes with horseradish and soybean peroxidase. *Biotechnology Letters*, 27: 753-758.

[169] Camarero, S., Canas, A.I., Nousiainen, P., Record, E., Lomascolo, A., Martinez, M.J., & Martinez, A.T. (2008). *P*-hydroxycinnamic acids as natural mediators for laccase oxidation of recalcitrant compounds. *Environmental Science and Technology*, 42: 6703-6709.

[170] Cho, H.Y., Cho, N.S, Jarosa-Wilkolazka, A., Rogalski, J., Leonowicz, A., Shin, Y.S., & Ohga, S. (2007). Effect of fungal laccase and new mediators, acetovanillone and acetosyringone, on decolourization of dyes. *Journal of the Faculty of Agriculture Kyushu University*, 52: 275-280.

[171] Chhabra, M., Mishra, S., & Sreekrishnan, T.R. (2008). Mediator-assisted decolorization and detoxification of textile dyes/dye mixture by *Cyathus bulleri* laccase. *Applied Biochemstry and Biotechnology*, 151: 587-598.

[172] Khammuang, S., & Sarnthima, R. (2009). Mediator assisted Rhodamine B decolorization by Trametes vesicolor laccase. *Pakistan Journal of Biological Sciences*, 12: 616-623.

[173] Murugesan, K., Yang, I.H., Kim, Y.M., Jeon, J.R., & Chang, Y.S. (2009b). Enhanced transformation of Malachite Green by laccase of *Ganoderma lucidum* in the presence of natural phenolic compounds. *Applied Microbiology and Biotechnology*, 82: 341-350.

[174] Sasmaz, S., Gedikli, S., Aytar, P., Gungormedi, G., Cabuk, A., Hur, E., Unal, A., & Kolankaya N. (2010). Decolorization potential of some reactive dyes with crude laccase and laccase-mediated system. *Applied Biochemistry and Biotechnology*, 30: [Epub ahead of print].

[175] Chance, B. (1952). The kinetics and stoichiometry of the transition from the primary to the secondary peroxidase–peroxide complexes. *Archives of Biochemistry and Biophysics*, 41: 416-424.

[176] Dunford, H.B., & Stillman, J.S. (1976). On the function and mechanism of action of peroxidases. *Coordination Chemistry Reviews*, 19: 187-251.

[177] Kelder, P.P., de Mol, N.J., Fischer, M.J.E., & Janssen, L.H.M. (1994). Kinetic evaluation of the oxidation of phenothiazine derivatives by methemoglobin and horseradish peroxidase in the presence of hydrogen peroxide: Implications for the reaction mechanism. *Biochimica et Biophysica Acta*, 1205: 230-238.

[178] Goodwin, D.C., Aust, S.D., & Grover, T.A. (1995). Determination of rate constants for rapid peroxidase reactions. *Analytical Biochemistry*, 231: 333-338.

[179] Chung, N., & Aust, S.D. (1995). Veratryl alcohol-mediated indirect oxidation of pentachlorophenol by lignin peroxidase. *Archives of Biochemistry and Biophysics*, 322: 143-148.

[180] Chung, N., & Aust, S.D. (1995). Veratryl alcohol-mediated indirect oxidation of phenol by lignin peroxidase. *Archives of Biochemistry and Biophysics*, 316: 733-737.

[181] Uetrecht, J.P., Ma, H.M., MacKnight, E., & McClelland, R. (1995). Oxidation of aminopyrine by hypochlorite to a reactive dication: Possible implications for aminopyrineinduced agranulocytosis. *Chemical Research and Toxicology*, 8: 226-233.

[182] Biswas, M.M., Taylor, K.E., Bewtra, J.K., & Biswas, N. (2007). Enzymatic treatment of sulfonated aromatic amines generated from reductive degradation of reactive azo dyes. *Water Environmental Research*, 79: 351-356.

[183] Husain, Q. Husain, M., & Kulshrestha, Y. (2009). Remediation and treatment of organopollutants mediated by peroxidases: A review. *Critical Reviews in Biotehnology*, 24: 94-119.

[184] Shakeri, M., & Shoda, M. (2007). Change in turnover capacity of crude recombinant dye-decolorizing peroxidase (rDyP) in batch and fed-batch decolorization of Remazol Brilliant Blue R. *Applied Microbiology and Biotechnology*, 76: 919-926.

[185] Shah, M.M., & Aust, S.D. (1993). Iodide as the mediator for the reductive reactions of peroxidases. *The Journal of Biological Chemistry*, 268: 8503-8506.

[186] Koduri, R.S., & Tien, M. (1994). Kinetic analysis of lignin peroxidase: Explanation for the mediation phenomenon by veratryl alcohol. *Biochemistry*, 33: 4225-4230.

[187] Goodwin, D.C., Barr, D.P., Aust, S.D., & Grover, T.A. (1994) The role of oxalate in lignin peroxidase-catalyzed reduction: Protection from compound III accumulation. *Archives of Biochemistry and Biophysics*, 315: 267-272.

[188] Barr, D.P., & Aust, S.D. (1994). Effect of superoxide and superoxide dismutase on lignin peroxidase-catalyzed veratryl alcohol oxidation. *Archives of Biochemistry and Biophysics*, 311: 378-382.

[189] Sutherland, G.R., Khindaria, A., Chung, N., & Aust, S.D. (1995). The effect of manganese on the oxidation of chemicals by lignin peroxidase. *Biochemistry*, 34: 12624-12629.

[190] Koduri, R.S., & Tien, M. (1995). Oxidation of guaiacol by lignin peroxidase. Role of veratryl alcohol. *The Journal of Biological Chemistry*, 270: 22254-22258.

[191] Heinfling, A., Ruiz-Duen, F.J., Martynez, M.J., Bergbauer, H., Szewzyk, U., & Martynez, A.T. (1998). A study on reducing substrates of manganese oxidizing peroxidases from *Pleurotus eryngii* and *Bjenkandera adusta*. *FEBS Letters*, 428: 141-146.

[192] Verma, P., & Madamwar, D. (2002). Decolorization of synthetic textile dyes by lignin peroxidase of *Phanerochaete chrysosporium*. *Folia Microbiology (Praha)*, 47: 283-286.

[193] Yu, G., Wen, X., Li, R., & Qian, Y. (2006). *In vitro* degradation of a reactive azo dye by crude ligninolytic enzymes from nonimmersed liquid culture of *Phanerochaete chrysosporium*. *Process Biochemistry*, 41: 1987-1993.

[194] Chagas, E.P., & Durrant, L.R. (2001). Decolorization of azo dyes by *Phanerochaete chrysosporium* and *Pleurotus sajor-caju*. *Enzyme and Microbial Technology*, 29: 473-477.

[195] Urek, R.O., & Pazarlioglu, N.K. (2005). Production and stimulation of manganese peroxidase by immobilized *Phanerochaete chrysosporium*. *Process Biochemistry*, 40: 83-87.

[196] Bhunia, A., Durani, S., & Wangikar, P.P. (2001) Horseradish peroxidase catalyzed degradation of industrially important dyes. *Biotechnology and Bioengineering*, 72: 562-567.

[197] Mohan, S.V., Prasad, K.K., Rao, N.C., & Sarma, P.N. (2005). Acid azo dye degradation by free and immobilized horseradish peroxidase catalyzed process. *Chemosphere*, 58: 1097-1105.

[198] Maddhinni, V.L., Vurimindi, H.B., & Yerramilli, A. (2006). Degradation of azo dye with horseradish peroxidase (HRP). *Journal of Indian Insitute of Science*, 86: 507-514.

[199] Ulson de Souza, S.M.A.G., Forgiarini, E., & Ulson de Souza, A.A. (2007) Toxicity of textile dyes and their degradation by the enzyme horseradish peroxidase (HRP). *Journal of Hazardous Materials*, 147: 1073-1078.

[200] Matto, M., Satar, R., & Husain, Q. (2009). Application of calcium alginate-starch entrapped bitter gourd (*Momordica charantia*) peroxidase for the removal of colored compounds from a textile effluent in batch as well as in continuous reactor. *Applied Biochemistry and Biotechnology*, 158: 512–523.

[201] Satar R, & Husain, Q. (2009). Use of bitter gourd (*Momordica charantia*) peroxidase together with redox mediators to decolorize disperse dyes. *Biotechnology and Bioprocess Engineering*, 14: 213-219.

[202] Satar, R., & Husain, Q. (2009). Phenol-mediated decolorization and removal of disperse dyes by bitter gourd (*Momordica charantia*) peroxidise. *Environmental Technology*, 30: 1519-1527.

[203] Satar, R., & Husain Q. (2009). Applications of Celite-adsorbed white radish (*Raphanus sativus*) peroxidase in batch process and continuous reactor for the degradation of reactive dyes. *Biochemical Engineering Journal*, 46: 96-104.

[204] Zhang, X., Liu, Y., Yan, K., & Wu, H. (2001). Decolorization of anthraquinone-type dye by bilirubin oxidase-producing nonligninolytic fungus Myrothecium sp. IMER1. *Bioresource Technology*, 79: 171-177.

[205] Liu, Y., Huang, J., & Zhang, X. (2009b). Decolorization and biodegradation of remazol brilliant blue R by bilirubin oxidase. Journal of Bioscience and Bioengineering., 108: 496-500.

[206] Tsujimura, S., Tatsumi, H., Ogawa, J., Shimizu, S., Kano, K., & Ikeda, T. (2001). Bioelectrocatalytic reduction of dioxygen to water at neutral pH using bilirubin oxidase as an enzyme and 2,2'-azinobis (3-ethylbenzothiazolin-6-sulfonate) as an electron transfer mediator. *Journal of Electroanalytical Chemistry*, 496: 69-75.

[207] Zhou, M., Liu, G.F., Zhou, J.T., Jin, R.F., Chen, M.X., & Wang, Y.Q. (2009). Decolorization of azo dyes using quinone reductase and quinoid compounds. *Huan Jing Ke Xue*, 30: 1810-1817.

[208] Salony, Mishra, S., & Bisaria, V.S. (2006). Production and characterization of laccase from *Cyathus bulleri* and its use in decolourization of recalcitrant textile dyes. *Applied Microbiology and Biotechnology*, 71: 646-653.

[209] Sigoillot, C., Record, E., Belle, V., Robert, J.L., Levasseur, A., Punt, P.J., van den Hondel, C.A., Fournel, A., Sigoillot, J.C., & Asther, M. (2004). Natural and recombinant fungal laccases for paper pulp bleaching. *Applied Microbiology and Biotechnology*, 64: 346-352.

In: Non-Conventional Textile Waste Water Treatment   ISBN: 978-1-62100-079-2
Editor: Ahmed El Nemr   © 2012 Nova Science Publishers, Inc.

Chapter 7

ELECTRO-COAGULATION FOR TEXTILE DYES REMOVAL

Abeer A. Moneer and Ahmed El Nemr[*]

Environmental Division, National Institute of Oceanography and Fisheries
Kayet Bey, El Anfoushy, Alexandria, Egypt

ABSTRACT

The electrocoagulation (EC) process was developed to overcome the drawbacks of conventional wastewater treatment technologies. This process is very effective in removing organic pollutants including dyestuff wastewater and allows for the reduction of sludge generation. The word ''electrocoagulation'' sometimes used with the word ''electroflotation'' (EF) and hence the technique can be considered as the electrocoagulation/flotation (ECF) process. Through the process of electrolysis, coagulating agents such as aluminum or iron hydroxides are produced. When aluminum electrodes are used, the aluminum dissolves at the anode and hydrogen gas is released at the cathode and the coagulating agent combines with the pollutants to form large size flocs. As the gas bubbles rise to the top of the tank they adhere to particles suspended in the water and float them to the surface. A conceptual framework of the overall ECF process is linked to coagulant generation, contaminant aggregation, and contaminant removal by flotation and settling, when it has been applied efficiently to various water and wastewater treatment processes. This chapter has attempted to demystify electrocoagulation by showing that it is possible to classify a wide diversity of reactor systems on a simple basis, to obtain and interpret detailed dynamic data from a batch reactor system, and to show that the complexity of electrocoagulation is a natural (and understandable) consequence of the interactions between a number of processes occurring in parallel. It made to bring the chemistry and physical processes involved into perspective and to focus attention on those areas critically needing research.

This chapter also reports the effects of the operating parameters, such as pH, initial concentration, duration of treatment, current density, interelectrode distance and conductivity on the removal of a synthetic textile dyes wastewater in the batch electrocoagulation (EC)–electroflotation (EF) process. A significant number of common

[*] E-mail: ahmedmoustafaelnemr@yahoo.com; ahmed.m.elnemr@gmail.com.

applications of EC process, which have been used for textile dye removal are also considers in this chapter. It is hoped that this evaluation will play its part in focusing attention on electrocoagulation as a viable localized water treatment technology in the near future.

1. INTRODUCTION

The textile industry consumes considerable amounts of water during dyeing and finishing operations. Dye pollutants from this industry are a major source of environmental contamination. Rivers, canals, estuaries and other water-bodies are being constantly polluted due to indiscriminate discharge of industrial effluents as well as other anthropogenic activities and natural processes. Therefore, one of the major challenges facing mankind today is to provide clean water to a vast majority of the population around the world. For example, the need for clean water is particularly critical in Third-World Countries. At the turn of the last century, it was estimated that some 1.1 billion people (one-sixth of the world's population) were without an 'improved' water supply [1], while in the foreseeable future the demand for water is only expected to grow as human population and industrialization increases [2].

A great number of industries such as textile, paper, pulp, printing, iron-steel, coke, petroleum, pesticide, paint, solvent, pharmaceutics, wood preserving chemicals, consume large volumes of water, and organic based chemicals. Effluents of these industries may contain undesired quantities of pollutants and need to be treated before discharge. Synthetic dyestuffs are used extensively in textile, paper, printing industries and dye houses. It is reported that there are over 100,000 commercially available dyes with a production of over 7×10^5 to 1×10^6 metric tons per year [3, 4]. Dyeing industry effluents constitute one of the most problematic wastewaters to be treated not only for their high chemical and biological oxygen demands, suspended solids and content in toxic compounds but also for color, which is the first contaminant to be recognized by human eye. Dyes may significantly affect photosynthetic activity in aquatic life due to reduced light penetration and may also be toxic to some aquatic life because they containing aromatic compounds, metals, chlorides, etc., [3-8]. Dyes usually have a synthetic origin and complex aromatic molecular structures which make them more stable and more difficult to biodegrade. Dyes are classified as follows: anionic-direct, acid and reactive dyes; cationic-basic dyes; non-ionic-disperse dyes [5, 7]. The chromophores in anionic and non-ionic dyes are mostly azo groups or anthraquinone types. The reductive cleavage of azo linkages is responsible for the formation of toxic amines in the effluent. Anthraquinone-based dyes are more resistant to degradation due to their fused aromatic structures and thus remain colored for a longer time in the wastewater. Reactive dyes are typically azo-based chromophores combined with different types of reactive groups such as vinyl sulfone, chlorotriazine, trichloropyrimidine, difluorochloropyrimidine, which are differ from all other classes of dyes in that they bind to the textile fibers (cotton for example) through covalent bonds. They are used extensively in textile industries regarding favorable characteristics of bright color, water-fast, simple application techniques with low energy consumption. Water-soluble reactive and acid dyes are the most problematic, as they tend to pass through conventional treatment systems unaffected, which makes their removal is of great importance [8-15]. Basic dyes have high brilliance and intensity of colors as well as they are highly visible even in a very low concentration [3, 6, 7, 16-18]. Metal complex dyes are mostly based on chromium, which is carcinogenic [3, 5, 6, 19]. Disperse dyes do not ionize in an aqueous medium and some disperse dyes have also been shown to have a tendency to bioaccumulate [6]. The characteristics of wastewater from textile dying are pH in a broad range, high temperature and a high concentration of dying substance. Treatment of dyed wastewater can be achieved by biological treatment, chemical coagulation, activated carbon adsorption, ultrafiltration, ozonation and electrocoagulation–electroflotation (EC–EF) [20, 21]. Recently, electrochemical treatment methods such as electro-oxidation and electrocoagulation (EC) have attracted great attention as an eco-friendly and cost-effective process [22-25]. Conventional biological wastewater treatment systems are inefficient in treating dyes wastewater due to the chemical stability and low biodegradability of these dyes. Dyes wastewater is usually treated by physical- or chemical-treatment processes, which include chemical coagulation/flocculation, ozonation, oxidation, ion exchange, irradiation, precipitation and adsorption [5-8, 10, 19, 26-36].

2. ELECTROCHEMICAL TECHNIQUES FOR WASTES TREATMENT

Innovative, cheap and effective methods of purifying water for human consumption as well as to clean the wastewater from industrial effluents before discharging into any other water systems are needed. Electrochemical techniques such as, electro-flotation (EF), electro-decantation (ED), electro-coagulation (EC), electro-kinetic remediation (EKR) (for contaminated soil) offer the possibility to be easily distributed, require minimum amount and number of chemicals.

EC involves the in situ generation of coagulants by electrolytic oxidation of an appropriate sacrificial anode (Such as, iron and/or aluminum) upon application of a direct current. The metal ions generated hydrolyze in the electrocoagulator to produce metal hydroxide ions and neutral metal hydroxides [$M(OH)_3$]. The low solubility of the $M(OH)_3$ promotes the generation of sweep flocs inside the treated wastewater and the removal of the contaminants by their enmeshment into these flocs. EC process removes contaminants principally by coagulation, adsorption, precipitation and flotation [37, 38]. Robust and compact instrumentation is very easily achievable in the above mentioned electrochemical techniques, and hence, they will have the potential to replace sophisticated processes that require a large volume and/or number of chemicals, massive containers that are present in a typical wastewater treatment plant. Consequently, the electrochemical techniques can be considered as a very simple replacement able to prevent economically unfeasible capital cost. Rajeshwar et al. [39] reported that the advantages from using electrochemical techniques include: environmental compatibility, versatility, energy efficiency, safety, selectivity, amenability to automation, and cost effectiveness as well as the electrochemical based systems allow controlled and rapid reactions, smaller systems become viable and the systems employ only electrons instead of using chemicals and micro-organisms to facilitate water treatment. Of the known electrochemical techniques, there is much interest in using electro-coagulation for treatment of wastewater containing, heavy metals [40, 41], foodstuff [42, 43], food processing [44], oil wastes [45], the wastewaters of olive mill [46, 47], phosphate [48, 49], surfactant [50], textile dyes [20, 51-55] , fluorine [56], polymeric wastes [57], organic matter from land fill leachate [58], suspended particles [59-61] , semiconductor [62], restaurant [43], chemical and mechanical polishing wastes [63-65] , aqueous suspensions of ultrafine particles [66], nitrate [67], phenolic waste [68], metal plating [69], tannery [70], chromium(VI) [71], potato chips manufacturing [72], dairy [73], poultry slaughterhouse [74, 75], pulp and paper mill [76], and refractory organic pollutants including lignin and EDTA [77]. Another approach of EC is for drinking water treatment [78, 79]. The electrochemical treatment of wastewater has been reported [80-82], but only a few authors have focused on the variables that are crucial to the improvement of the performance of this application [83]. The classification of electrocoagulation reactor systems has been mentioned in Scheme 1 [84].

2. THEORY OF ELECTROCOAGULATION

Electrocoagulation (EC) is the process of destabilizing or removing suspended, emulsified, or dissolved contaminants in an aqueous medium by passing an electric current into the contaminated medium. Simple EC reactor may be made up of an electrolytic cell with only one anode and one cathode. The conductive metal plates are commonly known as 'sacrificial electrodes' and may be made of the same or different materials such as aluminum and iron (anode and cathode) [24]. EC is the electrochemical production of destabilization agents (such as Al hydroxides, Fe hydroxides) that brings about neutralization of electric charge for removing contaminants, which combined together via charge difference like small magnets to form a large mass. This process has proven very effective in removing contaminants from water and is characterized by reduced sludge production, no requirement for chemical use, and ease of operation [99]. EC is a complicated process involving many chemical and physical phenomena that use sacrificial electrode to continuously produce polymeric hydroxides that effect on-charge neutralization. For example, aluminum or iron anodes are used to produce aluminum or iron cations which have the same effect as the addition of Al or iron based coagulants in conventional treatment systems [100].

The electrocoagulation/flotation (ECF) process is an alternative technique for contaminants removal from aqueous medium. ECF process involves applying an electric current to 'sacrificial electrodes' inside a reactor tank where the current generates a coagulating agent at the anode and gas bubbles at the cathode. Moreover, ECF is a technique involving the electrolytic addition of coagulating metal ions directly from sacrificial electrodes. These ions coagulate with contaminants in the aqueous medium via adsorption or neutralization, similar to the addition of coagulating chemicals such as alum and ferric chloride, and allow for easier removal of the contaminants by sedimentation and flotation.

In an EC process the coagulating ions are produced 'in situ' and it involves three successive stages:

  i.   Electrode oxidation: formation of coagulants by electrolytic oxidation of the sacrificial electrode,
  ii. Coagulation: destabilization of the contaminants, particulate suspension, and breaking of emulsions, and
  iii. Flocs formation: aggregation of the destabilized phases to form flocs.

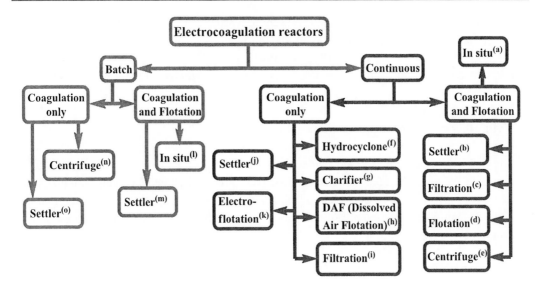

Scheme 1. Classification of electrocoagulation reactor systems.
(a) [43, 80]; (b) [56, 85, 86]; (c) [86-88]; (d) [89]; (e) [88]; (f) [90]; (g) [91, 92]; (h) [93]; (i) [94, 95];
(j) [59, 66, 94, 96, 97; (k) [89,98]; (l) [22, 84]; (m) [56]; (n) [24]; (o) [66].

The destabilization mechanism of the contaminants, particulate suspension, and breaking of emulsions may be summarized as follows:

i.   Compression of the diffuse double layer around the charged species by the interactions of ions generated by oxidation of the sacrificial anode,

ii. Charge neutralization of the ionic species present in wastewater by counter ions produced by the electrochemical dissolution of the sacrificial anode. These counter ions reduce the electrostatic interparticle repulsion to the extent that the van der Waals attraction predominates, thus causing coagulation. A zero net charge results in the process, and

iii. Floc formation; the floc formed as a result of coagulation creates a sludge blanket that entraps and bridges colloidal particles still remaining in the aqueous medium.

The solid oxides, hydroxides and polyhydroxides provide active surfaces for the adsorption of the pollutants. Fe/Al is dissolved from the anode generating corresponding metal ions, which almost immediately hydrolyze to polymeric iron or aluminum hydroxides, which are excellent coagulating agents. Coagulation occurs when the metal cations combine with the negative particles carried toward the anode by electrophoretic motion. Contaminants present in the wastewater stream are treated either by chemical reactions and precipitation or physical and chemical attachment to colloidal materials being generated by the electrode erosion. They are then removed by electroflotation, or sedimentation and filtration. Thus, rather than adding coagulating chemicals as in conventional coagulation process, these coagulating agents are generated in situ.

In a parallel reaction, water is electrolyzed producing small bubbles of oxygen at the anode and hydrogen at the cathode, which attract the flocculated particles and, through natural buoyancy, float the flocculated pollutants to the surface. In addition, the following physiochemical reactions may also take place in the EC cell:

    i.   cathodic reduction of impurities present in wastewater,

    iv.   discharge and coagulation of colloidal particles,

    v.   electrophoretic migration of the ions in solution,

    vi.   electroflotation of the coagulated particles by O_2 and H_2 bubbles produced at the electrodes,

    vii. reduction of metal ions at the cathode, and

    viii. other electrochemical and chemical processes.

In an EC experiment the electrode or electrode assembly is usually connected to an external DC source. The amount of metal dissolved or deposited is dependent on the quantity of electricity passed through the electrolytic solution. A simple relationship between current density (A cm^{-2}) and the amount of substances (M) dissolved (g of M cm^{-2}) can be derived from Faraday's law:

$$w = \frac{-itM}{nF} \tag{1}$$

where, w is the quantity of electrode material dissolved (g of M cm^{-2}), i is the current density (A cm^{-2}), t is the time in second, M is the relative molar mass of the electrode concerned, n is the number of electrons in oxidation/reduction reaction, and F is the Faraday's constant (96,500 C mol^{-1}).

It is expected that there should be an agreement between the calculated amount of substances dissolved as a result of passing a definite quantity of electricity and the experimental amount determined. Usually a good agreement is obtained [80] although significant error may be introduced if sufficient attention is not given to the geometry of the electrode assembly as well as the optimum conditions of operation of the EC cell. One area of uncertainty is in the measurement of potential of the EC cell. The measured potential is the sum of three components:

$$\eta_{AP} = \eta_k + \eta_{Mt} + \eta_{IR} \tag{2}$$

where: η_{AP} is the applied overpotential (V), η_k is the kinetic overpotential (V), η_{Mt} is the concentration overpotential (V), and η_{IR} is the overpotential caused by solution resistance or IR-drop (V). The IR-drop is related to the distance (d in cm) between the electrodes, surface area (A in m^2) of the cathode and specific conductivity of the solution (κ in mSm^{-1}) and current (I in A) by the equation 3 [80].

$$\eta_{IR} = \frac{Id}{Ak} \tag{3}$$

The IR-drop can be easily minimized by decreasing the distance between the electrodes and increasing the area of cross section of the electrodes and the specific conductivity of the solution. Concentration overpotential (η_{Mt}), also known as mass transfer or diffusion overpotential is caused by the change in analytical concentration occurring in the proximity of the electrode surface due to electrode reaction. This overpotential is caused by the differences in electro-active species concentration between the bulk solution and the electrode surface. This condition occurs when the electrochemical reaction is sufficiently rapid to lower surface concentration of electro-active species below that of the bulk solution. The concentration overpotential is negligibly small when reaction rate constant is much smaller than the mass transfer coefficient.

The mass transport overpotential (η_{Mt}) can be reduced by increasing the masses of the metal ions transported from the anode surface to the bulk of the solution and can be achieved by enhancing the turbulence of the solution. It can also be overcome by passing electrolyte solution from anode to cathode at a higher velocity by using some mechanical means.

Kinetic overpotential (also called activation potential) has its origin in the activation energy barrier to electron transfer reactions. The activation overpotential is particularly high for evolution of gases on certain electrodes. Both the kinetic and concentration overpotentials increase as the current increases. However, the effects of these changes need to be investigated for specific types of physical and chemical species in aqueous solution. The detailed effects of the electric field gradient on the relevant surface and solution reactions must also be clearly delineated. A survey of literature indicates that very little work has been done to characterize the deposits on the electrodes. The effect of pH and electrochemical potentials on both solution phases as well as interfacial reactions must also be clearly understood for optimization of the performances of EC techniques.

3. REACTIONS AT THE ELECTRODES

A simple electrocoagulating reactor is made up of one anode and one cathode (Figure 1). When a potential is applied from an external power source, the anode material undergoes oxidation, while the cathode will be subjected to reduction or reductive deposition of elemental metals. The electrochemical reactions with metal M as anode may be summarized as follows:

(*i*) At the anode:

$$M_s \longrightarrow M_{aq}^{n+} + ne^- \tag{4}$$

$$2H_2O \longrightarrow 4H_{aq}^+ + O_{2(g)} + 4e^- \tag{5}$$

(*ii*) At the cathode:

$$M_{aq}^{n+} + ne^- \longrightarrow M_s \tag{6}$$

$$2H_2O + 2e^- \longrightarrow H_{2(g)} + 2OH^- \tag{7}$$

If iron or aluminum electrodes are used, the generated $Fe_{(aq)}^{3+}$ or $Al_{(aq)}^{3+}$ ions will immediately undergo further spontaneous reactions to produce corresponding hydroxides and/or polyhydroxides. For example, Al^{3+} ions on hydrolysis may generate $Al(H_2O)_6^{3+}$,

$Al(H_2O)_5OH^{2+}$, $Al(H_2O)_4(OH)^{2+}$ and the hydrolysis products may form many monomeric and polymeric species such as, $Al(OH)^{2+}$, $Al(OH)_2^{+}$, $Al_2(OH)_2^{4+}$, $Al(OH)_4^{-}$, $Al_6(OH)_{15}^{3+}$, $Al_7(OH)_{17}^{4+}$, $Al_8(OH)_{20}^{4+}$, $Al_{13}O_4(OH)_{24}^{7+}$, $Al_{13}(OH)_{34}^{5+}$ [101] over a wide pH range. Similarly, ferric ions generated by electrochemical oxidation of iron electrode may form monomeric ions, $Fe(OH)^{3+}$ and polymeric hydroxyl complexes, namely: $Fe(H_2O)_6^{3+}$, $Fe(H_2O)_5(OH)^{2+}$, $Fe(H_2O)_4(OH)^{2+}$, $Fe_2(H_2O)_8(OH)_2^{4+}$ and $Fe_2(H_2O)_6(OH)_4^{4+}$ depending on the pH of the aqueous medium.

Table 1. The advantage and disadvantages of electrocoagulation

Advantages of EC	Disadvantages of EC
IT requires simple equipment and is easy to operate with sufficient operational latitude to handle most problems encountered on running.	The 'sacrificial electrodes' are dissolved into wastewater streams as a result of oxidation, and need to be regularly replaced.
Wastewater treated by EC gives palatable, clear, colorless and odorless water.	High conductivity of the wastewater suspension is required.
Sludge formed by EC tends to be readily settable and easy to de-water, because it is composed of mainly metallic oxides/ hydroxides. Above all, it is a low sludge producing technique.	Gelatinous hydroxide may tend to solubilize in some cases.
Flocs formed by EC are similar to chemical floc, except that EC floc tends to be much larger, contains less bound water, is acid-resistant and more stable, and therefore, can be separated faster by filtration.	An impermeable oxide film may be formed on the cathode leading to loss of efficiencyof the EC unit.
The EC process has the advantage of removing the smallest colloidal particles, because the applied electric field sets them in faster motion, thereby facilitating the coagulation.	
EC produces effluent with less total dissolved solids (TDS) content as compared with chemical treatments. If this water is reused, the low TDS level contributes to a lower water recovery cost.	The use of electricity may be expensive in many places
The EC process avoids uses of chemicals, and so there is no problem of neutralizing excess chemicals and no possibility of secondary pollution caused by chemical substances added at high concentration as when chemical coagulation of wastewater is used.	
The gas bubbles produced during electrolysis can carry the pollutant to the top of the solution where it can be more easily concentrated, collected and removed.	
The electrolytic processes in the EC cell are controlled electrically with no moving parts, thus requiring less maintenance.	
The EC technique can be conveniently used in rural areas where electricity is not available, since a solar panel attached to the unit may be sufficient to carry out the process.	

These hydroxides, polyhydroxides and polyhydroxymetallic compounds have strong affinity to disperse into the cell and attract pollutant ions to cause coagulation As well as the hydrogen and oxygen gases evolved at the cathode and anode, respectively, may impinge on and cause flotation of the coagulated materials. The success of the EF process is determined by the size of the bubbles as well as by the proper mixing of the bubbles with wastewater. It is generally believed that the smaller bubbles provide more surface area for attachment of the particles in aqueous stream, resulting in better separation efficiency of the EF process [25, 42, 43]. Table 1 shows the advantages and disadvantages of Electrocoagulation [24].

4. CONFIGURATIONS OF ELECTROCOAGULATION CELLS

To improve the performances of an EC it may be necessary to interchange the polarity of the electrode intermittently. However, a two-electrode EC cell (Figure 1) is not suitable for wastewater treatment, because for a workable rate of metal dissolution the use of electrodes with large surface area is required. Performance improvement has been achieved by using EC cells with monopolar electrodes either in parallel or series connections.

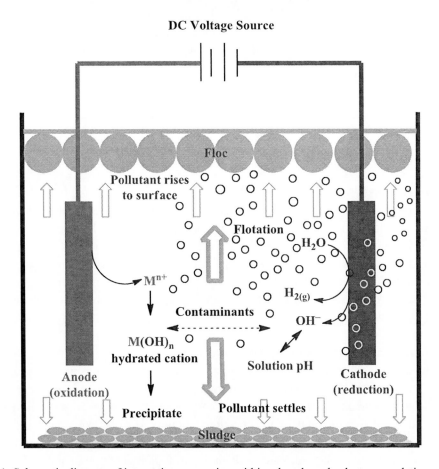

Figure 1. Schematic diagram of interactions occurring within a bench-scale electrocoagulation reactor.

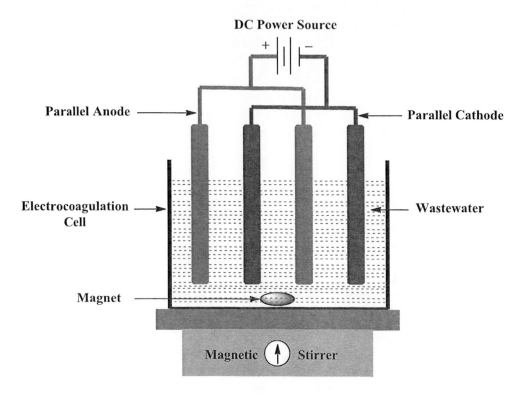

Figure 2. Schematic diagram of a bench-scale EC reactor with monopolar electrodes in parallel connections.

4.1. Monopolar Electrodes

4.1.1. Monopolar Electrodes in Parallel Connections

The anodes and cathodes are in parallel connection, the current is divided between all the electrodes in relation to the resistance of the individual cells. Hence, a lower potential difference is required in parallel connection, when compared with serial connections. The parallel arrangement essentially consists of pairs of conductive metal plates placed between two parallel electrodes and a DC power source. In the monopolar arrangement, each pair of sacrificial electrodes is internally connected with each other, and has no interconnections with the outer electrodes (Figure 2).

4.1.2. Monopolar Electrodes in Series Connections

Each pair of sacrificial electrodes is internally connected with each other, because the cell voltages sum up, a higher potential difference is required for a given current. This arrangement of the monopolar electrodes with cells in series is electrically similar to a single cell with many electrodes and interconnections (Figure 3). The experimental set-up also requires a resistance box to regulate the flow of current and a multimeter to read the current values. The conductive metal plates or rods used in EC fabrication are commonly known as sacrificial electrodes. The sacrificial anode lowers the dissolution potential of the anode and minimizes the reduction or reductive deposition of elemental metals on the cathode. The sacrificial electrode and the cathode may be made up of the same or of different materials.

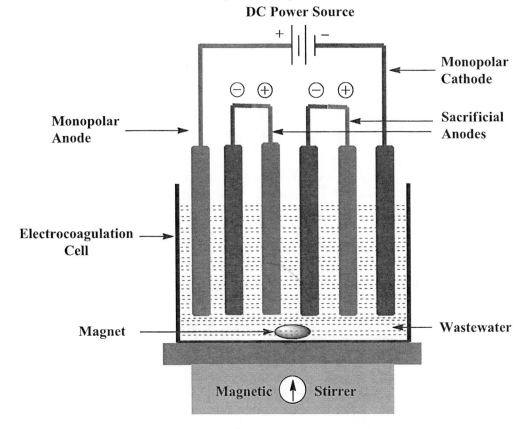

Figure 3. Schematic digram of a bench-scale EC reactor with monopolar electrodes in series connections.

Because the cells connected in series have higher resistance, a higher potential difference is required for a given current to flow in a series arrangement. However, the same current would flow through all the electrodes. On the other hand, in the parallel arrangement the electric current is divided between all the electrodes in relation to the resistance of the individual cells.

4.1.3. Bipolar Electrodes

Bipolar electrodes with cells in parallel have been used by some authors (Figure 4) [56, 78]. In this case, there is no electrical connection between inner electrodes 'sacrificial electrodes', only the outer electrodes 'monopolar electrodes' are connected to the power supply. Outer electrodes are monopolar and inner ones are bipolar. This connection mode has simple setup and has less maintenance cost during operation. This cell arrangement provides a simple set-up, which facilitates easy maintenance during use. When an electric current is passed through the two electrodes, the neutral sides of the conductive plate will be transformed to charged sides, which have opposite charge compared to the parallel side beside it. The sacrificial electrodes in this case are also known as bipolar electrodes [25]. Thus, during electrolysis, the positive side undergoes anodic reactions; while the negative side undergoes cathodic reactions. The ions released may remove the contaminants either by chemical reaction and precipitation, or by causing the colloidal materials to coalesce and then removed by electrolytic flotation. In addition, as water containing colloidal particulates, oils, or other contaminants move through the applied electric field, there may be ionization, electrolysis, hydrolysis, and free-radical formation, which may alter the physical and chemical properties of water and contaminants. As a result, the reactive and excited state causes contaminants to be released from water and destroyed or made less soluble [24].

5. DESIGN OF THE EC CELL

It is important to design the EC cell so that maximum efficiency can be achieved. In dealing with this problem, the following factors must be taken into consideration: (*i*) the IR-drop between the electrodes must be minimized, (*ii*) accumulation of O_2 and H_2 gas bubble nucleates at the electrode surfaces must be minimized, and (*iii*) impediment to mass transfer through the spaces between the electrodes must be minimum.

The IR-drop depends on: (*i*) the conductivity of the electrolyte solution, (*ii*) the distance between the two electrodes, and (*iii*) the electrode geometry.

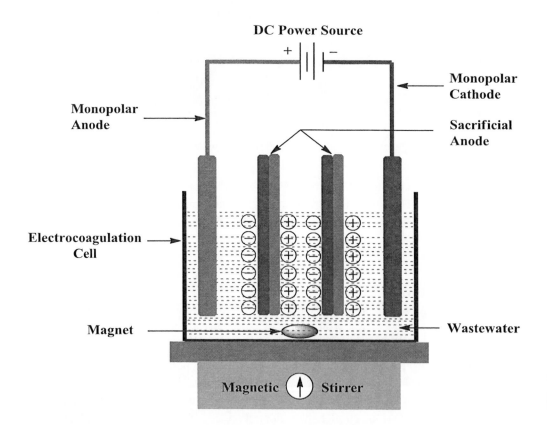

Figure 4. Schematic diagram of a bench-scale EC reactor with bipolar electrodes in parallel connections.

The magnitude of the error due to IR-drop can be minimized in three different ways: (*i*) use of highly conducting solution, (*ii*) decreasing the distance between the electrodes, and (*iii*) devising an electronic means to compensate for IR-drop (feedback action of a potentiostat).

The mass transport can be enhanced by increasing the turbulence level in the flow through the EC reactor. Turbulence can be increased by increasing the flow rate inside the EC reactor. The increase in turbulence level also reduces the passivation layer near the electrode plates. Oxygen and hydrogen gases are evolved at the anode and the cathode in the form of gas bubble nucleates. These gas bubbles are insulating spheres, and if allowed to accumulate at the electrode surfaces will increase the electrical resistance of the cell and, as a result, more electric energy must be used to achieve optimum removal efficiency. To minimize the accumulation of the gas bubbles, the electrolyte flow around the electrodes must be increased to sweep out the bubbles. Each EC reactor system has its own set of advantages and disadvantages, among which are varying degrees of treatment ability. The terms 'plates' or 'tubes' are used to refer to the anodic and cathodic surfaces, since the polarity is commonly reversed on a periodic basis in all reactors.

5.1. TALL VERTICAL-PLATE REACTOR

The tall vertical-plate EC reactor [56] uses electrodes made of flat steel plates whose vertical dimension significantly exceeds the horizontal dimension (Figure 5). The plates are typically arranged in a nonconductive case that may be open or closed at the top. The open case allows electrical contact above the solution level, while a closed case requires submerged contacts, which typically erode at a rate faster than the plates, which complicates the assembly unless they are coated with an insulating material. A number of attempts have been made using nonconductive (typically PVC) pipe or tubing as the outer case. These reactors use plates of various widths to fill the tube, as all must be equally spaced and parallel. The narrower plates near the inner tangent can offer more flow restriction, so that the flow in the reactor is not uniform. The narrower plates also have less surface area than adjacent plates closer to the center of the tubular case, causing uneven erosion and shortened plate life unless the plate thickness is varied. Flow must be from bottom to top to allow gas bubbles to move with the solution. These reactors typically use a plate spacing of 0.31 to 0.63 cm. and are subject to shorting as scale falling from the plates fills the void and collects at the bottom of the reactor within the plate field. The design usually includes an acid-wash step performed frequently to dissolve the scale, generating additional waste. Since plate spacing is not conducive to the additional bulk of bolts or connectors, assembly of the plates is typically done by welding operation, which results in an extended downtime during reactor rebuild unless a spare reactor is used. Some manufacturers have used a disposable reactor cell, which scrapped when the plates are exhausted by erosion. Corrosion will sometimes lock the plates to the case if the plates are contained in slots within the case to maintain their spacing. An open reactor with a wider plate gap and with all plates have the same dimensions within a rectangular case has also been used. The plates use a vertical to horizontal ratio of less than 2 so that the plates are removable even if corroded within the plate grooves in the case. The plates use contacts above the solution level so that welding and insulation are not required. The reactor itself contains the plates within a removable cartridge so that downtime is minimized when plate replacement is required. The reactor also has a large annular space below the plates to prevent shorting if sheets of scale occur. This reactor is capable of treatment to a degree far exceeding other vertical-plate reactors and can process water at a wide range of flow rates.

Serpentine flow is not practical with any of these vertical plate designs. Thus the fluid will be proximate to either an anode or cathode during most of its residence. The reactions necessary for treatment usually require exposure to both anodic and cathodic conditions, so that with the typical design the fluid is only partially reacted in a single pass through the reactor.

5.2. Long Horizontal Plate Reactor

These reactors use horizontal plates laying either flat or on edge (Figure 6). The plates are mounted within a rectangular nonconductive case with slots to maintain their spacing. The plates are nearly impossible to remove once corrosion occurs. When the plates are installed flat, the gas bubbles rise within the stream causing resistance at the bottom of the upper plate soon after the solution begins to move between the plates and continues down the long axis. The produced gases include oxygen, which causes rapid corrosion and scaling. When the scale falls, it causes short circuits between the plates. When the plates are installed vertically (on edge), the three phases of the solution (solid, liquid, and gas) can separate, so that only the central part of the plate is effective while the bottom is shorted with solids and the top is insulated by gas. The presence of solids at the base edge of each plate locks the plates to the case and complicates reactor service.

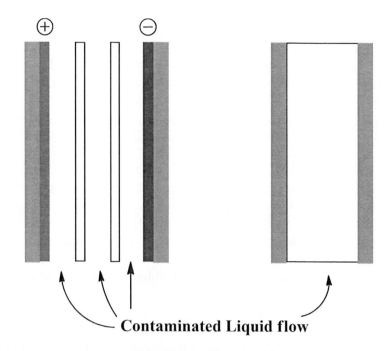

Figure 5. Schematic flow-diagram of EC reactor with tall, vertical-plate electrodes.

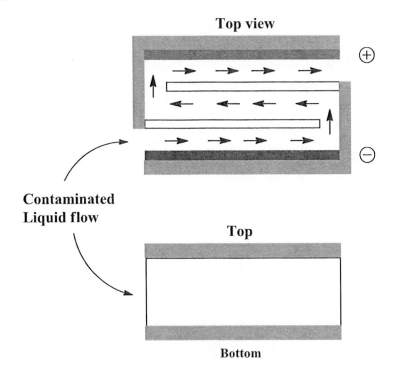

Figure 6. Schematic flow-diagram of EC reactor with long horizontal plate electrodes on edge.

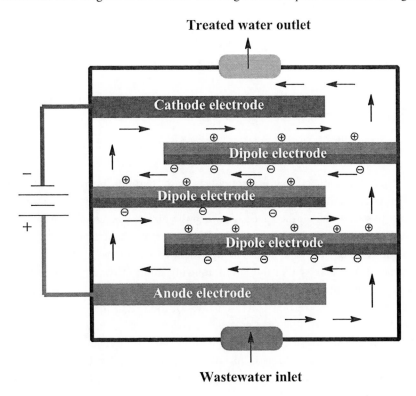

Figure 7. Schematic flow-diagram of EC reactor with short horizontal parallel plate electrodes.

Top view

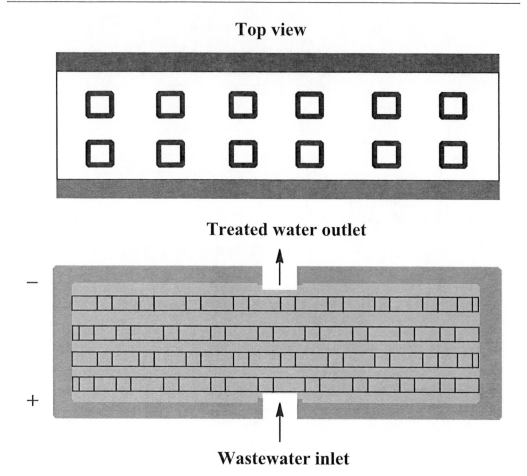

Treated water outlet

Wastewater inlet

Figure 8. Schematic diagram of EC reactor with perforated, flat and horizontal parallel plate electrodes..

5.3. Short Horizontal Plate Reactor

These reactors use plates that are roughly square, parallel, horizontal, and set apart by spacers or grooves within a non-conductive case (Figure 7). Flow is serpentine, so that the solution must pass through all the spaces between the plates. The configuration allows the use of multiple changes in polarity along the path. The water will have an opportunity to approach both anode and cathode, allowing complete treatment in a single pass [25].

The contacts are made within the case, requiring either difficult assembly or innovative methods of case design that allow electrical contacts without welding and insulation. The short contact area between the plates and the sides of the reactor case allows easy removal of corroded plates. Reactors of this type are considered to be most effective and are capable of treating high concentrations of waste. Some attempts with these reactors have used a low flow velocity to maximize residence time of the solution. A high fluid velocity ensures that there is no phase separation and removes scale in smaller pieces that do not foul the reactor.

5.4. Perforated Plate Reactor

Even though perforated plate reactor is not so commercialized due to the drawbacks mentioned below, it is worth to mention it here. Reactors with perforated, flat, horizontal, parallel plates within a non-conductive case can also be used (Figure 8). The flow of wastewater passes through the plates rather than between them. This configuration allows solids to collect rapidly between the plates in the dead space between adjacent perforations, causing electrical short circuits that can only be cleared with acid washing or disassembly.

The perforations erode with the plates, so that fluid velocity through the perforations changes with time. If any foreign matter is present the perforations can be plugged. A plugged perforation will accelerate fouling, as solids will build in that area. Since the many perforations amount to parallel flow there is no way to ensure uniform flow between all perforations. These reactors are effective if they are processing drinking water and do not use consumable plates, but they are difficult to assemble without leakage and usually operate at high pressure.

5.5. Solid Tube Reactor

A successful reactor with two concentric tubes employed as the sacrificial surfaces are usually contained within a third, non-conductive tube can also be fabricated (Figure 9). The tubes are held apart by wrapping with non-conductive cord or other, more complex fixtures. The annular space is minimized, keeping reaction voltage low and fluid velocity high. There is no opportunity to vary the current density by using non-charged surfaces, as one tube must always be the anode and the other the cathode. Since the inner and outer tubes have different surface areas, current reversal (switching anode and cathode electrically) requires differing forward and reverses times that vary with the amount of plate erosion. The current density at each reactive surface also varies depending on the direction of the current. These reactors are difficult to seal from leakage. They are also subject to massive shorting near the end of the tubing's useful life as stresses deform the tubes and short circuits occur. A short circuit commonly results in external leakage. The tubes are usually set in banks to increase residence time. In EC, the greatest erosion occurs near the solution inlet where the pH is at its lowest. With the tube-in-tube reactor there can be considerable waste if all tubes are replaced when the first set in a bank suffers break through or frequent downtime if they are not.

5.6. Perforated Tube Reactor

The perforated tube reactor is a variation of the tube in-tube that uses perforated inner or outer tubes or both (Scheme 2). These reactors suffer the same sealing problems as the solid tubes but have a shorter life. This is partially overcome by placing all the tubes in a case that becomes a manifold for the treated solution. This configuration results in attempting parallel flow through a number of tubes with resultant variations in flow and erosion. The tubes also suffer plugging and other disadvantages common with perforated plate reactors [25].

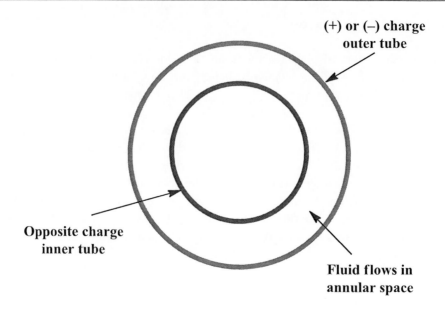

Scheme 2. Schematic diagram of EC reactor with two concentric tubes as sacrificial electrodes.

6. USING ALUMINUM ELECTRODES IN EC

In the case of EC with Al, the anodic reaction leads to soluble Al^{3+} ($E^\circ = 1.66$ V vs. Standard Hydrogen Electrode SHE) [102-105]. Aluminum dissolution at the anode was followed the reaction reported in equation 8.

$$Al \longrightarrow Al^{3+} + 3e^- \tag{8}$$

Water electrolysis at the cathode: the cathodic reaction produces hydroxide ion and H_2 gas:

$$3H_2O + 3e^- \longrightarrow 3OH + \left(\frac{3}{2}\right)H_{2(g)} \tag{9}$$

The overall reaction of Aluminum hydrolysis to give $Al(OH)_3$ is represented in equation 10.

$$Al + 3H_2O \longrightarrow Al(OH)_3 + \left(\frac{3}{2}\right)H_{2(g)} \tag{10}$$

However, when an Al cathode is also utilized, it can be chemically attacked by OH^- generated during H_2 evolution at high pH values as equation 11 [106, 107], and treated wastewater contains higher amount of aluminum ions than those expected from reaction equation 8. Note that a Fe or steel anode is not attacked by OH^- in alkaline medium, thus avoiding the formation of an excess of $Fe(OH)_4^-$ species.

$$Al + 3H_2O + OH^- \longrightarrow Al(OH)_4^- + \left(\tfrac{3}{2}\right)H_{2(g)} \tag{11}$$

Similarly to EC with Fe, the removal of dyes from wastewaters using Al can be explained by surface complexation and electrostatic attraction [102, 105, 108]. The surface complexes between dyes and hydrous aluminum moieties are formed as reported in equation 12.

$$Dye - H + (OH)OAl_{(s)} \longrightarrow Dye - OAl_{(s)} + H_2O \tag{12}$$

Several interactive mechanisms are possible between the dye molecules and hydrolysis products when the rate of these interactions depends on the pH of the solution. In this case interaction attractions between dye molecules and monomeric and polymeric aluminum cations via precipitation and/or adsorption mechanisms become more important in the EC process. Precipitation by neutralization of opposite charges predominates in acidic medium, taking place the reaction of dyes with monomeric species at pH = 4-5 (Equation 13) and at pH = 5-6 (Equation 14).

$$\tag{13}$$
$$Dye + monomeric\ Al \longrightarrow [Dye - monomeric\ Al]_{(s)}$$
$$Dye + polymeric\ Al \longrightarrow [Dye - polymeric\ Al]_{(s)} \tag{14}$$

Adsorption on $Al(OH)_3$ flocs, followed by coagulation to form particles, mainly occurs at pH > 6.5 (Equations 15 and 16).

$$Dye + Al(OH)_{3(s)} \longrightarrow [particle] \tag{15}$$

$$[Dye - polymeric\ Al]_{(s)} + Al(OH)_{3(s)} \longrightarrow [particle] \tag{16}$$

The large surface areas of freshly formed amorphous $Al(OH)_3$ flocs can also adsorb soluble organic compounds and/or trap colloidal particles, which are thus separated from the aqueous solution [102, 109].

Under experimental conditions, the negatively charged dye molecules were neutralized. The positive charge of the aggregates may be attributed to the adsorption of dye monomeric and dye polymeric colloidal particles on the $Al(OH)_3$ precipitates.

7. USING IRON AND STEEL ELECTRODES

Three main processes occur during electrocoagulation: electrolytic reactions at the surface of iron electrodes, formation of coagulants in aqueous phase, adsorption of soluble or colloidal pollutants on generated coagulants, which can be removed by sedimentation and/or floatation. The mechanism of removal of pollutants by EC process using iron electrodes can be explained as follows. When an iron or steel anode is utilized in EC; iron upon oxidation in an electrolytic system produces iron hydroxide, $Fe(OH)_n$ where n = 2 or 3. The mechanisms for the production of $Fe(OH)_n$ have been proposed as follows. Fe^{2+} is dissolved in the EC cell form iron oxidation at the anode (standard potential $E° = -0.44$ V vs. SHE) as equation 17 [53, 104, 110].

$$Fe \longrightarrow Fe^{2+} + 2e^- \tag{17}$$

whereas hydroxide ion and H_2 gas are generated at the cathode from the reaction ($E° = -0.83$ V vs. SHE), and

$$2H_2O + 2e^- \longrightarrow 2OH^- + H_{2(g)} \tag{18}$$

OH^- production from reaction (18) causes an increase in pH during electrolysis. Insoluble $Fe(OH)_2$ precipitates at pH > 5.5 and remains in equilibrium with Fe^{2+} up to pH 9.5 or with monomeric species such as $Fe(OH)^+$, $Fe(OH)_2$ and $Fe(OH)_3^-$ at higher pH values. The formation of insoluble $Fe(OH)_2$ can be written as equation 19.

$$Fe^{2+} + 2OH^- \longrightarrow Fe(OH)_{2(s)} \tag{19}$$

and the overall reaction for the electrolytic process from the sequence of reactions (Equations 18– 19) is:

$$Fe^{2+} + 2H_2O \longrightarrow Fe(OH)_{2(s)} + H_{2(g)} \tag{20}$$

In the presence of O_2, dissolved Fe^{2+} is oxidized to insoluble $Fe(OH)_3$ [53, 104, 110]:

$$4Fe^{2+} + 10H_2O + O_{2(g)} \longrightarrow 4Fe(OH)_{3(s)} + 8H^+ \tag{21}$$

and protons can be directly reduced to H_2 gas at the cathode:

$$8H^+ + 8e^- \longrightarrow 4H_{2(g)} \tag{22}$$

The corresponding overall reaction obtained by combining reaction equations 17, 21 and 22 is:

$$4Fe + 10H_2O + O_{2(g)} \longrightarrow 4Fe(OH)_{3(s)} + 4H_{2(g)} \tag{23}$$

The $Fe(OH)_{n(s)}$ formed remains in the solution as a gelatinous suspension, which can remove the pollutants from wastewater either by complexation or by electrostatic attraction, followed by coagulation [111].

In acidic media of pH < 5.0, however, a greater quantity of Fe anode than that expected from Faraday law following reaction equation 17 is dissolved owing to the chemical attack of protons [106]. $Fe(OH)_3$ coagulates from pH > 1.0, i.e., it is present in much stronger acidic media than $Fe(OH)_2$. Then, this precipitate can be in equilibrium with soluble monomeric species like Fe^{3+}, $Fe(OH)^{2+}$, $Fe(OH)_2^+$, $Fe(OH)_3$ and $Fe(OH)_4^-$ as a function of the pH range

[112]. Among them, hydroxy iron cations have a pronounced tendency to polymerize at pH 3.5–7.0 to give polymeric cations such as $Fe_2(OH)_2^{4+}$ and $Fe_2(OH)_4^{2+}$ [113]. Once the insoluble flocs of $Fe(OH)_3$ are produced, they can remove dissolved dyes by surface complexation or electrostatic attraction [108, 110]. The first mechanism considers that the dye can act as a legend to bind a hydrous iron moiety of the flocs yielding a surface complex:

$$Dye - H + (HO)OFe_{(s)} \longrightarrow Dye - OFe_{(s)} + H_2O \tag{24}$$

dissolved owing to the chemical attack of protons [106] and the second one supposes that $Fe(OH)_3$ flocs with surface complexes contain areas of apparent positive or negative charge that attract the opposite regions of the dyestuff. Coagulation of these flocs forms particles that are separated from the wastewater by sedimentation or electroflotation [109].

8. REMOVAL OF DYES USING EC TECHNIQUE

Table 2 reported the removal of different dyes using electrocoagulation technique and represented the different conditions used for the dye removal.

Table 2. Dye removal using EC technique

Dye	pH	No. of electrodes	Operating conditions	% Color removal	Ref.
Acid red 14	7.27	2 electrodes (Fe anode, st cathode) $50 \times 50 \times 3$ mm e = 10 mm	$C_i = 50$ mg l^{-1} V = 250 ml Current density = 102 Am^{-2} $t_r = 4.47$ min Batch reactor	> 93	[111]
Acid red 14	6-9	2 electrodes (Fe anode, steel cathode) 50 mm × 50 mm e = 10 mm	Ci = 150 ppm Current density = 80 Am^{-2} $t_r = 4$ min Batch reactor	93	[114]
A mixture of: Reactive red (confidential C.I) Reactive yellow 145 Reactive blue 221	11.5	6 monoploar St. St. electrodes $S = 38.5$ cm^2 e = 3 mm	C_i: R.R. = 41 mg l^{-1} R.Y = 25 mg l^{-1} R.B = 86 mg l^{-1} With NaCl (40 g l^{-1}) V = 1800 ml Current density = 220 A m^{-2} $t_r = 30$ min	85-100	[115]
		6 monoploar Al. electrodes $S = 38.5$ cm^2 e = 3 mm	Batch reactor	8-67	
Disperse Yellow 241 Reactive Yellow 135	4.5	4 monopolar Al electrodes $S = 137$cm^2 e = 20 mm	$C_i = 1000$ mg l^{-1} V = 1500 mL Current density = 105Am^{-2} $t_r = 15-20$ min Batch reactor	42-99 25.7-62	[116]

Table 2. Continued

Dye	pH	No. of electrodes	Operating conditions	% Color removal	Ref.
Bomaplex Red CR-L	3	5 pairs of monopolar Al electrodes $S = 1000$ cm^2 $e = 5$ mm	$C_i = 100$ mg l^{-1} Current density = 5 Am^{-2} $t_r = 30$ min MSS = 150 rpm Batch reactor	99.1	[117]
Direct red 81	6	2 Al electrodes $S = 40$ cm^2 $e = 15$ mm	$C_i < 200$ mg l^{-1} with NaCl (2g l^{-1}) Current density = 18.75 Am^{-2} $t_r = 60$ min MSS = 200 rpm Batch reactor	98	[118]
Reactive Blue 140 Disperse red 1	9.6	5 pairs of monopolar Fe electrodes $S = 1047$ cm^2 $e = 8$ mm	Ci = 100 mg l^{-1} Current density = 40Am^{-2} V = 1.8 L $t_r = 5$ min MSS = 150 rpm Batch reactor	>95	[119]
Mixture 1: reactive dyes: Yellow SPD (0.336%), Red S3B 195 (0.92%), Blue BRFS (0.8%)	7.5	2 Fe electrodes $S = 175$ cm^2 $e = 20$ mm	$C_i = 400$ mg l^{-1} Current density = 400 Am^{-2} $t_r = 20$ min batch reactor	>80	[120]
Mixture 2: disperse dyes: Yellow Terasil 4G (0.188%), Red disperse 343 150% (0.412%) and Blue Terasil 3R02 (0.9%)	6.2	2 Al electrodes $S = 175$ cm^2 $e = 20$ mm	$C_i = 400$ mg l^{-1} Current density = 286 Am^{-2} $t_r = 15$ min batch reactor	100	
Mixture 3: Mix.1 + Mix. 2	8.5-9	2 Fe electrodes $S = 175$ cm^2 $e = 20$ mm	$C_i = 400$ mg l^{-1} Current density = 457Am^{-2} $t_r = 20$ min batch reactor	>80	
Basic red 46	5.8	Fe anode and st. cathode $S = 56$ cm^2 $e = 15$ mm	$C_i < 80$ mg l^{-1} Current density = 60 Am^{-2} V = 250 ml $t_r = 5$ min Batch reactor	99	[110]
Basic blue 3	5.8	Fe anode and st. cathode $S = 56$ cm^2 $e = 15$ mm	$C_i < 80$ mg l^{-1} Current density = 80 Am^{-2} V = 250 ml $t_r = 5$ min Batch reactor	99	
2-naphthoic acid + 2-naphthol	6-9	2 Al electrodes $S = 48$ cm^2	$C_i < 200$ mg l^{-1} Current density = 312.5	85-95	[121]

(dispersive dye class)		e = 10 mm	Am^{-2} t_r = 14 min Continuous reactor F.R = 25-78 L h^{-1}		
levafix orange E3 GA	6.4	4 monopolar Al electrodes S = 78 cm^2 e = 11 mm	C_i < 500 mg l^{-1} Current density = 100 Am^{-2} V = 250 ml t_r = 12 min MSS = 200 rpm Batch reactor	95	[122]
Acid yellow 23	5.78	Fe anode, Al cathode S = 18 cm^2 e =15 mm	C_i = 40 mg l^{-1} with NaCl (400 mg l^{-1}) Current density = 120 A m^{-2} t_r = 6 min Batch reactor	100	[103]
Acid yellow 23	6	2 electrodes (Fe as anode and st.st. as cathode) Dimensions: 40 × 50 × 1 mm e = 15 mm	C_i = 50 mg l^{-1} Current density = 112.5 Am^{-2} V = 250 ml t_r = 5 min MSS = 200 rpm Batch reactor	98	[104]
Reactive black 5	5	4 bipolar Fe electrodes S = 218 cm^2 e = 25 mm	C_i = 100 mg l^{-1} with NaCl (3g l^{-1}) Current density = 45.75 Am^{-2} V = 500 ml t_r = 5 min Batch reactor	98.8	[123]
Methylene blue eosin yellowish	6.8	2 mild st. electrodes S = 6.2 cm^2 e = 12 mm	C_i = 200 mg l^{-1} with NaCl (400 mg l^{-1}) Current density = 240 Am^{-2} V = 70 ml t_r = 5 min MSS = 450 rpm Batch reactor	100 75	[124]
Orange II	8	2 Fe electrodes S = 106 cm^2 e = 20 mm	C_i < 200 mg l^{-1} Current density = 34.62 Am^{-2} V = 250 ml t_r = 5 min Batch reactor	>98	[125]
Orange II	6.5	5 Al bipolar electrodes Dimensions = 11.0 cm × 11.4 cm e = 6 mm	C_i = 10ppm with NaCl (4 g l^{-1}) Current density = 120 Am^{-2} V = 3 L Continuous reactor F.R = 350-550 ml min^{-1}	94.5	[126]
Blue reactive dye (Drimarene K2LR CDG Blue)	10	2 Al electrodes Dimensions = 100 mm × 50 mm e = 20mm	C_i = 50 mg l^{-1} current density = 120 Am^{-2} t_r = 60-120 min Continuous reactor F.R = 370 ml min^{-1}	95	[105]

Table 2. Continued

Dye	pH	No. of electrodes	Operating conditions	% Color removal	Ref.
Silica Gel	7.6	2 Al electrodes $S = 4.59$ cm^2 $e = 10$ mm	$C_i = 300$ mg l^{-1} Current density = 115.5 Am^{-2} $V = 1000$ ml $t_r = 10$ min Batch reactor	89.6	[127]
Basic Yellow 2 (BY2) Peroxi-coagulation	3	Carbon-nano tube (PTFE) cathode and Fe anode S (CNT-PTFE) = 233 m^2 g^{-1} S (iron) = 10 cm^2	$C_i = 20$ mg l^{-1} Current density = 1000 Am^{-2} $t_r = 10$ min Batch reactor	90	[128]
R12S (Drimarene Discharge X-3GL ®, Sandoz)	3-9	2 Fe electrodes $S = 5$ cm^2 $e = 15$ mm	$C_i = 300$ ppm Current density = 200Am^{-2} $V = 2$ L $t_r = 6$-20 min Batch reactor	90	[20]
D05H (Samaron Yellow 4 ®, CAS).	2.4	2 Al electrodes $S = 5$ cm^2 $e = 15$ mm	Ci = 300 ppm Current density = 200Am^{-2} $V = 2$ L $t_r = 6$-20 min Batch reactor	95	
Levafix Blue CA	6-8	6 Fe electrodes S: Outer diameter = 12 mm $e = 15$ mm	$C_i = 400$- 2000 mg l^{-1} with NaCl (3.1 g l^{-1}) Current density = 32-110 Am^{-2} $t_r = 26$ min	100	[129]
Levafix Red CA	6-8		$C_i = 400$- 1400 mg l^{-1} with NaCl (2.5 g l^{-1}) Current density = 72 Am^{-2} $t_r = 36$ min	84	
Levafix Yellow CA	6-8		$C_i = 400$- 2000 mg l^{-1} with NaCl (2.8 g l^{-1}) Current density = 10-107 Am^{-2} $t_r = 17$ min Batch reactor	100	
Crystal violet	5.9-8	7 monopolar 4 St. St cathodes 3 Al anodes $S = 120$ cm^2 $e = 11$ mm	$C_i = 200$ mg l^{-1} Current density = 28 Am^{-2} $t_r = 3$-30 min Batch reactor	85-100	[130]
	7.4	7 monopolar 4 St. St cathodes 3 Fe anodes $S = 120$ cm^2 $E = 11$ mm	$C_i = 200$ mg l^{-1} Current density = 28 Am^{-2} $t_r = 3$-30 min Batch reactor	85-100	
Reactive Red 141	6.1-6.5	2 Al electrodes $S = 3 \times 10 \times 0.2$cm $e = 40$ mm	$C_i = 50$ mg l^{-1} with NaCl (400 mg l^{-1}) Current density = 5 Am^{-2} $V = 500$ ml $t_r = 60$ min Batch reactor	41-96.4	[131]

Textile	6.9-7.8	4 monopolar Al electrodes Total S = 78 cm^2 e = 11 mm	C_i = COD = 3422 mg l^{-1} TSS = 1112 mg l^{-1} TOC = 900 mg l^{-1} Turbidity = 5700 NTU V = 250 cm^3 Current density = 100 Am^{-2} t_r = 10 min continuous reactor MSS = 2000 rpm	Turbidity = 99.5 COD = 80 with PAC COD =65 with Alum COD = 63 with no additives	[132]
Textile	<6	4 monopolar Al electrodes Total S = 78 cm^2 e = 11 mm	C_i = COD = 3422 mg l^{-1} TSS = 1112 mg l^{-1} TOC = 900 mg l^{-1} Turbidity, 5700 NTU V = 250 cm^3 Current density = 150 Am^{-2} t_r = 10 min continuous reactor MSS = 2000 rpm	Turbidity= 98 COD = 61-65	[133]
	3-7	4 monopolar Fe electrodes Total S = 78 cm^2 e = 11 mm	Current density = 80-100 Am^{-2}	Turbidity = 75-98 COD = 47-77	
Textile	10	2 Fe electrodes S = 6.4 cm^2	C_i = COD = 485 mg l^{-1} TSS = 70 m l^{-1} Turbidity = 1.45 NTU V = 100 cm^3 Batch reactor t_r = 3 min Potential = 600 mV	Turbidity = 100 COD = 84	[134]
Textile	13	2 Al electrodes Total S = 30 cm^2 e = 20 mm	C_i = COD = 4,800 mg l^{-1} TDS = 12,918 mg l^{-1} Turbidity = 252 NTU Current density = 400 Am^{-2} MSS = 700 rpm t_r = 60 min	Turbidity = 80 COD = 50	[135]
Textile	7	2 Al electrodes S = 105 cm^2 e = 20 mm	C_i: COD= 3260 mg l^{-}1 Turbidity = 310 NTU TSS = 1.7 g l^{-1} V = 2 L Current density = 50-200 A m^{-2} t_r = 60 min MSS = 200 rpm Continuous reactor FR = 50 ml min^{-1}	85-92 COD or TSS?	[136]
		2 Fe electrodes S = 105 cm^2 e = 20 mm	The same conditions	85-94	
Textile	--	Anode of carbon steel of dimensions: inner D = 1.2, outer D = 1.7, length = 33 cm Cathode of St. St. of dimensions: inner D = 2.1, outer D = 2.7, length = 33 cm	C_i: COD =450-766 ppm Turbidity = 33.2-78.1 NTU TSS = 28-146 ppm Current density = 426 A m^{-2} Continuous reactor	TSS=96 COD = 81	[137]

Table 2. Continued

Dye	pH	No. of electrodes	Operating conditions	% Color removal	Ref.
Textile	7.3-8.2	Al electrodes S = 0.6 cm diameter, 11 cm length, 6 connected electrodes forming anode, 6 connected electrodes forming cathode e = 2 mm	C_i: COD = 1316 mg l^{-1} TSS = 830 mg l^{-1} TDS = 4274 mg l^{-1} t_r = 5 min Current density = 300 Am^{-2} V = 2L Batch reactor	TSS =99 COD = 62	[138]
Textile	8.04-8.64	Mild steel electrodes S = 0.6 cm diameter, 11 cm length 6 connected electrodes forming anode, 6 connected electrodes forming cathode, e = 2 mm	C_i: COD = 530.7 mg l^{-1} TSS = 1500 mg l^{-1} TDS = 9190 mg l^{-1} Current density = 151.5-252.5 Am^{-2} t_r = 20-30 min V = 2L Batch reactor	TSS = 97 COD = 54	[139]
Three reactive dye bath of absorbance: 436, 525 and 620nm	5	6 monopolar Al electrodes Dimensions: (cylindrical) 11.9 × 1.02 cm e = 2 mm	C_i : A$_{436}$ = 0.532, A525 = 0.693, A620 = 0.808 (absorbance, cm^{-1}) Current density = 220 Am^{-2} t_r = 90 min Batch reactor	95	[140]
		6 monopolar St. St electrodes Dimensions: (cylindrical) 11.9 × 1.02 cm e = 2 mm	C_i : A$_{364}$ = 0.532, A$_{525}$ = 0.693, A$_{620}$ = 0.808 (absorbance, cm^{-1}) Current density = 220 Am^{-2} t_r = 60 min Batch reactor	99	
Procion Black 5B-Reactive dye	7-10	2 electrodes Al anode St. St. cathode 2 electrodes Fe anode St. St. cathode	V = 400 mL Current density = 100 Am^{-2} Batch reactor V = 400 ml Current density = 50 Am^{-2} Batch reactor	87.93 97.06	[108]

C_i is the initial concentration of dye; S is the surface area; e. is the electrode distance; t_r is the retention time; V is volume of solution; F.R. is flow rate; PAC = polyaluminium chloride, MSS is magnetic stirring speed.

8.1. Effect of pH

It has been established that pH is an important operating parameter influencing the performance of the electrochemical process [20, 21, 42]. Generally, pH of the medium changes during the process [43, 80]. This change depends on the type of electrode material and on initial pH. The effect of pH can be explained as follows. For aluminum electrode, at low pH, (2–3), cationic monomeric species Al^{3+} and $Al(OH)_2^+$ are predominate. When pH is between 4–9, the Al^{3+} and OH^- ions generated by the aluminum electrodes react to form various monomeric species such as $Al(OH)_2^+$, $Al(OH)_2^{2+}$, and polymeric species such as

$Al_6(OH)_{15}^{3+}$, $Al_7(OH)_{17}^{4+}$, $Al_{13}O_4(OH)_{24}^{7+}$, $Al_{13}(OH)_{34}^{5+}$ and finally transform into insoluble amorphous $Al(OH)_{3(s)}$ through complex polymerization mechanism and precipitated. When pH is higher than 8, the monomeric $Al(OH)_4^-$ anion concentration increases, reducing the significance of solid $Al(OH)_{3(s)}$. When the value of pH is higher than 10, the monomeric anion, $Al(OH)_4^-$, is increased and $Al(OH)_{3(s)}$ is decreased. In addition, the cathode may be chemically corroded by OH^- ions generated together with H_2 at high pH values. Therefore, the dye removal ratios of initial pH 4-9 were larger than those of initial pH larger than 10.

Two main mechanisms are generally considered: precipitation for pH lower than 4 and adsorption for higher pH. Adsorption may proceed on $Al(OH)_3$ or on monomeric $Al(OH)_4^-$ anion depending on the pollutant chemical structure. The formation of $Al(OH)_{3(s)}$ is therefore optimal in the 4–9 pH range [118, 126, 130, 141, 142].

Numerous workers studied the effect of the solution pH on the efficiency of the EC process. Kim et al. [142] studied the effect of pH of the solution on the removal of Reactive Blue 49 (RB-49), Reactive Yellow 84 (RY-84), Disperse Blue 106 (DB-106), and Disperse Yellow 54 (DY-54) by EC. They found that the pH value of the solution had no significant influence on the dye removal as long as the initial pH was kept between 4 and 9, which is close to the optimal pH for $Al(OH)_{3(s)}$ formation. They found that the dye removal decreased slowly from pH 4 to 9 but decreased rapidly from pH 10 to 12. The importance of pH in regard to coagulation has been well documented. In A1 anodes are used, the main mechanism of coagulation at pH 2-3 is double-layer compression, while the coagulation is carried out by adsorption, charge neutralization or enmeshment/entrapment at initial pH ranged between 4 to 9.

Gürses et al. [113] studied the effects of temperature, pH, and concentrations of the cationic surfactant and electrolyte concentration on the removal of Remazol Red (RB) textile dye. They showed that as pH increases, the solubility of the solid aluminum hydroxide increases, which causes an increase in the negative charge density of solid matrix, because of the adsorption on solid matrix of surfactant ions and $Al(OH)_4^-$ ions produced at high pH values. High settling velocities were observed in pH 10.05 and 10.15 indicating that the compact flocs were produced. This production was done as the additional negative charge acquired by adsorption of ions on solid matrix increases flocs stability.

The decolorization of the Levafix Orange (LO) textile dye solution by electrocoagulation using aluminum sacrificial anode has been investigated by Kobya et al. [122]. They concluded that the decolorization efficiency decreased slowly with increased in pH from 3 to 9, while the efficiency decreased rapidly at pH values above 9. Maximum (99.9%) and minimum (76.6%) decolorization efficiencies occurred at pH values of 3 and 11, respectively, which indicate that the higher decolorization efficiency is obtained in acidic to neutral mediums.

Essadki et al. [143] applied a 20 L external-loop airlift reactor as an electrochemical cell to carry out water pollution removal using batch electrocoagulation without mechanical agitation, pumping requirements or air injection. Mixing and complete flotation of the pollutants were achieved by the overall liquid recirculation induced by H_2 micro-bubbles generated by water electrolysis. They used a Red Dye from the Moroccan textile industry to validate this innovative application of airlift reactors, which drives the overall liquid circulation by the gas hold-up difference between the riser (ε_r) and the down-comer (ε_d), and also from the dispersion height. The gas hold-up is defined as the ratio of volume occupied by the gas phase over the total volume of the corresponding section. Dispersion height (h_D)

corresponds to the distance from the surface in which a gas phase can be observed in the riser. On the other hand, wall friction effects oppose to the overall liquid circulation. The influence of the initial pH on COD and turbidity removals was studied and found for the initial pH values ranged between 7.0 and 8.0 are the optimal pH. EC process exhibits some buffering capacity because of the balance between the production and the consumption of OH^-, which prevents high change in pH. The buffering pH seems just above 7; pH decreases during EC when the initial pH is above 7, otherwise, the opposite behavior is observed.

8.2. Effect of Electrode Number

Kim et al. [142] studied the number of electrodes using 4.45 mA cm^{-2} of current density, 1 cm of electrode gap, 500 mg l^{-1} of Disperse Blue 106 (DB-106), 100 ml min^{-1} of flow rate and 1.0 g l^{-1} of NaCl. They found that the electrical conductivity is directly proportional to cross-sectional area. Increase of the number of electrodes causes proportionally increase in the cross-sectional area for the current supply. High current efficiency was also caused by the large surface area of the electrode. Increase of the electrode number from four to seven pairs causes increases in the dye removal ratio from 87.9% to 98.3%. However, the increases in dye removal and k value between six and seven pairs were relatively small. Conversely, the power consumption disproportionally decreased as the number of pairs of electrode was increased.

8.3. Effect of Initial Dye Concentration

Merzouk et al. [121] carried out a study on removal of dispersive Red Dye from its aqueous solution using an EC cell, with a total initial concentration (C_i) varied between 25 and 200 mg l^{-1}. Their results showed that the continuous EC process gave satisfactory results for all the concentrations studied, as % dye removal was always higher than 80% in the exit stream of the EC cell. When the dye concentration increased from 25 to 100 mg l^{-1}, the dye concentration in the effluents C_f decreased from about 11 to 4 mg l^{-1}. This behavior may stem both from a thermodynamic limitation resulting from the shape of the adsorption isotherm and from a kinetic limitation at low C_i values. The kinetic limitation seems however to be the most probable because of the dye concentrations used: when C_i decreases, longer residence times are required to achieve dye removal. Conversely, % dye removal decreased from 96 to 89% when C_i was increased from 100 to 200 mg l^{-1} and C_f doubled approximately. This shows clearly that the adsorption capacity of the flocs became exhausted when C_i was higher than 100 mg l^{-1}, as the total amount of sludge was constant for all concentrations at constant current density. The EC process is robust because it can achieve more than 80% color removal for C_i between 25 and 200 mg l^{-1}.

Direct Red 81 (DR-81) dye removal was investigated by Aoudj et al. [118] using different dye concentrations ranged from 25 to 200 mg l^{-1} under constant current intensity. They reported that increasing initial dye concentration led to decrease in removal efficiency, for example, when the initial concentration increased from 25 to 200 mg l^{-1}, the removal percentage was decreased from 98.86% to 76.86%. They reported that for DR-81 dye, the lower dye concentration is the better decolorization efficiency. Adsorption on aluminum hydroxide is the main dye molecule removal pathway, so, for a constant current intensity, there is obviously the same amount of electro generated aluminum cations and hence the same amount of coagulating species. This may led toless available adsorption sites to capture dye molecules in high concentrations.

Crystal Violet (CV) Dye removal was studied by Durango-Usuga *et al.* [130], and they concluded that by increasing the dye concentration, there is an evident increase in the elimination rate of the dye. Mollah *et al.* [126] studied the effect of dye concentrations (10–50 $\mu g\ l^{-1}$) on the removal of Orange II (O-II) azo dye using the EC process by applying constant current density (120 A m^{-2}), 4 g l^{-1} of NaCl concentration and constant temperature of the dye solution (25°C). They found that the O-II dye removal efficiency decreased almost linearly with increasing dye concentration. The highest dye removal efficiency (~86.5%) was obtained at 10.0 $\mu g\ l^{-1}$, while the lowest dye removal efficiency (~37.0%) was attained at 50.0 $\mu g\ l^{-1}$ The lower dye removal efficiency at higher dye concentration was caused by less than required number of coagulant, $Al(OH)_{n(s)}$ species generated from the sacrificial anode for a given conductivity and applied current density. However, the dye removal efficiency at higher concentration may be enhanced by lowering the flow rate of the solution in the EC cell.

Kim *et al.*, [142] studied the removal of Reactive Blue 49 (RB-49), Reactive Yellow 84 (RY-84), Disperse Blue 106 (DB-106) and Disperse Yellow 54 9dy-54) dyes using EC technique. They investigated the effects of dyes concentration and power consumption on the EC efficiency of dye removal. They used initial dye concentrations ranged between 200 and 1000 mgl^{-1} and found that, as the concentration of dyes increased from 200 to 1000 mg l^{-1}, the dye removal ratio decreased from 97.5 to 69.2%. However, between 200 and 500 mg l^{-1} of dyes concentration, the decreases in the dyes removal was not relatively significant; thus, the effect of initial dyes concentration between 200 and 500 mg l^{-1} on the removal efficiency of EC was small. While increase of initial dyes concentration above 500 mg l^{-1} required increasing of the amounts of coagulant produced electrochemically to maintain the removal efficiency constant.

Gürses *et al.* [113] studied the removal of Remazol Red RB textile dye to investigate the effects of temperature, pH, and concentrations of the cationic surfactant and electrolyte concentration on the settling velocity of the simulated textile wastewater. They reported that the settling velocity decreased with the increase of the initial dye concentration, for example, the settling velocity at -75 mg l^{-1} was lower than it at 25 mg l^{-1}, as well as, the average mean size at 75 mg l^{-1} was higher than at 25 mg l^{-1}. Because the settling velocity is significantly depend on floc characteristics, the dye concentration may affect floc characteristics. They observed an increase in the settling velocity at 1 mg l^{-1}, and a decrease in average floc size was measured. While changing dye concentrations from 25 mg l^{-1} to 75 mg l^{-1}, the average floc size increases, which suggested that low-density flocs are produced at 75 mg l^{-1}. This proves well with the fact that decreased electrostatic repulsions among charged flocs in suspensions may destabilize the dispersions. The low stable dispersions result in the production of low density flocs due to the neutralization between negatively charged dye molecules and positively charged polymer molecules.. Therefore, settling velocity decreases with decreasing flocs density. However, they observed an increase in the settling velocities after 75 mg l^{-1}, which may be due to the electrostatic stability acquired by inversion of the surface charge of flocs in high dye concentrations, and also may be attributed to the production of compact flocs. The settling velocity index (SVI) was investigated and was found to be high (170 ml g^{-1}) at 25 mg l^{-1} and a low value (95 ml g^{-1}) at 100 mg l^{-1}, another low SVI value (70 ml g^{-1}) was observed at 150 mg l^{-1}.

The effect of initial dye concentration on the removal of the Levafix Orange (LO) textile dye in aqueous solution by EC using aluminum sacrificial anode has been studied by Kobya et al. [122]. They stated that the removal efficiency falls in a linear fashion from 99.6 to 88% with increase in initial dye concentration from 100 to 500 mg l^{-1}. This is likely due to the formation of insufficient number of aluminum hydroxide complexes produced by the electrode to coagulate the greater number of dye molecules at higher concentrations. Therefore, it is quite clear that for LO removal, the lower initial dye concentration is the better removal efficiency.

Golder et al. [144] reported the potential of electrocoagulated metals hydroxide sludge (EMHS) generated during removal of Cr^{3+} using Al electrode for adsorption of Congo Red (CR) from aqueous solution. They studied the effect of initial CR day concentration of 100, 200 and 300 mg l^{-1} on the removal efficiency of EC process. Their study showed that 51.8% of CR dye was removed within 1st 10 min using 100 mg l^{-1}, whereas 27.3 and 18.7% were removed within the 1st 10 min when 200 and 300 mg l^{-1} initial day concentrations are used, respectively. However, corresponding cumulative mass of CR dye removed were slightly increased from 64.75 to 70.13 mg g^{-1} with increase in initial concentration from 100 to 300 mg g^{-1}, which may be attributed to more effective contact with higher number density of dye molecules in solution.

8.4. Effect of Current Density

Operating current density is critical in batch electrocoagulation, as it is the only operational parameter that can be controlled directly. In this system electrode spacing is fixed and current is a continuous supply. Current density directly determines both coagulant dosage and bubble generation rates, as well as strongly influencing both solution mixing and mass transfer at the electrodes. The current density is expected to exhibit a strong effect on EC process especially on the kinetics of turbidity removal; the higher the current is the shorter the treatment required, which ascribed to the fact that at high current density, the dissolution of aluminum anode increases, resulting in a greater amount of precipitate for the removal of pollutants. Moreover, bubble generation rate increases and the bubble size decreases with increasing current density. These effects are both beneficial for high pollutant removal by H$_2$ flotation [118, 126, 130, 141, 142].

Merzouk et al. [127] investigated the effect of current density and inter electrode distance on the efficiency of turbidity removal using EC–EF process carried out using various current densities and distance between the electrodes. They used current density from 11.55 to 91.5 mA cm^{-2}, and electrode gap ranged from 1 to 3 cm. When the current density was increased from 11.55 to 91.5 mA cm^{-2} and the electrode gap varied from 1 to 3 cm, the turbidity removal efficiency decreased. The optimal values for the current density, electrode gap and EC time for removal of the simulated wastewater were shown to be 11.55 mA cm^{-2}, 1 cm, and 10 min, respectively, to have 89% turbidity removal efficiency. They also concluded that the turbidity has a very particular variation: it increases at the beginning of treatment under the effect of the accumulation of the aluminum hydroxide in the polymer form to reach very strong values.

The negative removal efficiencies of the turbidity at low times and high current densities can be explained as follows: dissolved aluminum is polymerized in the shape of aluminum hydroxide and thus increases turbidity. In the second period of the run, turbidity reaches a low level, in particular for low current density. For larger current densities, the steady-state plateau of the remaining turbidity was far higher, likely because of the presence of Al hydroxides in excess. The decrease of turbidity removal with increased current density is also due to the adsorption of the hydrogen bubbles produced by the electrodes; although the cathode is perforated, hydrogen bubbles adsorb on the lower face of cathode and remain blocked on this area.

Mollah et al. [126] studied EC-floc removal of Orange II dye using 120 -160 mA cm^{-2} and 30 µg l^{-1}. They found the removal efficiency did not change significantly. However, inhibition efficiency increased from 61.0% at 120 mA cm^{-2} to 83.0% at 215 mA cm^{-2}. Further increase of current density did not change the dye removal efficiency significantly; it is, however, advisable to limit the current density in order to avoid excessive evolution of hydrogen and other gases as well as to minimize other adverse effect including higher cost of operation.

8.5. Effect of Conductivity

Sodium chloride (NaCl) is usually employed to increase the conductivity of the water or wastewater to be treated. Wastewater conductivity affects faradic yield, cell voltage and therefore energy consumption in EC cells. In addition, increasing water conductivity using NaCl has other advantages: e.g., chloride anions could significantly reduce the adverse effects of other anions, such as HCO_3^- and SO_4^{2-}. Indeed, the existence of carbonate anion would lead to the precipitation of Ca^{2+} ion. These can form an insulating layer on the surface of the cathode (Equations 25 and 26), which could increase the ohmic resistance of the electrochemical cell.

$$HCO_3^- + OH^- \rightarrow CO_3^{2-} + H_2O \qquad (25)$$

$$Ca^{2+} + CO_3^{2-} \rightarrow CaCO_3 \qquad (26)$$

Conversely, an excessive amount of NaCl induces an over consumption of the aluminum electrodes due to "corrosion pitting"; Al dissolution may become irregular [141].

Aoudj et al. [118] studied the effect of salt type on dye removal efficiency using NaCl, Na_2SO_4, $NaNO_3$ and Na_2CO_3 as supporting electrolytes (SE) with a concentration of 2 g l^{-1}. Runs were performed at initial pH 6 and current density of 1.875 mA cm^{-2}. The higher removal rates are achievable with NaCl as supporting electrolyte comparing to other salts. The lower rates are encountered in the presence of carbonate. It is well known that Cl$^-$ anions can destroy the formed passivation layer on aluminum electrode and therefore enhance anodic dissolution rate of metal which lead to produce more aluminum hydroxide. It has been reported that carbonate has strong affinity to Al(OH)$_3$. The observed reduction in dye removal in the presence of CO_3^{2-} may be due to competition for adsorption sites on aluminum hydroxide from this anion and dye molecules. The inhibiting effect of carbonate may be also due to the passivation of anode which hinders the dissolution process.

9. ELECTROCOAGULATION FUTURE RESEARCH NEEDED

Electrocoagulation is an enigmatic technology has a very complex chemical and physical system, which has not been delineated. Despite having been widely used for over a century, there appears to be no real consensus on the most appropriate approach for any given application, little in the way of systematic reactor design rules, and almost nothing in the way of a generic a priori modeling approach. The root cause of this situation seems to be that electrocoagulation is a technology that lies at the intersection of three more fundamental technologies: (i) electrochemistry, (ii) coagulation and (iii) flotation. Each of these three technologies is well-studied in its own right. The voltage ranges used are found in anodization and electrolysis but are not commonly used in fundamental electrochemical studies. Therefore, there is a need for fundamental electrochemical studies of both the interfacial reactions affecting the electrodes and the multiphase reactions in these voltage ranges.

The overpotential required for EC performance (η_{AP}) is the result of three components equation 2, where η_k is the kinetic overpotential, which may have several contributions such as gas evolution, η_{Mt} is the mass transfer overpotential, and η_{IR} is the IR-drop due to solution and electrode deposits. The solution part of the η_{IR} is controlled by equation 3, where I is the current (A), d is the distance between the electrodes, A is the active electrode surface area, and κ is the specific conductivity (10^3 mSm^{-1}). The IR drop is reduced by lowering d and increasing A and κ. The effects of these changes need to be precisely studied for specific types of chemical and physical species in aqueous solutions. Moreover, the detailed effects of the electric field gradient on the relevant interfacial and solution reactions need more investigation, and the nature of the deposits on the electrodes need better characterization as well as the influences of pH and electrochemical potentials on both solution phase and interfacial reactions need further study. It is clear from the published literature that what is lacking is a quantitative appreciation of the way in which these technologies interact to provide an electrocoagulation system. For electrocoagulation to play a wider role as an accepted and dependable water treatment technology, research is required that focuses neither on simply making a specific (contaminant-centered) application work nor on any one of the foundation technologies, but rather the emphasis needs to be on explaining and quantifying the key interactions between electrochemistry, coagulation and flotation. Experimentation and modeling of these reactions need to be done to establish steady-state and equilibrium status. Reactions under kinetic control need to be established and their controlling parameters defined [22, 24, 25, 80].

Scheme 3 shows one possible conceptual framework explains that each foundation area brings a certain perspective to electrocoagulation, as represented by each lobe of this Venn diagram, which aims to show how the complexity of EC can be simplified using a reductionist approach. Relevant phenomena, characterization methods and tools are highlighted. Information presented in the intersection between two lobes represents knowledge that links the foundation areas. For example, thermodynamic modeling of the solution chemistry of hydrolyzed metal cations links the electro-chemistry and coagulation lobes. Central to understanding and describing electrocoagulation as a whole are the contact pattern (i.e. mixing) and process kinetics. The first of these describes how the various species (coagulant, contaminant particles, and bubbles) move and are brought into proximity with each other, while the latter describes the rate at which interactions between the various species occurs. Hence, these aspects are placed at the intersection of all three lobes. It is a combination of physico-chemical processes occurring within an electrocoagulation reactor that shifts the dominant contaminant separation mechanism between settling (gravity driven) and flotation (buoyancy driven). The vertical arrows in Scheme 3 represent these two removal paths with the relative importance of each being set by a combination of reactor design and operating parameters. As an example, current density (represented by a double-headed arrow at the base of Scheme 3) shifts the relative importance between the flotation and coagulation lobes, as it determines both the coagulant dosage and bubble production rates, as well as influencing the extent of mixing within a reactor. The message here is that decisions about reactor design cannot be made in isolation, as there is an inseparable link between design and operational parameters brought about by the complex interactions between the three foundation technologies. In many areas of engineering, short-cut methods (such as the correlation of experimental data via dimensionless analysis) have been successfully employed as design/operational tools long before a process has been understood at a mechanistic level. However the electrocoagulation literature is almost completely devoid of such short-cut (or scale-up) methods, a testimony to the complexity of the process and the myriad possible interactions occurring within. Indeed it is the authors' view that meaningful short-cut methods will never be developed for general application to electrocoagulation and that in terms of research effort it would be a mistake to pursue such a goal. Rather electrocoagulation is a process where some level of mechanistically based mathematical modeling is almost certainly required for the technology to progress beyond its present state of enlightened empiricism. Thus the future focus should be on quantifying the interactions that occur between each of the three underlying technologies (i.e. the lobes in Scheme 3) for a range of systems where the pollutant itself can be readily quantified [22, 100].

10. CONCLUSIONS

EC is still an empirically optimized process that requires more fundamental understanding for improved engineering design and the fact that electrocoagulation is being successfully applied to contaminated water is testament to its potential which is yet to be fully realized. The EC comprises complex chemical and physical processes involving many surface and interfacial phenomena. Clearly more fundamental information is needed on the physical chemistry involved in EC process. There is, however, a paucity of scientific understanding of these phenomena, which limits the engineering design of EC reactor for optimum performance and future progress of this novel and innovative technology. This technology will continue to make inroads into the water treatment arena because of numerous advantages and the nature of the changing strategic water needs in the world.

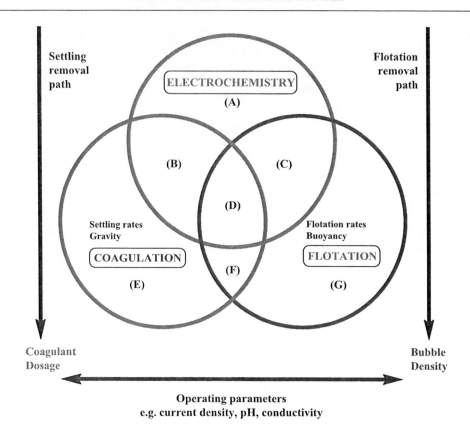

Scheme 3. Venn diagram represents the relationship between scientific bases of electrocoagulation process. (A) Electrochemical characterization such as kinetics, power, passivation, half-cell reactions, and electrodes material and their arrangement; (B) coagulant produced, thermodynamic model, solution chemistry, pH, speciation, and hydrolyzed metal salts; (C) electrolytic gases produced, gas type, agitation, and mixing due to bubbles; (d) electrocoagulation contact patterns and kinetics; (E) particle characterization such as particle size distribution, zeta potential and fractal dimension; (F) force balance between gravity and buoyancy (dissolved air flotation); (G) bubble characterization such as bubble size, bubble distribution and bubble density.

From the electrochemical, surface and interfacial chemical and aqueous chemical perspective there appear to be several approaches that can be taken based on fundamental principles. Hydrogen evolution would have to be controlled by the size of the cathodic reaction area and the electrode overpotential of hydrogen evolution. At the same time, an anode would have to carry out several fundamental processes at highest efficiencies. These include a corrodable part, which supplies the polyvalent coagulant ions to the solution at the lowest overpotential, a part that must be an efficient electro-oxidation catalyst to form charged organics by partial oxidation, and an oxygen evolution part, that must generate the oxygen at the highest efficiency but in controlled amounts. The latter may be achieved by limiting the oxygen evolution electrode area. Electro-oxidation catalysts are available for shallow oxidation. These may be achieved by composite electrodes or unique multi-electrode arrangements. In addition, the presence of sacrificial surfactants at low concentration may be helpful to improve the efficiency of the coagulation process and ad/absorption processes. In addition the ionic make-up of the solution may be adjustable for optimization of the processes involved.

The electrocoagulation technology is considered to be potentially an effective tool for treatment of color from textile wastewaters with high removal efficiency. The removal efficiency was found to be dependent on the initial pH, the dye concentration, the applied current density, and the electrolysis time in batch model. The capacity and efficiency of the EC process for treatment of industrial wastewaters was found to be dependent on the nature of the liquid waste and initial pollutant concentrations. Research studies showed that EC process is more efficient than coagulation process for potable water treatment. Less aluminum dosage was needed to get the same removal efficiency in EC process, which is related to chemical cost and sludge production.

This chapter addresses electrocoagulation's surprising lack of acceptance as a mainstream option and puts forward the following reasons for this failure by identifying deficiencies in a number of key areas:

(i)   The lack of any systematic evaluation of existing applications leading to an agreed set of guidelines suitable for the design/operation of new applications.

(ii) An almost complete lack of detailed experimental data on the operation of batch electrocoagulation reactors, one of the more suitable options for (modest size scale) localized water treatment.

(iii) No widely applicable mechanistically based approach to the mathematical modeling of electrocoagulation reactors.

(iv) Failure to fully appreciate that the performance of an electrocoagulation reactor is largely determined by the interactions that occur between the three 'foundations Technologies' of electrochemistry, coagulation and flotation. No generic solution to the problem of electrode passivation.

REFERENCES

[1]   WHO/Unicef (2000). Global water supply and sanitation assessment 2000 report. *World Health Organization and United Nations Children's Fund*, USA.

[2]   Asmal, P.K. (2000). Water is a catalyst for peace. In: *Stockholm Water Symposium Laureate Lecture World Commission on Dams*, Stockholm.

[3]   Clarke, E.A. & Anliker, R. (1980). Organic dyes and pigments. In: *Handbook of environmental chemistry, anthropogenic compounds*, 3, part A. New York: Springer-Verlag, p. 181-215.

[4]   Zollinger, H. (1987). Azo dyes and pigments. *Color chemistry-synthesis, properties and applications of organic dyes and pigments*. New York: VCH, p. 92-100.

[5]   Mishra, G., & Tripathy, M. (1993). A critical review of the treatment for decolourization of textile effluent. *Colourage*, 40: 35-38.

[6]   Banat, I.M., Nigam, P., Singh, D., & Marchant, R. (1996). Microbial decolourization of textile-dye containing effluents: a review. *Bioresource Technology*, 58: 217–227.

[7]   Fu, Y., & Viraraghavan, T. (2001). Fungal decolorization of wastewaters: a review. *Bioresource Technology*, 79: 251–262.

[8]   Robinson, T., Mcmullan, G., Marchant, R., & Nigam, P. (2001). Remediation of dyes in textile effluent: a critical review on current treatment technologies with a proposed alternative. *Bioresource Technology*, 77: 247–255.

[9]   Hu, T.L. (1992). Sorption of reactive dyes by Aeromonas biomass. *Water Science and Technology*, 26: 357–366.

[10] Juang, R.-S., Tseng, R.-L., Wu, F.-C., & Lee, S.-H. (1997). Adsorption behavior of reactive dyes from aqueous solutions on chitosan. *Journal of Chemical Technology and Biotechnology*, 70: 391–399.

[11] Karcher, S., Kornmuller, A., & Jekel, M. (2000). Removal of reactive dyes by sorption/complexation with cucurbituril. *Water Science and Technology*, 40: 425–433.

[12] Sumathi, S., & Manju, B.S. (2000). Uptake of reactive textile dyes by *Aspergillusfoetidus*. *Enzyme Microbial Technology*, 27: 347–355.

[13] Aksu, Z., & Tezer, S. (2000). Equilibrium and kinetic modeling of biosorption of Remazol Black B by *R. arrhizus* in a batch system: effect of temperature. *Process Biochemistry*, 36: 431–439.

[14] O'Mahony, T., Guibal, E., & Tobin, J.M. (2002). Reactive dye biosorption by *Rhizopusarrhizus* biomass. *Enzyme Microbial Technology*, 31: 456–463.

[15] Moran, C., Hall, M.E., & Howell, R.C. (1997). Effects of sewage treatment on textile effluent. *Journal Society of Dyers Colour*, 113: 272–274.

[16] Mittal, A.K., & Gupta, S.K. (1996). Biosorption of cationic dyes by dead macro fungus *Fomitopsiscarnea*: batch studies. *Water Science Technology*, 34: 157–181.

[17] Chu, H.C., & Chen, K.M. (2002). Reuse of activated sludge biomass: I. Removal of basic dyes from wastewater by biomass. *Process Biochemistry*, 37: 595–600.

[18] Fu, Y., & Viraraghavan, T. (2002). Removal of Congo Red from an aqueous solution by fungus *Aspergillusniger*. *Advances in Environmental Research*, 7: 239–247.

[19] Gupta, G.S., Prasad, G., & Singh, V.N. (1997). Removal of chrome dye from aqueous solutions by mixed adsorbents: fly ash and coal. *Water Research*, 24: 45–50.

[20] Do, J.-S. & Chen, M.-L. (1994). Decolorization of dye-containing solutions by electrocoagulation. *Journal of Applied Electrochemistry*, 24: 785-790.

[21]   Lin, S.H., & Chen, M.L. (1997). Treatment of textile wastewater by electrochemical methods for reuse. *Water Research*, 31: 868-876.

[22] Holt, P.K., Barton, G.W., & Mitchell, C.A. (2005). The future for electrocoagulation as a localized water treatment technology. *Chemosphere*, 59: 355–367.

[23] Calvo, L.S., Leclerc, J.P., Tanguy, G., Cames, M.C., Paternotte, G., Valentin, G., Rostan, A., & Lapicque, F. (2003). An electrocoagulation unit for the purification of soluble oil wastes of high COD. *Environmental Progress*, 22: 57–65.

[24] Mollah, M.Y.A., Schennach, R., Parga, J.R., & Cocke, D.L. (2001). Electrocoagulation (EC) science and applications, *Journal of Hazardous Materials*, 84: 29–41.

[25] Mollah, M.Y.A., Morkovsky, P., Gomes, J.A.G., Kesmez, M., Parga, J., & Cocke, D.L. (2004). Fundamentals, present and future perspectives of electrocoagulation. *Journal of Hazardous Materials*, 114: 199–210.

[26] El-Geundi, M.S. (1991). Color removal from textile effluents by adsorptiontechniques. *Water Research*, 25: 271–273.

[27] McKay, G., & Poots, J.P. (1980). Kinetics and diffusion processes in color removal from effluent using wood as an adsorbent. *Journal of Chemical Technology Biotechnology*, 30: 279–292.

[28] Lambert, S.D., Graham, N.J.D., & Sollars, C.J. (1997). Fowler, G.D. Evaluation ofinorganic adsorbents for the removal of problematic textile dyesand pesticides. *Water Science and Technology*, 36: 173–180.

[29] Low, K.S., & Lee, C.K. (1997). Quaternized rice husk as sorbent for reactivedyes. *Bioresource Technology*, 61: 121–115.

[30] Ramakrishna, K.R., & Viraraghavan, T. (1997). Dye removal using low costadsorbents. *Water Science and Technology*, 36: 189–196.

[31] Morais, L.C., Freitas, O.M., Gonçalves, E.P., Vasconcelos, L.T., & GonzalezBeça, C.G. (1999). Reactive dyes removal from wastewaters by adsorption eucalyptus bark: variables that define the process. *Water Research*, 33: 979–988.

[32] Ho, Y.S., & McKay, G. (1999). Comparative sorption kinetic studies of dye and aromatic compounds onto fly ash. *Journal of Environmental Science and Health*, A34: 1179–1204.

[33] Otero, M., Rozada, F., Calvo, L.F., Garcia, A.I., & Moran, A. (2003). Kinetic andequilibrium modeling of the methylene blue removal from solutionby adsorbent materials produced from sewage sludge. *Biochemical Engineering Journal*, 15: 59–68.

[34] Slokar, Y.M., & Le Marechal, A.M. (1997). Methods of decoloration of textile wastewaters. *Dyes and Pigments*, 37: 335–356.

[35] Lee, C.K., Low, K.S., & Gan, P.Y. (1999). Removal of some organic dyes byacid-treated spent bleaching earth. *Process Biochemistry*, 34: 451–465.

[36] Aksu, Z. (2005). Application of biosorption for the removal of organic pollutants: a review. *Process Biochemistry*, 40: 997-1026.

[37] Cañizares, P., Martinez, F., Carmona, M., Lobato, J., & Rodrigo, M.A. (2005). Continuous electrocoagulation of synthetic colloid-polluted wastes. *Industrials Engineering and Chemistry Research*, 44: 8171–8177.

[38] Carmona, M., Khemis, M., Lecler, J.-P., & Lapicque, F. (2006). A simple model to predict the removal of oil suspensions from water using the electrocoagulation technique. *Chemical Engineering Science*, 61: 1237–1246.

[39] Rajeshwar, K., Ibanez, J. G., & Swain, G.M. (1994). Electrochemistry and the environment. *Journal of Applied Electrochemistry*, 24: 1077-1091.

[40] Pogrebnaya, V.L., Klimenko, A.A., Bokovikova, T.N., Tsymbal, E.P., & Pronina, N.P. (1995). Purification of waste water of heavy metals by electrocoagulation. *Chemistry and Petroleum Engineering*, 31: 280-281.

[41] Balasubramanian, N., & Madhavan, K. (2001). Arsenic removal from industrial effluent through electrocoagulation. *Chemical Engineering and Technology*, 24:519-521.

[42] Chen, G., Chen, X., & Yue, P.L. (2000a). Electrocoagulation and electroflotation of restaurant wastewater. *Journal of Environmental Engineering*, 126: 858-863.

[43] Chen, X., Chen, G., & Yue, P.L. (2000b). Separation of pollutant from restaurant wastewater by electrocoagulation. Separation and Purification Technology, 19: 65-76.

[44] Barrera-Diaz, C., Roa-Morales, G., Avila-Cordoba, L., Pavon-Silva, T., & Bilyeu, B. (2006). Electrochemical treatment applied to food-processing industrial wastewater. *Industrials Engineering and Chemistry Research*, 45: 34–38.

[45] Biswas, N., & Lazarescu, G. (1991). Removal of oil from emulsions using electrocoagulation. *International Journal of Environmental Study*, 38: 65-75.

[46] Adhoum, N., & Monser, L. (2004). Decolorization and removal of phenolic compounds from olive mill wastewater by electrocoagulation. *Chemical Engineering Process*, 43: 1281–1287.

[47] Un, U.T., Ugur, S., Koparal, A.S., & Ogutveren, U.B. (2006). Electrocoagulation of olive mill wastewaters. *Separation and Purification Technology*, 52: 136–141.

[48] Irdemez, S., Demircioglu, N., & Yildiz, Y.S. (2006). The effects of pH on phosphate removal from wastewater by electrocoagulation with iron plate electrodes. *Journal of Hazardous Materials*, 137: 1231–1235.

[49] Golder, A.K., Samanta, A.N., & Ray, S. (2006b). Removal of phosphate from aqueous solutions using calcined metal hydroxides sludge waste generated from electrocoagulation. *Separation and Purification Technology*, 52: 102–109.

[50] Zor, S., Yazici, B., & Erbil, A. (2006). Removal of linear alkyl benzene sulphonate (LAS) from aqueous solutions by electrocoagulation. *Bulletin Electrochemistry*, 22: 241–248.

[51] Vlyssides, A. G., Loizidou, M., Karlis, P.K., Zorpas, A.A., & Papaioannou, D. (1999). Electrochemical oxidation of a textile dye wastewater using a pt/Ti electrode. *Journal of Hazardous Materials*, 70(1–2): 41-52.

[52] Vlyssides, A. G., Papaioannou, D. P., Loizidoy, M., Karlis, P.K., & Zorpas, A.A. (2000). Testing an electrochemical method for treatment of textile dye wastewater. *Waste Management*, 20: 569-574.

[53] Singh, M.M., Szafran, Z. & Ibanez, J.G., (1998). Laboratory experiments on the electrochemical remediation of environment. Part 4: color removal of simulated wastewater by electrocoagulation-electroflotation. *Journal of Chemical Education*, 75: 1040-1041.

[54] Gürses, A., Yalçin, M., & Dõgar, C. (2002). Electrocoagulation of some reactive dyes: a statistical investigation of some electrochemical. *Waste Management*, 22: 491-499.

[55] Xiong, Y., Strunk, P.J., Xia, H., Zhu, X., & Karlsson, H.T. (2001). Treatment of dye wastewater containing acid orange II using a cell with three-phases three dimensional. *Water Research*, 35(17): 4226-4230.

[56] Mameri, N., Yeddou, A.R., Lounici, H., Belhocine, D., Grib, H., & Bariou, B. (1998). Defluoridation of septentrional Sahara water of North Africa by electrocoagulation process using bipolar aluminum. *Water Research*, 32: 1604-1612.

[57] Panizza, M., Bocca, C., & Cerisola, G. (2000). Electrochemical treatment of wastewater containing polyaromatic organic pollutants. *Water Research*, 34(9): 2601-2605.

[58] Tsai, C. T., Lin, S.T., Shue, Y.C., & Su, P.L. (1997). Electrolysis of soluble organic matter in leachate from landfills. *Water Research*, 31: 3073-3081.

[59] Donini, J.C., Kan, J., Szynkarczuk, J., Hassan, T.A., & Kar, K.L. (1994). Operating cost of electrocoagulation. *Canadian Journal of Chemical Engineering*, 72: 1007–1012.

[60] Abuzaid, N.S., Bukhari, A.A., & Al-Hamouz, Z.M. (2002). Ground water coagulation using soluble stainless steel electrodes. *Advances in Environmental Research*, 6: 325-333.

[61] Szynkarczuk, J., Kan, J., Hassan, T.A.T., & Donini, J.C. (1994). Electrochemical coagulation of clay suspensions.*Clays and Clay Minerals*, 42: 667-673.

[62] Hu, C.Y., Lo, S.L., Kuan, W.H., & Lee, Y.D. (2005). Removal of fluoride from semiconductor wastewater by electrocoagulation–flotation. *Water Research*, 39: 895–901.

[63] Belongia, B. M., Harworth, P.D., Baygents, J.C., & Raghavan, S. (1999). Treatment of Alumina and silica chemical mechanical polishing waste by electrodecantation and electrocoagulation. *Journal of Electrochemical Society*, 146: 4124-4130.

[64] Lai, C.L., & Lin, S.H. (2004). Treatment of chemical mechanical polishing wastewater by electrocoagulation: system performances and sludge settling characteristics, *Chemosphere*, 54: 235–242.

[65] Den, W., Huang, C.P., & Ke, H.C. (2006). Mechanistic study on the continuous flow electrocoagulation of silica nanoparticles from polishing wastewater. *Industrials Engineering and Chemistry Research*, 45 (2006) 3644–3651.

[66] Matteson, M.J., Dobson, R.L., Glenn Jr., R.W., Kukunoor, N.S., Waits III, W.H., & Clayfield, E.J. (1995). Electrocoagulation and separation of aqueous suspensions of ultrafine particles.*Colloids and Surfaces A: Physicochemical Engineering Aspects*, 104: 101-109.

[67] Koparal, S., & Ogutveren, U.B. (2002). Removal of nitrate from water by electroreduction and electrocoagulation. *Journal of Hazardous Materials*, 89(1): 83-94.

[68] Phutdhawong, W., Chowwanapoonpohn, S., & Buddhasukh, D. (2000). Electrocoagulation and Subsequent Recovery of Phenolic Compounds. *Analytical Science*, 16: 1083-1084.

[69] Adhoum, N., Monser, L., Bellakhal, N., & Belgaied, J.E. (2004). Treatment of electroplating wastewater containing Cu^{2+}, Zn^{2+} and Cr^{6+} by electrocoagulation. *Journal of Hazardous Materials*, 112: 207–213.

[70] Murugananthan, M., Bhaskar, & R.G., Prabhakar, S. (2004). Separation of pollutants from tannery effluents by electroflotation. *Separation and Purification Technology*, 40: 69–75.

[71] Gao, P., Chen, X., Shen, F., & Chen, G. (2005). Removal of chromium (VI) from wastewater by combined electrocoagulation–electroflotation without a filter. *Separation and Purification Technology*, 43: 117–123.

[72] Kobya, M., Hiz, H., Senturk, E., Aydiner, C., & Demirbas, E. (2006a). Treatment of potato chips manufacturing wastewater by electrocoagulation, *Desalination*, 190: 201–211.

[73] Sengil, I.A., & Ozacar, M. (2006). Treatment of dairy wastewaters by electrocoagulation using mild steel electrodes. *Journal of Hazardous Materials*, 137: 1197–1205.

[74] Kobya, M., Hiz, H., Senturk, E., Aydiner, C., & Demirbas, E. (2006a). Treatment of potato chips manufacturing wastewater by electrocoagulation, *Desalination*, 190: 201–211.

[75] Bayramoglu, M., Kobya, M., Eyvaz, M., & Senturk, E. (2006). Technical and economic analysis of electrocoagulation for the treatment of poultry slaughterhouse wastewater, *Separation and Purification Technology*, 51: 404–408.

[76] Mahesh, S., Prasad, B., Mall, I.D., & Mishra, I.M. (2006). Electrochemical degradation of pulp and paper mill wastewater. Part 1. COD and color removal, *Industrials Engineering and Chemistry Research*, 45: 2830–2839.

[77] Chiang, L.C., Chang, J.E., & Tseng, S.C. (1997). Electrochemical oxidation pretreatment of refractory organic pollutants. *Water Science and Technology*, 36(2–3): 123-130.

[78] Pouet, M.F., & Grasmick, A. (1995). Urban wastewater treatment by electrocoagulation and flotation. *Water Science and Technology*, 31: 275-283.

[79] Chen, G. (2004). Electrochemical technologies in wastewater treatment. *Separation and Purification Technology*, 38: 11-41.

[80] Vik, E. A., Carlson, D.A., Eikum, A.S., & Gjessing, E.T. (1984). Electrocoagulation of potable water. *Water Research*, 18(11): 1355-1360.

[81] Chen, X., Chen, G., & Yue, P.L. (2002). Investigation on the electrolysis voltage of electrocoagulation. *Chemical Engineering Science*, 57: 2449-2455.

[82] Jiang, J.-Q., Graham, N., Andre, C., Kelsall, G.H., & Brandon, N. (2002). Laboratory study of electro-coagulation-flotation for water treatment. *Water Research*, 36: 4064-4078.

[83] Mollah, M.Y.A., Morkovsky, P., Gomes, J.A.G., Kesmez, M., Parga, J., & Cocke, D.L. (2004). Fundamentals, present and future perspectives of electrocoagulation. *Journal of Hazardous Materials*, 114: 199–210.

[84] Holt, P.K., Barton, G.W., & Mitchell, C.A. (2001). The role of current in determining pollutant removal in a batch electrocoagulation reactor. In: 6th World Congress of Chemical Engineering Conference Media CD, Melbourne, Australia.

[85] Osipenko, V.D., & Pogorelyi, P.I. (1977). Electrocoagulation neutralization of chromium containing effluent. *Metallurgist*, 21: 44–45.

[86] Sanfan, W. (1991). Studies on economic property of pretreatment process of brackish water using electrocoagulation (EC) method. *Desalination*, 82(1–3): 365–373.

[87] Balmer, L.M., & Foulds, A.W. (1986). Separating oil from oil-in water emulsions by electroflocculation/electroflotation. *Filtration and Separation*, 23: 366–370.

[88] Nikolaev, N.V., Kozlovskii, A.S., & Utkin, I.I. (1982). Treating natural waters in small water systems by filtration with electrocoagulation. *Soviet Journal of Water Chemistry and Technology*, 4(3): 244–247.

[89] Weintraub, M.H., Gealer, R.L., Golovoy, A., Dzieciuch, M.A., & Durham, H. (1983). Development of electrolytic treatment of oily wastewater. *Environmental Progress*, 2: 32–37.

[90] Koren, J.P.F., & Syversen, U. (1995). State-of-the-art electroflocculation. *Filtration and Separation*, 32(2): 153–156.

[91] Cerisier, S.D.M., & Smit, J.J. (1996). The electrochemical generation of ferric ions in cooling water as an alternative for ferric chloride dosing to effect flocculation. *Water South Africa*, 22(4): 327–332.

[92] Woytowich, D.L., Dalrymple, C.W., Gilmore, F.W., & Britton, M.G. (1993). Electrocoagulation (CURE) treatment of ship bilge water for the US coast guards in *Alaskan Material Technology Society Journal*, 27: 62–67.

[93] Pouet, M.F., & Grasmick, A. (1995). Urban wastewater treatment by electrocoagulation and flotation. *Water Science and Technology*, 31: 275-283.

[94] Groterud, O., & Smoczynski, L. (1986). Phosphorus removal from water by means of electrolysis. *Water Research*, 20(5): 667–669.

[95] Zabolotsky, V.I., Nikonenko, V.V., Pismenskaya, N.D., & Istoshin, A.G. (1996). Electrodialysis technology for deep demineralization of surface and ground water. *Desalination*, 108(1–3): 179–181.

[96] Barkley, N.P., Farrell, C.W., & Gardner-Clayson, T.W. (1993). Alternating current electrocoagulation for superfund site remediation. *Air Waste*, 43: 784–789.

[97] Pretorius, W.A., Johannes, W.G., & Lampert, G.G. (1991). Electrolytic iron flocculant production with a bipolar electrode in series arrangement. *Water South Africa*, 17(2): 133-138.

[98] Gott, R. (1977). Development of wastewater treatment at the Climax Mine. *American Mining Congress Journal*, 64(4): 28–34.

[99] Rajeshwar, K., & Ibanez, J. (1997). Environmental electrochemistry: fundamentals and applications in pollution abatement. In: Tarr, Matthew A. (Ed.), *Chemical Degradation Methods for Wastes and Pollutants*. Academic USA Press 720 pp.

[100] Emamjomeh, M.M., & Sivakumar, M. (2009). Review of pollutants removed by electrocoagulation and electrocoagulation/flotation processes. *Journal of Environmental Management*, 90: 1663–1679.

[101] Rebhun, M., & Lurie, M. (1993). Cost effective wastewater treatment and recycling in a large industrial complex. *Water Science and Technology*, 27: 1-20.

[102] Can, O.T., Bayramoglu, M., & Kobya, M. (2003). Decolorization of reactive dye solutions by electrocoagulation using aluminum electrodes. *Industrial Engineering and Chemical Research*, 42: 3391–3396.

[103] Modirshahla, N., Behnajady, M.A., & Kooshaiian, S. (2007). Investigation of the effect of different electrode connections on the removal efficiency of Tartrazine from aqueous solutions by electrocoagulation. *Dyes and Pigments*, 74: 249-257.

[104] Daneshvar, N., Khataee, A.R., Ghadim A.R.A., & Rasoulifard, M.H. (2007). Decolorization of C.I. Acid Yellow 23 solution by electrocoagulation process: Investigation of operational parameters and evaluation of specific electrical energy consumption (SEEC). *Journal of Hazardous Materials*, 148: 566-572.

[105] Alinsafi, A., Khemis, M., Pons, M.N., Leclerc, J.P., Yaacoubi, A., Benhammou, A., & Nejmeddine, A. (2005). Electrocoagulation of reactive textile dyes and textile wastewater. *Chemical Engineering and Processing: process intensification*. 44: 461–470.

[106] Cañizares, P., Jimenez, C., Martinez, F., Saez, C., & Rodrigo, M.A. (2007). Study of the electrocoagulation process using aluminum and iron electrodes. *Industrial Engineering Chemistry Research*, 46: 6189–6195.

[107] Picard, T., Cathalifaud-Feuillade, G., Mazet, M., & Vandensteendam, C. (2000).Cathodic dissolution in the electrocoagulation process using aluminum electrodes. *Journal of Environmental Monitoring*, 2: 77–80.

[108] Raghu, S., & Basha, C.A. (2007). Chemical or electrochemical techniques, followed by ion exchange, for recycle of textile dye wastewater. *Journal of Hazardous Materials*, 149: 324–330.

[109] Martinez-Huitle, C.A., & Brillas, E. (2009). Decontamination of wastewaters containing synthetic organic dyes by electrochemical methods: A general review. *Applied Catalysis B: Environmental*, 87: 105-145.

[110] Daneshvar, N., Oladegaragoze, A., & Djafarzadeh, N. (2006). Decolorization of basic dye solutions by electrocoagulation: An investigation of the effect of operational parameters. *Journal of Hazardous Materials*, 129: 116-122.

[111] Aleboyeh, A., Daneshvar, N. & Kasiri., M.B. (2008). Optimization of C.I. Acid Red 14 azo dye removal by electrocoagulation batch process with response surface methodology. *Chemical Engineering and Processing*, 47: 827–832.

[112] Barrera-Diaz, C., Ureña-Nuñez, F., Campos, E., Palomar-Pardavé, M., & Romero-Romo, M. (2003). A combined electrochemical-irradiation treatment of highly colored and polluted industrial wastewater. *Radiation Physical Chemistry*, 67: 657–663.

[113] Gürses, A., Yalcin, M., & Dŏgar, C. (2003). Removal of *Remazol Red RB* by using Al (III) as coagulant-flocculant: Effect of some variables on settling velocity. *Water, Air and Soil Pollution*. 146: 297-318.

[114] Daneshvar, N., Sorkhabi, H.A., & Kasiri, M.B. (2004). Decolorization of dye solution containing Acid Red 14 by electrocoagulation with a comparative investigation of different electrode connections. *Journal of Hazardous Materials*, 112: 55-62.

[115] Kabdaslı, I., Vardar, B., Arslan-Alaton, I. & Tünay, O. (2009). Effect of dye auxiliaries on color and COD removal from simulated reactive dye bath effluent by electrocoagulation. *Chemical Engineering Journal*, 148: 89–96.

[116] Eyvaz, M., Kirlaroglu, M., Aktas, T.S., & Yuksel, E. (2009).The effects of alternating current electrocoagulation on dye removal from aqueous solutions. *Chemical Engineering Journal*, 153: 16–22.

[117] Yalcın, S., & Yildiz, E., (2008). Optimization of Bomaplex Red CR-L dye removal from aqueous solution by electrocoagulation using aluminum electrodes. *Journal of Hazardous Materials*, 153: 194-200.

[118] Aoudj, S., Khelifa, A., Drouiche, N., Hecini, M., & Hamitouche, H., (2010). Electrocoagulation process applied to wastewater containing dyes from textile industry. *Chemical Engineering and Processing*, 49: 1176–1182.

[119] Phalakornkule, C., Polgumhang, S., Tongdaung, W., Karakat, B., & Nuyut, T. (2010). Electrocoagulation of blue reactive, redisperse and mixed dyes, and application in treating textile effluent. *Journal of Environmental Management*, 91: 918-926.

[120] Balla, W., Essadkia, A.H., Gourich, B., Dassaa, A., Chenik, H., & Azzi, M. (2010). Electrocoagulation/electroflotation of reactive, disperse and mixture dyes in an external-loop airlift reactor. *Journal of Hazardous Materials*, 184: 710-716.

[121] Merzouk, B., Gourich, B., Sekki, A., Madani, K., Vial, Ch., & Barkaoui, M. (2009). Studies on the decolorization of textile dye wastewater by continuous electrocoagulation process. *Chemical Engineering Journal*, 149: 207-214.

[122] Kobya, M., Demirbas, E., Can, O.T., & Bayramoglu, M. (2006). Treatment of levafix orange textile dye solution by electrocoagulation. *Journal of Hazardous Materials*, 132: 183-188.

[123] Ayhan, I., Engil, S., & Ozacar, M. (2009). Thedecolorization of C.I. Reactive Black 5 in aqueous solution by electrocoagulation using sacrificial iron electrodes. *Journal of Hazardous Materials*, 161: 1369–1376.

[124] Golder, A.K., Hridaya, N., Samanta, A.N., & Ray, S. (2005). Electrocoagulation of methylene blue and eosin yellowish using mild steel electrodes. *Journal of Hazardous Materials*, 127: 134-140.

[125] Daneshvar, N., Ashassi-Sorkhabi, H., & Tizpar, A. (2003). Decolorization of orange II by electrocoagulation method. *Separation and Purification Technology*, 31: 153-162.

[126] Mollah, Y.M.A., Gomes, J.A.G., Das, K.K., & Cocke, D.L. (2010). Electrochemical treatment of Orange II dye solution—Use of aluminum sacrificial electrodes and floc characterization. *Journal of Hazardous Materials*, 174: 851-858.

[127] Merzouk, B., Madani, K., & Sekki, A. (2010). Using electrocoagulation–electroflotation technology to treat synthetic solution and textile wastewater, two case studies. *Desalination*, 250: 573-577.

[128] Zarei, M., Niaei, A., Salari, D., & Khataee, A.R. (2010). Removal of four dyes from aqueous medium by the peroxi-coagulation method using carbon nanotube–PTFE cathode and neural network modeling. *Journal of Electroanalytical Chemistry*, 639: 167-174.

[129] Korbahti, B.K. (2007). Response surface optimization of electrochemical treatment of textile dye wastewater. *Journal of Hazardous Materials*, 145: 277-286.

[130] Durango-Usuga, P., Guzmán-Duque, F., Mosteo, R., Vazquez, M.V., Penuela, G., & Torres-Palma, R.A. (2010). Experimental design approach applied to the elimination of crystal violet inwater by electrocoagulation with Fe or Al electrodes. *Journal of Hazardous Materials*, 179: 120–126.

[131] Zidane, F., Drogui, P., Lekhlif, B., Bensaid, J., Blais, J.-F., Belcadi, S., & El kacemi, K. (2008). Decolourization of dye-containing effluent using mineral coagulants produced by electrocoagulation. *Journal of Hazardous Materials*, 155: 153-163.

[132] Can, O.T., Kobya, M., Demirbas, E. & Bayramoglu, M. (2006). Treatment of the textile wastewater by combined electrocoagulation. *Chemosphere*, 62: 181-187.

[133] Kobya, M., Can, O.T., & Bayramoglu, M. (2003). Treatment of textile wastewaters by electrocoagulation using iron and aluminum electrodes. *Journal of Hazardous Materials*, 100: 163-178.

[134] Zaroual, Z., Azzi, M., Saib, N., & Chainet, E. (2006). Contribution to the study of electrocoagulation mechanism in basic textile effluent. *Journal of Hazardous Materials*, 131: 73-78.

[135] Aouni, A., Fersi, C., Ali M.B.S., & Dhahbi, M. (2009). Treatment of textile wastewater by a hybrid electrocoagulation/nanofiltration process. *Journal of Hazardous Materials*, 168: 868-874.

[136] Zodi, S., Potier, O., Lapicque, F., & Leclerc, J.-P. (2009). Treatment of the textile wastewaters by electrocoagulation: Effect of operating parameters on the sludge settling characteristics. *Separation and Purification Technology*, 69: 29-36.

[137] Shin, S.-H., Kim, Y.-H., Jung, S.-K., Suh, K.-H., Kang, S.-G., Jeong, S.-K., & Kim, H.-G. (2004). Combined Performance of Electrocoagulation and Magnetic Separation Processes for Treatment of Dye Wastewater. *Korean Journal of Chemical Engineering*, 21(4): 806-810.

[138] Raju , G.B., Karuppiah , M.T., Latha, S.S., Parvathy, S. & Prabhakar, S. (2008). Treatment of wastewater from synthetic textile industry by electrocoagulation–electrooxidation. *Chemical Engineering Journal*, 144: 51-58.

[139] Raju, G.B., Karuppiah M.T., Latha, S.S., Priya, D.L., Parvathy, S., & Prabhakar, S. (2009). Electrochemical pretreatment of textile effluents and effect of electrode materials on the removal of organics. *Desalination*, 249: 167-174.

[140] Arslan-Alaton, I., Kabdaslı, I., Vardar, B., & Tünay, O. (2009). Electrocoagulation of simulated reactive dyebath effluent with aluminum and stainless steel electrodes. *Journal of Hazardous Materials*, 164: 1586–1594.

[141] Merzouka, B., Gourichb, B., Sekkic, A., Madanid, K., Vial, Ch., & Barkaoui, M. (2009). Studies on the decolorization of textile dye wastewater by continuouselectrocoagulation process. *Chemical Engineering Journal*, 149: 207–214.

[142] Kim, T.-H., Park, C., Shin, E.-B., & Kim, S. (2002). Decolorization of disperse and reactive dyes by continuous electrocoagulation process. *Desalination*, 150: 165-175.

[143] Essadki, A.H., Bennajah, M., Gourich, B., Vial, Ch., Azzi, M., & Delmas, H. (2008). Electrocoagulation/electroflotation in an external-loop airlift reactor—Application to the decolorization of textile dye wastewater: A case study. *Chemical Engineering and Processing: Process Intensification*, 47: 1211–1223.

[144] Golder, A.K., Samanta, A.N., & Ray, S. (2006a). Anionic reactive dye removal from aqueous solution using anew adsorbent—Sludge generated in removal of heavy metal by electrocoagulation. *Chemical Engineering Journal*, 122: 107–115.

In: Non-Conventional Textile Waste Water Treatment   ISBN: 978-1-62100-079-2
Editor: Ahmed El Nemr   © 2012 Nova Science Publishers, Inc.

Chapter 8

CLEANER (SUSTAINABLE) PRODUCTION IN TEXTILE WET PROCESSING

*E. Alkaya[1], M. Böğürcü[1], F. Ulutaş[1], G.N.Demirer[2]**
[1]Technology Development Foundation of Turkey, Bilkent 06800 Ankara, Turkey
[2]Middle East Technical University, Department of Environmental Engineering,
06800 Ankara, Turkey

ABSTRACT

The textile industry includes a variety of processes ranging from the manufacture of synthetic fibers and fabric production to retail sales. The wet-processing operations, namely preparation, dyeing and finishing of textile products which are used to give the desired characteristics to the yarn or fabric, require the use of several chemical baths. They consume vast amount of energy, chemicals and water. Emissions of volatile organic compounds (VOCs) mainly arise from textiles finishing, drying processes, and solvent use. VOC concentrations vary from 10 mg m^{-3} for the thermosol process to 350 mg carbon m^{-3} for drying and condensation process. Process wastewater is a major source of pollutants. It is typically alkaline and has high BOD5 (700 to 2,000 mg l^{-1}) and chemical oxygen demand (COD) (approximately 2 to 5 times the biochemical oxygen demand (BOD) level), solids, oil and possibly toxic organics including phenols (from dyeing and finishing) and halogenated organics (from processes such as bleaching). Dye wastewaters are frequently highly colored and may contain heavy metals such as copper and chromium. Wool processing may release bacteria and other pathogens. Pesticides are sometimes used for the preservation of natural fibers and these are transferred to wastewaters during washing and scouring operations. Pesticides are also used for moth proofing, brominated flame retardants for synthetic fabrics, and isocyanates for lamination wastewaters may also contain heavy metals such as mercury, arsenic, and copper. Air emissions include dust, oil mists, acid vapors, odors, and boiler exhausts.

Towards the search for sustainable industrial enterprises, recent studies indicated that there are many cleaner (sustainable) production opportunities which lead to waste reduction as well as increased raw material use efficiency in textile wet processing

---

*Corresponding author. Tel.: +90-312-210 58 67; Fax: +90-312-210 26 46. E-mail address: goksel@metu.edu.tr
(G.N. Demirer).

industry. The relevant reduction/conservation strategies, process modifications, chemical substitutions and reclamation/reuse techniques which reduce the wastes (air, water and solid/hazardous) originating from preparation, dyeing, printing, finishing, and other sources in textile mills were reported.

The objective of this chapter is to: (a) provide an environmental profile of the wet textile industry, (b) review cleaner (sustainable) production opportunities in textile wet processing industry, and (c) report the progress obtained in the textile demonstration project in the context of the UNIDO Eco-efficiency (cleaner production) project which has been implemented in Turkey since 2008.

1. INTRODUCTION

The textile wet processing industry is characterized by its comparatively high specific water consumption and chemical usage. The textile wet processing industry uses water as the principal medium for removing impurities, applying dyes and finishing agents. For each ton of produced fabric 20-350 m^3 of water are consumed, the rather wide range reflecting the variety of processes and process sequences. Among the largest industrial consumers of water, the textile wet processing industry is a prime candidate for the development of intensive water recycling strategies and the recovery of valuable chemical products through cleaner production strategies [1, 2].

1.1. The Cleaner Production Concept

Cleaner Production is a general term that describes a preventive environmental approach, aimed at increasing resource efficiency and reducing the generation of pollution and waste at source, rather than addressing and mitigating just the symptoms by only technically "treating" an existing waste/pollution problem. In essence, Cleaner Production is about:

- Preventing waste and pollution at source
- Minimizing the use of hazardous raw materials
- Improving water and energy efficiency
- Reducing risks to human health
- Saving money
- Improving efficient management practices
- Promoting sustainable development

Cleaner Production includes measures to conserve raw materials, water and energy and measures to reduce at source the quantity and toxicity of all emissions and wastes being emitted to air, land and water. Furthermore, this approach embraces the '*cradle-to-grave*' principle, the '*precautionary principle*' and the '*preventive principle*'. Because Cleaner Production addresses the problem at several levels at once, it is a holistic integrated preventive approach to environmental protection.

The term "Cleaner Production" describes a *comprehensive* preventive approach to environmental protection. It is a broad term, encompassing what is sometimes also referred to as *waste minimization, pollution prevention, cleaner technology, waste reduction, non-waste technologies* and *source reduction*, which all form part of the Cleaner Production approach. *Waste minimization* is a key concept driving CP and CP-related programs and initiatives. Terms such as *industrial ecology, green business* and *eco-efficiency* similarly describe aspects of the CP approach to business. All of the terms mentioned above, however, describe a proactive approach that embraces a forward-looking "anticipate and prevent" philosophy.

Although various definitions of Cleaner Production exist, the concept is relatively straightforward. The definition used in this report is that proposed by the United Nations Environment Program (UNEP) for Cleaner Production as: "*The continuous application of an integrated preventive environmental strategy to processes, products, and services, to increase overall efficiency, and reduce risks to humans and the environment. Cleaner Production can be applied to the processes used in any industry, to products themselves and to various services provided in society. Specifically for:*

- *Production processes: Cleaner Production results from one or a combination of conserving raw materials, water and energy; eliminating toxic and dangerous raw materials; and reducing the quantity and toxicity of all emissions and wastes at source during the production process;*
- *Products: Cleaner Production aims to reduce the environmental, health and safety impacts of products over their entire life cycles, from raw materials extraction, through manufacturing and use, to the 'ultimate' disposal of the product; and*
- *Services: Cleaner Production implies incorporating environmental concerns into designing and delivering services*" [3].

The term Cleaner Production has recently been replaced by Sustainable Consumption and Production (SCP) by organizations such as UNEP, UNIDO and UN-Division of Economics and Society. Since Agenda 21 the issues of unsustainable consumption have been addressed through a series of meetings, dialogues, research and publications from UN CSD, UNEP, UNDP and other business, consumer and research organizations. The idea of Sustainable Consumption has been developed and clarified through that process, emerging as an umbrella term bringing together various issues, such as: "*meeting needs, enhancing quality of life, improving resource efficiency, minimizing waste, taking a life-cycle perspective and taking into account the equity dimension; integrating these component parts in the central question of how to provide the same or better services to meet the basic requirements of life and the aspiration for improvement, for both current and future generations, while continually reducing environmental damage and risks to human health* [4, 5].

"Cleaner production" concept is still used by many related institutions while "sustainable production" concept has been rapidly adopted [6, 7]. Therefore, the term "cleaner (sustainable) production" is adopted in this study.

In 1992, Cleaner Production found mention at the United Nations Conference on Environment and Development (UNCED), held in Rio de Janeiro, as an important strategy to take forward the concept of sustainable development. The commitment of governments to achieving Sustainable Development is set out in Agenda 21, which made significant references to Cleaner Production and has in fact served as a guiding framework for the implementation of Cleaner Production. It also provided a direction and focus to the adoption of Cleaner Production on a multi-stakeholder and multi-partnership basis.

Today, Cleaner Production is a flagship program of UNEP and several organizations in the world that have adopted and adapted it. It has truly become a global movement. The emphasis on Cleaner Production today is more on action and the establishment of an enabling framework embodying the spirit of partnership.

The growing attention to issues of sustainable consumption is a natural outcome of decades of work on Cleaner Production. Action focused on consumption has highlighted the need to address the creation of new systems of production and consumption, systems that might be truly sustainable, both environmentally and economically. Both consuming and producing more efficiently will be fundamental to any successful strategies for eradicating poverty and creating business opportunities [8].

1.2. The Cleaner Production Techniques

Cleaner Production can be achieved in many different ways. The most important are:

- *Changing attitudes* and finding a new approach to the relationship between industry and the environment.
- *Applying expertise and know-how* by improving efficiency, adopting better management techniques, changing housekeeping practices, and revising policies, procedures and institutions as necessary.
- *Improving technology* or simply rethinking an industrial process or product in terms of Cleaner Production may produce the required results without importing new technology.

The mechanism or tools used to implement CP include:

- Measuring and monitoring key performance indicators
- Waste, pollution & resource efficiency audits
- Environmental life cycle assessments
- Process integration
- Industrial symbiosis
- Green chemistry
- Dematerialization
- Waste minimization
- Design for Environment.

In a business, Cleaner Production should be seen as the responsibility of entire the company, starting from top management all the way to cleaning staff. While it is business itself that ultimately must implement C(S)P, this needs to be supported by many external factors. These include: the policies of government, enforcement by local authorities, objectives of financial institutions, research and development of academic and research institutions, assistance of service providers, the commitment of business and industry associations, and the lobbying of NGOs.

The role of government is to lead by providing an environment conducive to accelerating the process and encouraging industry to initiate its own cleaner production programs. The range of tools available for governments trying to catalyze industry to adopt cleaner production is large and different countries will select those combinations of tools they regard as most suited to their needs. Such tools include: establishing cleaner production programs, requiring cleaner production audits, publishing environmental performance data, providing technical assistance, revising existing laws and regulations, setting new regulations, changing permitting system, encouraging voluntary reduction schemes, making special enforcement provisions, changing use of technology standards, providing subsidies, offering grants for the development of cleaner production technology, and investing revenues from waste treatment and taxes in cleaner production development. All these and other tools can be classified in four main categories, namely: applying regulations, using economic instruments, providing support measures and obtaining external assistance.

In defining targets for action and policy implementation, towards *Sustainable Consumption* there is broad agreement that it must embrace:

- Poverty eradication
- Change pursued by all countries, with the developed countries taking the lead
- A mix of policies including regulations; economic and social instruments targeted to land use, transport, energy and housing; information; products and services
- Partnership between governments, relevant international organizations, the private sector and consumer groups
- Special attention to unsustainable consumption patterns among the richer segments in all countries.

Global business and industry – for example through the World Business Council for Sustainable Development (WBCSD) – has approached Sustainable Consumption as an extension of eco-efficiency approaches to include:

- Technological and social innovations to improve quality of life
- Provide and inform consumer choice and
- Improved market conditions through appropriate legislation and regulation.

The need to reduce resource consumption in production and products and to provide information to consumers, to improve the effectiveness and quality of product use, is also recognized. Reducing end-of-life waste (usually through recycling) is also a common feature of product stewardship programs across most industry sectors [8].

2. Environmental Issues in Textile Wet Processing

Textile wet processes consume dyes, auxiliaries, chemicals, detergents and finishing agents in the conversion of raw materials to finished product. The specific water use varies from 60 to 400 l kg^{-1} of fabric, depending on the type of fabric wet application. Generally, textile effluents are highly colored and saline, contain non-biodegradable compounds, and are high in Biological and Chemical Oxygen Demand (BOD, COD). These factors combine to present numerous operational problems in municipal wastewater treatment works, which are biological processes and not intended for the breakdown of complex organic molecules. The presence of metals and other dye compounds inhibits microbial activity and in some cases may cause failure of biological treatment systems. Various indicators may be used to classify strength of effluent from the textile process; these are shown in Table 1 [9].

Table 1. Overall effluent characteristic for textile mills

Parameter	Woven Fabric	Knit fabric	Yarn dyeing/finishing
Biological Oxygen Demand (mg l^{-1})	550	250	200
Suspended Solids (mg l^{-1})	185	300	50
Chemical Oxygen Demand (mg l^{-1})	850	850	524
Sulphide (mg l^{-1})	3	0-2	-
Colour (ADMI)	325	400	600
pH	7-11	6-9	7-12
Water Use (l kg^{-1})	297	277	297

Emissions from the textile industry take the form of liquid effluents, wet fabric/fiber wastes from dye processes, solid wastes from the dry processes, hazardous wastes and air emissions. Liquid effluents contain many different components such as: dyes and chemicals, leveling and dispersing agents, alkalis and salts, metals and acids. Table 2 shows the environmental releases from textile wet processing [10].

In addition to high volumes of liquid effluent (wet processes have a high specific water usage), solid wastes comprising waste fiber and fabric, paper waste, sludge from effluent treatment and dyebath wet wastes are also produced. Most dyes are not readily biodegradable. The microbial populations present in the aerobic systems of municipal works cannot breakdown the molecules that cause color in the effluent. Some dyes though, particularly those containing the azo bond, may be partially reduced by anaerobic microbes in biological systems. Other dyes may be adsorbed onto the sludge in the digesters or sludge beds of aerobic systems. Generally, acid and reactive dyes have poor adsorption capabilities due to their solubility in the effluent. Direct, disperse and vat dyes are readily adsorbed onto the sludge [9].

In textile industry, operations exist that are not linked directly with the production process, but which become essential in order to develop continuous production. This is the case for some cleaning done with solvents, which constitute sources of diffuse origin emissions. These solvents and degreasing agents are used for cleaning printing machines, specifically in the print injectors and other parts which are in contact with dyes, pigments and printing pastes. Textiles stored can, in some cases, emit volatile compounds due to their use in the operations to which they have been subjected and the residual presence in manufactured products, especially auxiliary materials, with which, the textile products are impregnated [11].

Table 2. Environmental releases from textile wet processing

Process	Wastewater	Air Emissions	Residual Waste
Knitting	Little or no wastewater emissions generated	Little or no air emissions generated	Packaging waste; yarn and fabric scraps; off-spec fabric
Desizing	BOD from water-soluble sizes, synthetic size, lubricants, biocides, antistatic compounds	VOCs from glycol ethers	Little or no residual waste generated
Scouring	Disinfectants and insecticide residues: NaOH, detergents, fats, oils, pectin, wax, knitting lubricants, spin finishes, spent solvents	VOCs from glycol ethers and scouring solvents	Little or no residual waste generated
Bleaching	Hydrogen peroxide, sodium silicate or organic stabilizer, high pH	Little or no air emissions generated	Little or no residual waste generated
Singeing	Little or no wastewater generated	CO_2 emissions, exhaust gases from burners	Little or no residual waste generated
Mercerizing	High pH, NaOH	Little or no air emissions generated	Little or no residual waste generated
Dyeing	Metals, salts, surfactants, toxics, organic processing assistants, cationic materials, color, BOD, COD, sulphide, acidity/alkalinity, spent solvents, sequestering agents	VOCs	Little or no residual waste generated
Printing	Suspended solids, urea, solvents, color, metals, heat, BOD, foam	CO_2 emissions, solvents, acetic acid from drying and curing oven emissions, combustion gases, particulate matter	Leftover color, little or no other residual waste generated
Finishing (Wet)	BOD, COD, suspended solids, toxics, spent solvents	CO_2 emissions, VOCs, contaminants in purchased chemicals, formaldehyde vapors, combustion gases, particulate matter	Fabric scraps and trimmings, packaging waste, waste chemicals from finishing (i.e., water softeners)

3. CLEANER (SUSTAINABLE) METHODS APPLICABLE TO THE WET PROCESSING TEXTILE INDUSTRY

C(S)P can be applied to wet textile processing industry by improving current operations and by product design changes and reformulation.

Table 3. The strategies for material or other feedstock substitution in wet processing textile industry

Purchase Chemicals with Lowest Toxicity		
☑	Substitute surfactants containing NP, NPEs, octylphenol and octylphenol ethoxylates (OP and OPEs) with surfactants with more favorable toxicological profiles.	[10, 12, 13]
☑	Purchase the least toxic, appropriate dyes where possible	
☑	Substitute other process chemicals with less toxic alternatives where possible	
☑	Substitute surfactants with biodegradable surfactants	[11]
☑	Substitute conventional lubricants with hydrosoluble oils in the manufacturing of knitted fabric	[11]
Ensure There are No Contaminants in your Raw Materials		
☑	Perform quality control of incoming raw materials to reduce contamination since biocides may be present on some raw materials and some oily residues on yarns can contribute to your effluent toxicity.	[14]
☑	Try to work with suppliers who - demonstrate environmental responsibility and/or have an EMS or ISO 14001 program in place - develop a system to deal with unused chemicals - develop new dyes and chemicals which have lower toxic ingredients with the same or better performance - have take-back program for shipping containers	
Purchase Chemicals that Provide Greater Process Efficiencies		
☑	If you do cotton dyeing use sodium sulphate rather than sodium chloride (NaCl) which results in use of less chemical bleach and extends the life of the machinery	[15]
☑	If you do knitting then be aware that some chemicals used in the dry processes may affect TMEs toxicity	

CS Brooks reduces chemicals containing NPEs by 99%

1.1.1. CS Brooks, which is a dyeing, printing and finishing plant in Quebec, did a thorough review of the chemicals they purchase. They reduced NPE use by over 99% and in the process made other important product substitutes and changes that resulted in savings of about $75 000 per year. Examples of how they achieved these savings include purchasing more concentrated chemicals and purchasing only one product whereas before many were purchased for similar operations [15].

Hafner Inc. reduces toxicity of wastewater

1.1.2. Hafner Inc. produces furniture fabric and stretch knitted fabric in Granby, Quebec. Quebec's Ministère de l'Environnement asked the Hafner plant to assess the nature of its wastewater and to help improve the water quality going into the municipal wastewater treatment plant. An impact study suggested that the wastewater from the treatment plant had the potential to adversely affect aquatic life and fish-eating wildlife.

1.1.3. The company completed a series of effluent characterizations and reviewed their MSDSs and the handling of chemical products used. Sources of chlorinated dioxins and furans, and NP/NPEs were identified, along with petroleum hydrocarbons (C10-C50). Working with suppliers, they identified equally effective, acceptably priced replacement products. NPE loadings were reduced more than 97%, chemical oxygen demand (COD) reduced by 48% and C10-C50 petroleum hydrocarbons loads were reduced by 87%. Hafner has improved its operating efficiency, reduced environmental liability and reduced workplace exposure to hazardous substances. The reduction in COD reduced the annual effluent disposal costs by $15 000 [15].

Textile mills in Toronto work with suppliers to remove NP/NPEs from chemicals purchased

1.1.4. Textile mills in Toronto have been developing and implementing C(S)P plans over the last few years as part of a requirement of the City's sewer use by-law. This by-law requires all facilities that discharge any of 38 subject pollutants to develop and implement a C(S)P plan. Subject pollutants of interest to the textile industry include AP and APEs (which also include NP/NPEs and OP/OPEs), as well as numerous metals found in textile processing chemicals. Textile chemical suppliers have been taking notice of this new by-law and many have been manufacturing products that do not contain any of these subject pollutants. The suppliers have become more aware of environmental issues and the need to provide alternative products after communication with the Ontario Chapter of the Canadian Association of Textile Colorists and Chemists. Through this association, the mills asked for information on the contents of the chemicals purchased, and alternatives to chemicals containing subject pollutants, and alerted suppliers to the new requirements in the Toronto by-law. Alternatives for NP/NPE chemicals in particular are becoming more widely available [15].

Savings through chemical substitution

1.1.5. A Scottish finishing company saves 20 000 pounds year^{-1} in effluent disposal costs by reducing the COD of their effluent from 2 460 mg l^{-1} to 700 mg l^{-1}. This was achieved through replacing the use of soap in scouring with anionic/non-ionic detergents and conducting trials to ensure that minimum detergent was used [16].

3.1. Improving Current Operations

Improving current operations is a general C(S)P method that can be divided into six types. This section provides examples of each of the six types. In some cases, the type can further be divided into sub-categories that are more applicable to the wet processing textile industry.

3.1.1. Material or other Feedstock Substitution

This C(S)P method refers to replacing raw materials which make your effluent more toxic with substances that are non-toxic or less toxic. For example, you can identify toxic chemicals used in wet processes or toxic chemicals in the textile materials you purchase from suppliers and then request substitutions. Finding an appropriate substitute may require some investigation with suppliers, consultants and industry experts. On-site trials may have to be conducted. Some of the relevant strategies in wet processing textile industry are provided in Table 3.

3.1.2. Equipment or Process Modifications

Production systems often operate in a manner that generates unnecessary toxic compounds or other wastes. By optimizing how a textile facility operates, and/or upgrading or replacing production equipment, a textile mill can increase production efficiency and reduce operating costs. Higher initial costs are usually associated with equipment purchases and therefore are not usually the first C(S)P measure undertaken. Some of the relevant strategies in wet processing textile industry are provided in Table 4.

Table 4. The strategies for equipment or process modifications in wet processing textile industry

Process modifications that optimize chemical use		
☑	Use automated systems to measure exact amount of surfactants, oxidants and other chemicals and reduce their usage	[12, 15]
☑	Use automated dissolving and dispensing of dyes for better quality, optimized consumption and reduction of re-dyes	
☑	Reduce the concentration or use of chemicals suspected to contribute to effluent toxicity	
☑	Consider conducting optimization tests on existing equipment and determine where process inefficiencies occur. Add microprocessor controller for dyeing machines: reduces cycle times, increases production.	
☑	Replace the after chroming wool dyeing process with the dyeing process using reactive dyes	[11]
Explore new equipment that results in less-toxic discharges		
☑	Low liquor ratio dyeing machines	[12, 15]
☑	High-pressure jet-dying machines. Results in decreased dyeing time, lower liquor ratio (14:1 – 8:1) and reduces chemical use.	
☑	Wet on wet finishing system using vacuum technology. 25% reduction of raw materials, lower toxicity, with energy savings for evaporation.	
☑	Cold pad batch dyeing. Primarily for processing cotton fabrics	
☑	Microprocessor controller for dyeing machines reduces cycle times, increases production.	
Purchase equipment designed to reduce energy and water use		
☑	Pulsating rinse technology to reduce water consumption during rinsing and	[12, 15]

	energy reduction due to shorter cycles	
☑	Install dyeing process cooling water recovery system	
☑	Recover cooling water with heat recovery system and storage tanks: reduces freshwater use	
☑	Install an exhaust stack recovery system to take emissions from boiler, recover heat, and reduce CO_2 emissions	
☑	Install new process controllers on dyeing machines, which reduces energy consumption and CO_2 emissions	

The installation of an automated chemical dispensing system at a dyehouse optimizes chemical use with a short payback time.

    1.1.6. A dyehouse located in Montreal was producing 42,000 kg of dyed yarn each week and using \$564 000 worth of chemicals each year. By converting all chemicals supplied in drums to totes an initial saving of 5% was achieved. By installing an automatic chemical dispensing system to distribute 20 liquid chemicals from totes and bulk storage tanks to 13 packages dyeing machines a reduction in the use of chemicals produced an extra 13% savings. The project resulted in total chemical cost savings of \$101,520 per year and labor cost savings of \$90 000. Payback for this project was calculated at 1.2 years [15].

New high-pressure jet-dyeing machine reduces chemical usage with payback of 2.4 years

    1.1.7. A Quebec-based textile manufacturer was producing 22000 kg week^{-1} of tubular knitted fabrics in atmospheric dye becks. These dye becks were replaced by three high-pressure jet-dyeing machines equipped with "SmartFill" pulsating rinse, blend fill, automatic dosing, differential pressure controls, microprocessor controllers and a cooling water recovery system.

    1.1.8. The new technology reduced the liquor ratio from 13:1 to 8:1. Savings were due to less chemical use, reduced water use, and reduced energy consumption. The initial cost of \$584 000 resulted in savings of \$244 935 per year, with a simple payback of 2.4 years.

    1.1.9. Additional savings due to a reduction in the dye cycle times also resulted in a reduction of total overhead costs. The installation of more efficient high pressure jet dyeing machines also resulted in space savings as bulky jet machines were replaced [15].

3.1.3. Good Operating Practices and Training

Good operating practices and training focus on improving work procedures and employee skills. In many cases improved operational efficiencies can be implemented relatively easily through the introduction of work procedures which target process control systems. The result is often improved productivity, increased reliability, more efficient resource and energy use and reduced waste of financial resources and production materials. Training employees is key to identifying and implementing good operating practices. Some of the relevant strategies in wet processing textile industry are provided in Table 5.

Table 5. The strategies for good operating practices and training in wet processing textile industry

Good housekeeping practices		
☑	Production scheduling. Schedule dyeing activities to start with light colored dyes, followed by darker dyes, which will decrease washing in between color changes.	[12, 15, 16]
☑	Develop a prescreening program for raw materials. Test raw materials for easy-to-perform tests using on-site laboratory i.e., pH, viscosity and refractive index.	
☑	Management practices. Review management practices to ensure they support pollution prevention. Provide incentives for employees to develop pollution prevention approaches.	
☑	Implement an Environmental Management System	
☑	Optimize equipment layout. Replace old, bulky equipment with smaller more efficient equipment to provide more working space: results in more efficient use of space and chemicals and higher productivity.	
☑	Operation and maintenance procedures. Develop and undertake regular preventative maintenance procedures for all equipment and improve maintenance scheduling.	
☑	Ensure incoming materials in drums are dated and labeled correctly by manufacturer. Early detection of mislabeled drums can reduce spoiled batches.	
☑	Material handling. Don't mix waste streams, i.e. hazardous with non-hazardous wastes, as it will all become hazardous waste.	
☑	Control of the number of re-operations and additions. Identify the possible factors that influence the indices of re-operations and additions through the analysis, during a certain period of time, of the registry of process parameters that are made up of parts of production	[11]
☑	Product storage. Use and store containers in accordance with the supplier's recommendations. Use suitable containers for the products they contain: they must be stable, easy to handle, closed, and it may be useful for them to have a dispenser device, etc.	
☑	Demineralization and desizing of woven cotton fabric by the padbatch System	
☑	Washing and dyeing of knitted polyester fabrics in a single bath	
☑	Single stage desizing, scouring and bleaching of cotton fabric	
Training		
☑	Develop staff training programs to ensure appropriate tasks are carried out with new C(S)P initiatives.	[12, 15]
☑	Develop new employee training programs which include promotion of pollution prevention.	
☑	Train staff on occupational, health and safety aspects of chemical handling.	
☑	Train staff on spill management.	

3.1.4. Inventory Management and Purchasing

This C(S)P method which is often complimentary to other C(S)P methods includes two distinct practices:

- Environmentally preferable purchasing, which involves the integration of environmental considerations into existing and new purchasing practices, can help reduce material consumption and avoid unnecessary use of toxic substances in products;
- Environmentally responsible inventory management, which entails the incorporation of environmental considerations into inventory management systems.

Some of the relevant strategies in wet processing textile industry are provided in Table 6.

Table 6. The strategies for Inventory management and purchasing in wet processing textile industry

Inventory management and purchasing		
☑	Set up a purchasing system where new product or chemical purchases must be assessed for potentially toxic constituents before purchase.	[12, 15]
☑	Reduce the amount of unused chemicals left in packaging by purchasing chemicals in the largest container suitable for your facility.	
☑	Purchase in totes rather than drums, if suitable. Install bulk storage systems for large-volume chemicals such as sodium hydroxide, brine, hydrogen peroxide and acetic acid.	
☑	Review your purchasing practices and, if possible, reduce the number of chemicals that you need to buy.	
☑	Purchase concentrated chemicals where practical and safe	
☑	Consider just-in-time purchase of chemicals to reduce storage and disposal of old, unwanted chemicals	
☑	Centralize all material purchase records to facilitate easy tracking.	
☑	Purchase in quantity only what you definitely consume	

3.1.5. Spill and Leak Prevention

Spill and leak prevention seeks to avoid prevention of raw material losses as well as formation of corresponding wastes. This C(S)P method is often complimentary to other C(S)P methods. The amount of money and chemicals saved by not undertaking spill and leak prevention activities is difficult to measure but can be estimated by working through a few possible spill scenarios on site. Some of the relevant strategies in wet processing textile industry are provided in Table 7.

3.1.6. On-site Reuse, Recycling or Recovery

Re-use and recycling of wasted materials on-site can help save on raw material and disposal costs. Effective reuse and recycling requires viewing waste as a loss of valuable process materials, which could have significant environmental benefits when recycled. Some of the relevant strategies in wet processing textile industry are provided in Table 8.

Table 7. The strategies for spill and leak prevention in wet processing textile industry

Spill and leak prevention		
☑	Conduct a spill prevention audit of your facility.	[15]
☑	Reduce manual handling of chemicals where possible to reduce spills and employee exposure to chemicals	
☑	Develop environmental emergency plans to compliment C(S)P plans	
☑	Fix all leaks as soon as they are detected	

Montreal Woolens improves brine delivery system and reduces risk to water quality
Montreal Woolens Canada Ltd. is a textile manufacturer in Cambridge, Ontario. Following an on-site pollution prevention assessment, they improved their existing brine delivery system by replacing older underground tanks with above ground tanks. This has eliminated the production downtime of the old system and reduced costs per ton of brine through the delivery of larger volumes of materials at a time. The company also reduced the risk of spills or leaks [15].

Table 8. The strategies for on-site reuse, recycling or recovery in wet processing textile industry

On-site reuse, recycling or recovery		
☑	Explore salt bath recovery system for salts from textile dye waste process water baths	[12]
☑	Chemical recovery and reuse of dyebaths, caustics used in mercerizing, and size baths	
☑	Recycling and reuse of non-process water such as cooling water and condensate water	
☑	Process water recycling and reuse using various technologies	
☑	Reuse of spent rinse water and wash water from bleach baths	
☑	Substitution of starch-type sizing products with synthetic, hydrosoluble sizes in the sizing of warps for manufacturing woven fabric	[11]

Saving water through recycling and reuse
1.1.10. Recycling of their cooling and condensate water saves a medical textile company in Lancashire 11 000 m^3 of borehole water. Estimated savings in effluent disposal are about 3000 pounds year^{-1}. In addition, recycling of the last rinse water from beam and winch dyeing saves a further 7 000 m^3 of water and about 2700 pounds in effluent disposal costs.
1.1.11. A Wigan-based dyer and finisher halved its water consumption by recycling the bleach effluent for the scouring process. Approximately 10300 pounds year^{-1} are saved in effluent disposal costs [16].

Acabats Barberá, S.L.: Recycling at source of an enzyme desizing bath
All cotton finishing processes require prior desizing so that the processes to which the garment is later subjected have an effect. When the size used is starch, the simplest desizing process and through which the best results may be obtained is that carried out by means of enzymes, specifically amylases and cellulases. A process that allows its recycling at source in turn

allows the significant reduction in the process cost and the wastewater pollutant load and, as a consequence, the treatment cost. The company built a system that would send the desizing bath to a storage tank once the process had finished. The desizing baths from the different operational machines are accumulated in this tank. Automatically, the necessary bath volume for the next machine to become operative is measured and sent. When reaching the machine which starts the new desizing process, 30% of the enzymes that would have been used if the bath had been prepared again are added and 100% of the auxiliaries. This process may be repeated up to 20 times per day, five days per week. Once per week, all desizing baths are renewed and are poured into the company's treatment system [11].

3.2. Product Design Changes and Reformulation

Product design and reformulation integrates environmental criteria into the usual design drivers of performance, cost, quality, cultural, legal and technical criteria. Design for the Environment (DfE) looks at the product life cycle after the design stage and groups these activities into five stages:

- How raw materials are obtained
- How the materials are manufactured
- Filling, packaging and distribution systems
- Use, reuse and maintenance
- Disposal

Product reformulation is a very invasive step and may not be easily accepted by a manufacturer who has had a product on the market for many years and has a demanding customer. Environmentally aware customers, however, have started to demand textile products produced in a sustainable manner. Some of the relevant strategies in wet processing textile industry are provided in Table 9.

4. TEXTILE DEMONSTRATION PROJECT IN UNIDO ECOEFFICIENCY (CLEANER PRODUCTION) PROGRAM IN TURKEY

Cleaner (sustainable) production concept has been firstly brought to the agenda of Turkey by The Scientific and Technological Research Council of Turkey (TUBITAK) and Technology Development Foundation of Turkey (TTGV) in 1999 (Science-Technology-Industry Discussion Platform, 1999). Cleaner Production concept is placed in the priority areas of the Supreme Council for Science and Technology (BTYK) which determines the national science and technology policies. This concept has also been emphasized in the Environment and Sustainable Development Panel in the scope of the TUBITAK's Vision 2003 Project [19]. Moreover, it was among the main themes stated in 8th Five Year [20] and 9th Seven Year Development Plans [21] and documents prepared for European Union (EU) accession efforts [22].

Table 9. The strategies for Product Design and Reformulation (Design of Environmentally Friendly Products) in wet processing textile industry

Product Design and Reformulation (Design of Environmentally Friendly Products)		
☑	Educate the final consumer (and brand name companies who make the final product), who may not be aware of the toxicity issues of some of the substances they demand. Customers may not be aware that the products they require result in toxic wastes and may contribute to an unhealthy working environment and discharges to the environment. Educate customers on the availability of alternatives that do not contain substances which are toxic or contain materials of concern (i.e. some of the dyes).	[15,18]
☑	Develop a working group with sectoral textile associations and the brand name companies to promote awareness of these issues.	
☑	Develop and promote new product lines that show reduced environmental impact through product reformulation that use less or no toxic materials	
☑	Increase product life by development of more durable products where appropriate.	
☑	Develop and promote new product lines that allow for maximum reuse of materials and recycling of components after use.	
☑	Design for re-manufacturing or reuse of the product after its life.	

Climatex Lifecycle: An award-winning compostable, upholstery fabric that contains no toxic ingredients

   1.1.12.DesignTex, an international design team, the Swiss textile mill Rohner Textil AG, and McDonough Braungart Design Chemistry developed a compostable, non-toxic upholstery fabric so toxin free that the local garden club uses factory trimmings as mulch. When Swiss inspectors tested the mill's effluent, they thought their instruments were broken—the water leaving the factory was as clean as when it entered. The resulting product from Climatex contains a combination of freerange wool and ramie. Partnering with Swiss chemical manufacturer Ciba and EPEA, the design team selected 38 chemical dyes, auxiliaries, and fixatives that met performance criteria and were not harmful to plants, animals, humans or ecosystems. This fabric has garnered gold medals and design awards and has proved to be tremendously successful in the marketplace. Climatex Lifecycle exemplifies what is possible with intelligent design: ecological soundness, social fairness, success in the marketplace, creativity rather than regulation, and an entirely new way of making and consuming [15].

Sustainable Textile Standard developed in USA provides global benefits

   1.1.13. Members of the U.S.-based Sustainable Textile Committee of the Institute for Market Transformation to Sustainability (MTS) worked for three years with the textile and design community to produce an unprecedented Approved National Consensus Sustainable Textile Standard for carpet, fabric, and apparel that contains the following:

1.1.14.
- Textile rating system: certified, silver, gold and platinum sustainable textile
- Multiple environmental, social, and economic benefits over the supply chain
- Business benefits: cost savings, design innovation, product differentiation, long-term customer relationships, liability reduction
- Market definition of sustainable textile
- Life cycle environmental performance requirements for sustainable textile
- Social performance requirements for sustainable textile over the supply chain
- Defines sustainable agriculture for textile

1.1.15. These new product standards will help identify and market textiles made in an environmentally preferable manner [18].

The term cleaner (sustainable) production has been cited in many other policy and strategy documents of the top level agency/institutions on science, technology, development, etc. in Turkey for over a decade. However, it is not sufficiently known and applied except its energy efficiency aspect in Turkey. The most important reason of this problem is the lack of capacity on this subject.

In order to overcome this deficiency, there are two national level projects being executed in Turkey since 2008. The first one is the UNIDO Eco-efficiency (Cleaner Production) Program which has been executed by TTGV since 2008 as the subprogram of "Enhancing the Capacity of Turkey to Adapt to Climate Change United Nations Joint Program" [23]. The second one is the "Determination of the Framework Conditions and Research-Development Needs for the Dissemination of Cleaner (Sustainable) Production Applications in Turkey" project [24] supported by the Ministry of Environment and Forestry and carried out by TTGV and Prof. Dr. Göksel N. Demirer, as the consultant.

4.1. Determination of the Framework Conditions and Research-Development Needs for the Dissemination of Cleaner (Sustainable) Production Applications in Turkey Project

In this project, the current situation on "cleaner (sustainable) production" subject is evaluated in terms of capacity, source, legal arrangement, incentive mechanism and existing studies, and they are compared with international applications and finally proposals are prepared in accordance with country's needs and conditions. Final Project Report that is the most important output of the project includes the evaluations made and results obtained [25].

During preparation of the Report, it has been aimed to include all stakeholders representing public institutions, universities, research institutions, non-governmental organizations, chambers and unions, organized industrial zones, sectoral institutions, international organizations, media and financial institutions in the preparation and discussion period of the report. Within the scope of the project, 128 stakeholders for the determination of the existing institutional capacity about cleaner (sustainable) production; 37 stakeholders for the criteria evaluation in the scope of determination of the priority sectors for cleaner production and finally 151 stakeholders for taking opinions and contributions for the Draft Report, involved in the report preparation process. As a result of this, 66 institutions for determination of existing capacity and 23 institutions for determination of the priority sectors have been included into process; and the feedback taken during and after the Project Workshop which was conducted on December 29, 2009 with 125 participants from 62 institutions, has been reflected to the Report.

4.2. UNIDO Eco-efficiency (Cleaner Production) Program

"Enhancing the Capacity of Turkey to Adapt to Climate Change Joint Program" compromises development, environment, industry, agriculture related components and is collectively carried out by related cooperation connected to United Nations (UN). Pilot region for UN Joint Program is Seyhan River Basin and Ministry of Environment and Forestry is the main beneficiary of this program. One of the most important outputs expected from UN Joint Program is the determination of national strategy for adapting climate change and arrangement within the framework of development plans.

Eco-efficiency (Cleaner Production) Program was actualized as an industry component of Joint Program. In the context of Joint Program, from the point of view that " adaptation to climate change can be procurable with cleaner production and eco-efficiency applications", studies related to adaptation in industry is conducted by UNIDO (United Nations Development Program) and TTGV (Technology Development Foundation of Turkey). Within this scope, development of capacity in the field of cleaner production and eco-efficiency, implementation of pilot projects in Seyhan River Basin (Adana, Niğde, Kayseri) and dissemination of them on national basis are targeted.

In Seyhan River Basin and many regions of Turkey, most distinct impact of climate change directly affecting the industry is foreseen as "reduction of usable water amount". From this point of view, "reduction of water consumption in production" forms the focus of the UNIDO Eco-efficiency Program.

In the scope of this program, firstly priority sectors in Seyhan River Basin were determined via environmental and economical parameters. These are, Textile-Leather, Food-Beverages, Chemical Products and Metal Processing-Machinery sectors.

Scope of the program is composed of:

- Informative meetings for related institutions, organizations and project stakeholders oriented to concept and example applications related to "cleaner production" and "eco-efficiency" besides "United Eco-efficiency Program";
- Training for industry and experts;
- Pilot project implementations for eco-efficiency (primarily water consumption) in six companies placed in Seyhan River Basin and active in priority sectors;
- Dissemination of pilot project results;
- Formation of Information Unit coordinated with related eco-efficiency institutions at national and international level [26];
- Preparation of guide documents for the implementation of eco-efficiency programs and environmental friendly technologies in priority sectors.

4.3. Textile Demonstration Project

In the scope of UNIDO Ecoefficiency (Cleaner Production) Program six demonstrations projects have been implemented. One of them has been conducted in a textile company located in Bursa which is accepted as the centre of textile manufacturing in Turkey.

4.3.1. Company and Process Description
Fabric production compromises the main activity area of the company. The Company employing 147 people and produces nearly 2000 ton fabric per year.

The flow chart of the process is given in Figure 1.

4.3.2. Ecoefficiency (Cleaner Production) Implementations
The aim of the proposed eco-efficiency project is to reduce water intensity of the company by good-housekeeping practices, better process control in the whole system and technological renovation in water softening system.

In the old process, water is mostly used in textile dyeing and finishing purposes. Approximately 260,000 tons of distilled water is used annually for dyeing and finishing purposes, accounting for 80-85% of water consumption in the company. Distilled water is obtained by water softening (ion exchange) equipment in old technology operated manually and doesn't meet the required parameters (especially hardness) anymore. During regeneration of water softening device, the water consumption is 15 m^3 reg^{-1} and salt consumption is 450 kg reg^{-1}.

In the cleaner production implementation, the old water softening system has been changed with the fully automated one that enables to enhance the production quality. With the new system water consumption for regeneration purpose have been decreased to 8 m^3 reg^{-1} and salt consumption to 138 kg reg^{-1}. Besides the renovation of the ion exchange system a list of good-housekeeping and process control practices are in the scope of the project. After the determination of high water intensive areas in the process, the below listed practices were determined to be implemented:

- Better control of water consumption amounts for each process and examination of the adequate water amounts (high water consumption is identified in fabric washing, washing after dyeing units and cloth expanding machine)
- Renovation of valves in the inputs and outputs of the cooling water part of dyeing machines
- Reuse of tumbler dryer cooling water in the system
- Reuse of nap trimming cooling water in the system

4.3.3. Environmental Benefits
With the renovation of water softening device and other listed good housekeeping implementations water, energy and salt consumption in the company has been reduced.

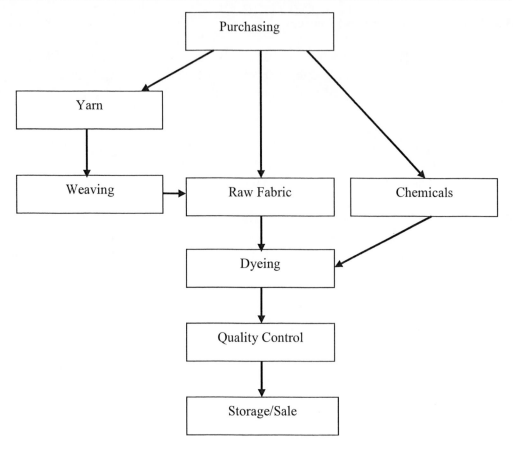

Figure 1. Flowchart of the company.

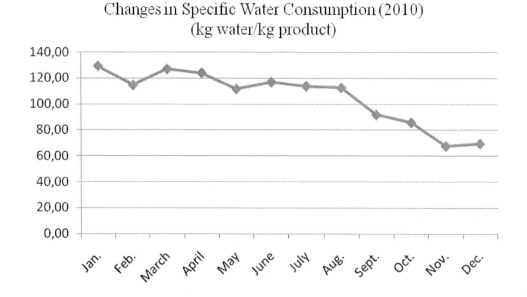

Figure 2. Changes in specific water consumption in the company.

Water Consumption

As it can also be seen from the graphic above, with the start of the project (September 2010), enhancements in the processes has decreased the specific water consumption amounts.

Furthermore, data regarding the water consumption for the months before and after the project and product amounts can be seen from Table 10 below.

Table 10. Water consumptions before and after the project

Period	Water Consumption (m^3 month^{-1})	Production Amount (kg month^{-1})	Specific Water Consumption (m^3 ton^{-1})
Before the renovation of water softening device	25.000	203.977	122,6
After the renovation of water softening device	11.500	198.989	57,8

Values in the above table showed that there is an important reduction in water consumption amounts with the project implementations. The amount of specific water consumption is decreased from 122,6 kg kg^{-1} to 57,8 kg kg^{-1}. At this point, the reduction in the water consumption is identified as %53. In textile sector specific water consumption in dyeing and finishing processes is said to be around 150-200kg kg^{-1} [27]. This comparison reveals the efficiency of the company in water consumption.

When only the water consumption data of water softening device is analyzed, effects of this implementation on the data can be seen since the month that system is put into use (in December 2010). Amount of softened water produced by this device versus amount water used for backwash and regeneration are showed in the figure below.

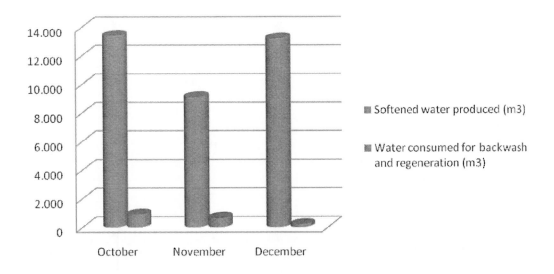

Figure 3. Amount of softened water produced versus amount water used for backwash and regeneration.

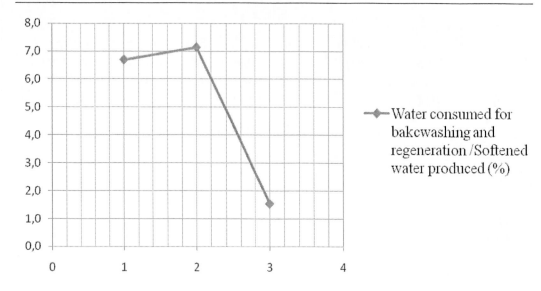

Figure 4. Ratio of amount of water consumed for backwashing and regeneration to amount of softened water produced.

As it can be seen from the graph, amount of water consumed for backwashing and regeneration has been decreased by the renovation of water softening device. The graphic above displays the changes in the ratio of water consumed for backwashing and regeneration to amount of softened water produced which is reduced from 6.9% to 1.5% by the renovation of the softening device.

In Table 11 water saving expected to be gained via project implementations were listed. Before the project implementation, company's water consumption is reported as 300,000 m^3 $year^{-1}$. When this value is taken into account the below table is reported.

Table 11. Theoretical Water Saving Calculation Results
(Before the project implementations)

Water saving practices	Water Saving ($m^3 day^{-1}$)	Annual Water Saving (%)
Adjustment of water consumption in fabric washing, washing after dyeing units according to adequate amounts	200	20
Renovation of valves in the inputs and outputs replaced in the cooling water part of dyeing machines	50	5
Reuse of tumbler dryer cooling water in the system	20	2
Adjustment of water consumption in tumbler dryer cooling water in the system	10	1
Reuse of nap trimming cooling water in the system	2	0.2
Renovation of water softening device	20	2
Total	302	30,2

Although 30% saving in water consumption is expected with this assumptions; with the renovation of water softening device and good housekeeping implementations water saving more than the expected value has been achieved (53%).

Energy Consumption

In the context of this cleaner production project there isn't any implementation directly affecting the energy consumption. However, reductions in water consumption have also an impact on the reduction of energy consumption due to pumping of water. Another factor reducing the energy consumption is the reduction of wash water used in dyeing and finishing processes. When it is considered that reactive and disperses dyeing is done at 60-80°C and 80-120°C, respectively. Reduction in the water that needs to be heated brought the reduction in the energy requirement for heating. According to monitoring results nearly 11% energy (as natural gas and electricity) has been saved with the project.

Other Benefits

Amount of wastewater generated is expected to be decreased by 53% due to reduction in the use of water. Furthermore, salts that were used in the process and in the softening device have been reduced by 67% (192 ton/year NaCl) that also reduced the regarding transportation costs. In total project has a pay back period less than one month.

4.3.4. Evaluation of the Dissemination Impact of the Project

This project has a potential to be disseminated to other companies due to often use of softened water in the industrial processes. In addition, good housekeeping practices implemented in the context of this project can be easily adapted to the other companies in the sector. Moreover, implementations such as; optimization of wash water, usage of water meters and reuse of cooling water are good examples to be implemented in all industries including these processes.

5. CONCLUSIONS

Cleaner (sustainable) production concept is defined as "decreasing risks on human and environment by continuous application of an integrated and preventive environment strategy on products and processes". "Pollution Control" approaches try to overcome the environmental problems after they arise. Pollution control approaches accept the production and design phases as unchangeable factors; therefore pollution is seen as an inevitable result of these phases and solutions are sought after pollution occurs. Consequently, these approaches require additional costs for the institutions by focusing on the waste treatment facilities. On the other hand, cleaner production approaches accept the pollution as a result of deficiencies and inefficiencies during design, raw material utilization and production processes; and aim to find solution by providing necessary developments during these processes.

The textile industry is one of the longest and most complicated industrial chains in manufacturing industry. It is a fragmented and heterogeneous sector dominated by SMEs, with a demand mainly driven by three main end-uses: clothing, home furnishing and industrial use. The textile industry is composed of a wide number of sub-sectors, covering the entire production cycle from the production of raw materials (man-made fibers) to semi-processed (yarn, woven and knitted fabrics with their finishing processes) and final products (carpets, home textiles, clothing and industrial use textiles).

The textile industry is characterized not only by the vast quantity of water required, but also by the variety of chemicals used. Generally, there is a long sequence of wet processing stages, and therefore many requirements for resource inputs and several sources of waste generation. Amongst the contributions to waste, liquid wastes tend to dominate over solid wastes and air emissions in terms of severity of environmental impact. As an integrated and holistic solution to many of the listed problems and regarded economical issues, cleaner production implementation possible list of which is tried to be summarized in Section 3. Improving current operations and by product design changes and reformulation are the main topics of the implementations for textile sector cleaner production implementations. As it can be concluded from the case studies in which the different cleaner production opportunities have been realized, results of the projects are very impressive for the companies when considering the environmental benefits as well as related cost savings.

In the demonstration project conducted in the scope of UNIDO Eco-efficiency (Cleaner Production) Program which has been executed by TTGV, cleaner production implementations including simple technological change and good housekeeping measured have been realized. As a result of this implementation, company has reduced its water consumption at rate of 53% that brings the reduction of wastewater generation in addition to reduction of 11% in energy and 67% in salt consumption. All of these environmental saving goes hand in hand with regarding cost savings that have reduced the payback period of the project.

REFERENCES

[1]   Schoeberl, P., Brik, M., Braun, R., & Fuchs, W. (2004). Treatment and recycling of textile wastewater case study and development of a recycling concept, *Desalination*, 171: 173-183.

[2]   Ozturk, E., Yetis, U., Dilek, F.B., & Demirer, G.N. (2009). A chemical substitution study for a wet processing textile mill in Turkey. *Journal of Cleaner Production*, 17: 239-247.

[3]   UNEP (1996). Cleaner Production: A Training Resource Package, Industry and Environment.

[4]   http://www.un.org/esa/dsd/dsd_aofw_scpp/scpp_index.shtml.

[5]   Narayanaswamy, V., & Stone, L. (2007). From cleaner production to sustainable production and consumption in Australia and New Zealand: achievements, challenges, and opportunities. *Journal of Cleaner Production*, 15: 711-715.

[6]   Veleva, V., & Ellenbecker, M. (2001). Indicators of sustainable production: framework and methodology. *Journal of Cleaner Production*, 9: 519–549

[7]   Glavic, P., & Lukman, R. (2007). Review of sustainability terms and their definitions, *Journal of Cleaner Production*, 15: 1875-1885.

[8]   Assessment of the Status Quo of Cleaner Production in South Africa, (2004). Department of Environmental Affairs and Tourism, Final Report, August 2004.

[9]   Waste Minimization Guide for the Textile Industry – A step towards Cleaner Production (1998). Pollution Research Group, University of Natal, Volumes 1 and 2.

[10]   Crechem Technologies Inc. (2003). *Determination of Aqueous Releases of Chemicals from Wet Processing Textile Mills*. New Substances Division, Health Canada, Ottawa, Ontario.

[11]   RAC CP (2002). Pollution Prevention in the Textile Industry within the Mediterranean Region.

[12]   Marbek Resource Consultants (2001). *Identification and Evaluation of Best Available Technologies Economically Achievable (BATEA) for Textile Mills Effluents*. Environment Canada – Quebec Region, Montreal.

[13]   ToxEcology – Environmental Consulting Ltd. (2002). *Alternatives to Nonylphenol Ethoxylates: Review of Toxicity, Biodegradation, and Technical-Economic Aspects*. Environment Canada.

[14]   U.S. EPA – United States Environmental Protection Agency (1996). *Best Management Practices for Pollution Prevention in the Textile Industry*. EPA/625/R-96/004. Cincinnati, Ohio, USA.

[15]   Environment Canada (2004). Technical Resource Guide, Wet Processing Textile Mills, Environmental Protection Branch, EN154-28/2004E, Montréal, Québec, Canada.

[16]   Barclay, S., & Buckley, C. (2000). Waste Minimization Guide for the Textile Industry, A Step Towards Cleaner Production, The Pollution Research Group, University of Natal, Durban South Africa.

[17]   United Kingdom Department of Trade and Industry, and Department of the Environment, Transport and the Regions (1998). *EMS in Textiles: How to Set Up Environmental Management Systems in the Textiles Industry*. Blacksburg, Virginia.

[18]   Institute for Market Transformation to Sustainability (2003). *Sustainable Textile Standard*. Sustainable Textile Committee Members in the USA. Washington, DC.

[19]   http://www.tubitak.gov.tr/home.do?ot=1&sid=472&pid=468.

[20]   http://ekutup.dpt.gov.tr/plan/viii/plan8.pdf.

[21]   http://ekutup.dpt.gov.tr/plan/plan9.pdf.

[22]   http://www.did-cevreorman.gov.tr/duyuru-doc/uces_tr.pdf.

[23]   http://www.undp.org.tr/Gozlem2.aspx?WebSayfaNo=1392.

[24]   http://www.cygm.gov.tr/CYGM/AnaSayfa/tumProjeler/10-04-27/Temiz_S%c3%bcrd%c3%bcr%c3%bclebilir_%c3%9cretim.aspx?sflang=tr

[25]   http://www.ttgv.org.tr/en/cleaner-production.

[26]   http://www.ecoefficiency-tr.org.

[27]   Environmental Technology Best Practice Program (1997). Guide Code EG98, Water Use in Textile Dyeing and Finishing.

In: Non-Conventional Textile Waste Water Treatment ISBN: 978-1-62100-079-2
Editor: Ahmed El Nemr © 2012 Nova Science Publishers, Inc.

Chapter 9

LIPID INTERACTION WITH TEXTILE FIBERS AND CONTROL RELEASE OF A MICROENCAPSULATED ACID DYE PROMOTED BY CATIONIC SURFACTANTS

M. Elisabete C. D. Real Oliveira[*]

Centro de Física da Universidade do Minho (CFUM),
Campus de Gualtar, 4710–057 Braga, Portugal

ABSTRACT

There is an increasing interest in the textile industry for eco-friendly textile processing, in which the use of naturally occurring materials such as phospholipids becomes important. The non-uniformity that occurs in the dyeing process of polyamide, caused by the irregularities in the surface properties of the fiber, is reduced by the use of leveling agents. The leveling agents can promote both levelness and coverage of fiber irregularities, blocking the accessible sites in the fiber. The use of natural products such as soybean lecithin, as auxiliary in the dyeing of polyamide and cotton, instead of chemical products can improve the effluent characteristics and also reduce the initial rate of dye uptake. The present chapter shows the different affinities of phosphatidylcholine with the polyamide fibers and cotton and also compares the retarding effect of the acid dye Telon[®] Blue RR (C.I. Acid Blue 62) release on polyamide fibers dyeing by encapsulation of the dye in mixed cationic liposomes of dioctadecyldimethylammonium bromide (DODAB)/soybean lecithin (containing a 10% molar fraction of DODAB) with pure soybean lecithin liposomes or synthetic auxiliaries. The retarding effect of liposomes on the dye release was analyzed through changes in the absorption and fluorescence spectra of the acid dye at different conditions. The effect of temperature (in the range of 25 - 70°C) on the spectroscopic behavior of the dye in the absence and in presence of polyamide was also investigated, in order to simulate the dyeing conditions. Exhaustion curves obtained in dyeing experiments showed that, below 45°C, the retarding effect of the mixed liposomes (lecithin/DODAB (9:1)) was similar to that of the auxiliaries, but better than the one of pure lecithin liposomes. At higher temperatures (above 45°C), the system lecithin/DODAB presents a better performance, achieving a

[*] e-mail: beta@fisica.uminho.pt

higher final exhaustion level when compared with the commercial leveling agent without losing the smoothing effect of lecithin.

1. INTRODUCTION

In textile industry, there is a growing interest in the development of eco-friendly textile processing, with the use of naturally occurring materials [1-4]. The non-uniformity that occurs in the dyeing process of polyamide, caused by the irregularities in the surface properties of the fiber, is reduced by the use of leveling agents. The leveling agents can promote both levelness and coverage of fiber irregularities, blocking the accessible sites in the fiber. These products reduce the initial rate of dye uptake and the extent of this retardation in the dyeing rate decreases with the increasing temperature of dyeing. The interactions between lipids or surfactants and textile fibers are not completely established. Auxiliaries, as their name implies, are used to assist in dyeing, by wetting, leveling or when necessary by dispersing dyes of low solubility.

Their interaction with fibers plays a very important role in achieving level dyeing or in controlling dye adsorption by fibers. The use of natural products, as soybean lecithin, as auxiliary in the dyeing of polyamide and cotton, instead of chemical products can improve the effluent characteristics [1]. Previous work showed that soybean lecithin liposomes have a retarding effect on the microencapsulated acid dyes, in the dyeing of polyamide [1, 2]. This effect is very important to achieve level dyeing. It was interesting to observe that some of this same effect (to less extent) is also present when the dyeing was processed in the presence of lecithin liposomes and non-microencapsulated dyes.

Maza and his co-workers [3] reported a number of investigations on unilamellar or multilamellar vesicles of egg phosphatidylcholine as vehicles of dyes or oxidative reagents for dyeing and finishing wool. The role of the liposomes can be attributed to the fact that bilayer structure of lipids from cell membrane complex of wool is similar to that of the liposomes. Kim [4] proposed to use double tailed surfactants for preparing synthetic vesicles in disperse dyeing of polyamide to improve dyebath exhaustion and color uniformity. They concluded that there might be fairly strong interactions between those surfactants and the fiber by virtue of electrostatic and hydrophobic interactions.

In this chapter it is presented the study of the interactions between lecithin and textile fibers (polyamide and cotton) are investigated by reflectance, fluorescence and FTIR spectroscopy and SEM (scanning electronic microscopy) characterization techniques and also the retarding effect of soybean lecithin/cationic liposomes.

Liposomes are defined as spherical structures (vesicles) constituted by a phospholipid bilayer that entraps an aqueous core. Depending on the nature of the lipids, different types of liposomes (multilamellar, unilamellar) ranging from very small (20 nm) to very large vesicles (dozens of micrometers) can be formed. Due to their amphiphilicity, hydrophobic molecules can be trapped within the bilayer while hydrophilic molecules can be entrapped in the aqueous compartment [5-8]. Physical-chemical properties such as permeability, phase transition temperature or stability depend on the phospholipids fatty acid composition (hydrocarbon chain length, degree of saturation as well as properties of the constituting polar head groups) [9, 10].

Liposomes release the microencapsulated dye slowly, promoting a retarding effect, comparable with the one obtained with retarding agents, making them a good and eco-friendly alternative to commercial leveling products [2, 3, 5].

In previous research concerning the interaction of soybean lecithin liposomes with polyamide and cotton fibers was observed a retarding effect of these liposomes in dyeing assays [2, 11]. The effect of temperature, pH and surfactant addition on the control release of the dye was also studied [12, 13]. The retarding effect is crucial to achieve level dyeing and is also present (although in less extent) when the dyeing assay is performed with non-encapsulated dyes but in the presence of liposomes. The retarding effect of liposomes at the first stage of dyeing process with hydrophobic dyes may be due to the higher affinity of the dyes to the liposomes in the bath in comparison to the fibers. Another factor can be the chemical structure of the dyes that may affect both the assembly properties of the dye-liposome system and the hydrophobic interactions with the hydrophobic regions within the fiber [14-16].

The encapsulation efficiency of the liposomes depends on the chemical structure of the trapped agent (reactive or non-reactive dye), the type of media solution and the additives on the liposome formulation [14]. Liposomes may be prepared using amphoteric, anionic or cationic amphiphilic molecules.

A number of synthetic cationic surfactants have been found to form stabilized vesicles and has been widely used in several biological applications such as gene delivery [17-20], antiseptic and disinfectant [21-23]. The double-chain quaternary ammonium surfactant DODAB (dioctadecyldimethylammonium bromide) is a synthetic vesicles-forming lipid when dispersed in water above the gel to liquid-crystalline phase transition temperature (T_m) [24-26]. Since T_m of aqueous DODAB dispersions is between 44.8 and 45.5°C, it is generally accepted that DODAB vesicles at room temperature are in the gel phase [24, 25].

Commercial soybean lecithin, containing (% mol/mol) 22% phosphatidylcholine, 20% phosphatidylethanolamine, 20% phosphatidylinositol and 10% phosphatidic acid as main components, presents a very low $T_m \sim -20°C$ and forms large lamellar liposomes in aqueous media.

In this chapter, it is shown the potential usefulness of mixed cationic lecithin/DODAB liposomes for the encapsulation and dyeing with acid dyes is assessed for the case of polyamide. The main objective is to increase the retarding effect of acid dye release and, consequently, improving the equalizing effect of the color, without losing the smoothing effect of lecithin.

Dyeing assays were performed with N-Rh-PE using the rhodamine group emission by excitation at 463 nm and also the acid dye Telon® Blue RR (C.I. Acid Blue 62) encapsulated in mixed lecithin/DODAB liposomes and in pure lecithin liposomes, for comparison.

To understand the interaction between liposomes and the encapsulated dye, fluorescence spectroscopy was used, due to its high sensitivity and dependence on the environment. As Telon® Blue RR dye is itself fluorescent, the use of external probes is avoided and information about lipid/dye interactions is obtained through the intrinsic fluorescence of the dye.

2. MATERIALS AND METHODS

The material to be mentioned in this chapter, were polyamide 6.6 knitwear without any special treatment and cotton. Commercial soybean lecithin, containing (% mol/mol) 22% phosphatidylcholine, 20% phosphatidylethanolamine, 20% phosphatidylinositol and 10% phosphatidic acid as main components, was supplied by Stern (USA). Acetic acid and sodium acetate were purchased from Sigma-Aldrich, while the synthetic lipid dioctadecyldimethylammonium bromide (DODAB) was obtained from Tokyo Kasei. The dye Telon® Blue RR (Acid Blue 62) sodium salt was purchased from DyStar. Structures of the dye and DODAB are shown below.

Telon® Blue RR dye (sodium salt)

DODAB

N-Rh-PE

2.1. Liposome Preparation

Liposomes were prepared according to the thin film hydration method. Briefly, lipids were dissolved in chloroform and dried under an argon stream. The lipid film was then hydrated with a buffered aqueous solution (pH = 5.5) containing the dye (1.02×10^{-5} M) and sonicated for 15 minutes at room temperature for lecithin vesicles and above 45°C (the melting temperature of DODAB) [24-26] for lecithin: DODAB mixed vesicles (containing 10% molar fraction of DODAB). The quantity of dye that was not encapsulated into the liposomes was removed by gel filtration chromatography through a Sephadex G-50 (from Sigma-Aldrich) column.

2.2. Dyeing Conditions

Laboratory dyeing was done in an Ahiba Turbo Color dyeing machine with a dyebath ratio 50 : 1. The following dyeings were carried out: 1) with soybean lecithin liposomes (2 g l^{-1}); 2) with PC liposomes (0.1 g l^{-1}); 3) with PE liposomes (0.1 g l^{-1}); 4) with N-Rh-PE liposomes (0.01 g l^{-1}) and 5) with soybean lecithin (2 g l^{-1}) and N-Rh-PE (0.01 g l^{-1}) mixed liposomes. Dyeing was started at 40°C and the temperature was increased to 95°C (or 85°C in presence of liposomes) at a gradient of 0.8°C min^{-1}, keeping the dyebath at this temperature during 30 minutes. The percentage of dyebath exhaustion was measured on a Shimadzu UV/Vis. spectrophotometer at λ_{max} of absorption of the dye. The percentage of dyebath exhaustion (% E) was calculated according to the following equation:

$$\%E = \left(\frac{A_0 - A_F}{A_0} \right) \times 100$$

where A_0 and A_F are the concentrations of the dyebath before and after dyeing, respectively.

2.2.1. Dyeing of Polyamide

To the aqueous solution with lecithin liposomes, 2 g l^{-1} of ammonium sulphate was added and the pH adjusted with acetic acid to reach pH five. Dyeing was started at 40°C and the temperature was increased to 98°C at a gradient of 1°C min^{-1}, keeping the dyebath at this temperature during 30 minutes.

2.2.2. Dyeing of Cotton

To the aqueous solution with lecithin liposomes, 50 g l^{-1} of sodium sulphate was added and the dyeing carried on at 45°C during 30 minutes, then pH is adjusted to 12 using 15 g l^{-1} of sodium carbonate and the dyeing process was kept during further 60 minutes at the same temperature.

2.3. Spectroscopic Measurements

All the solutions were prepared using spectroscopic grade solvents and ultrapure water (Milli-Q grade). Absorption spectra were recorded in a Shimadzu UV-3101PC UV-Vis-NIR spectrophotometer, equipped with a Peltier temperature controllable cuvette holder. Fluorescence measurements were performed using a Spex Fluorolog 3 spectrofluorimeter, equipped with double monochromators in both excitation and emission and a temperature controllable cuvette holder.

In order to study the effect of temperature on the dye release, aliquots obtained from the chromatographic column, containing liposomes with encapsulated dye, were submitted to increasing temperatures (from 25 to 70°C), to simulate the first part of the dyeing process of polyamide. Telon® Blue RR emission was obtained with an excitation wavelength of 640 nm.

Spectroscopic measurements in the presence of polyamide were also performed, to a more realistic simulation of the dyeing conditions. For this purpose, a piece of polyamide was placed at one face of the fluorescence cuvette containing the solution with the encapsulated dye. The temperature was raised from 25 to 70°C and absorption and fluorescence spectra of the remaining dye were measured at several temperatures.

The diffuse reflectance of the samples was measured with a spectrophotometer Shimadzu UV-3101 PC. The Michelson Series FT-IR Spectroscopy from Bomem was used to obtain infrared spectra of the cotton and the polyamide samples that were untreated, i.e., without any dyeing process, and dyed with lecithin. The pieces of fabrics were cut, put on top of sampling cup containing potassium bromide powder and scanned 100 times by diffuse reflectance spectroscopy. The images of the fibers surfaces and their cross-sections were obtained by a scanning electron microscope, Leica Cambridge S360.

3. INTERACTION OF LECITHIN WITH TEXTILE FIBERS

FTIR spectrum of polyamide and cotton before and after dyeing with lecithin are shown in Figure 1. The resulting difference spectrum for polyamide (Figure 1A) shows four peaks at around 1663, 1676, 1695 and 1740 cm^{-1} that correspond to the frequency region of carbonyl group present in lecithin showing that some or all of lecithin component are incorporated in the polyamide matrix. With the same technique the incorporation of lecithin in cotton is not so evident as in the case of polyamid.

The labeled phospholipid N-Rh-PE was included into the lecithin liposomes, in order to understand the interaction of lecithin with the fibers.

Figure 2 shows the fluorescence spectra of N-Rh-PE in polyamide (A) and cotton (B) samples.

It can be observed that the rhodamine spectra are red shifted relative to, for example, an ethanolic environment ($\lambda_{max} = 581$ nm). In aromatic compounds the usually electronic transitions are $\pi\pi^*$ and $n\pi^*$ [28]. The molecule in different electronic states interacts differently with environment originating dependences of the transition energy on the properties of the medium. The $\pi\pi^*$ transition shows red shift as the environment polarity increases. As the involved transition is a $\pi\pi^*$, we conclude that in both fibers rhodamine feels a polar media. Comparing both fibers we can conclude that in polyamide the sites where rhodamine is located, are more polar than in cotton as the emission maximum in polyamide are red shifted in relation to cotton. This can be understood if we consider the structures of the fluorescence probe [1] and the fibers [29].

During the dyeing process some polyamide sites are positively charged. As the probe has a negative charge, there is an electrostatic interaction (ionic binding) between the phospholipid fluorescent probe and polyamide.

For cotton the ionic binding is not feasible and thus N-Rh-PE goes to the fiber via dispersive interaction. With this information it could be expect that negatively charged PE would be lecithin's main binding component for polyamide and the zwitterionic PC should interact more efficiently with cotton. To see whether lecithin components can compete with N-Rh-PE for the fibers binding sites, mixed liposomes (soybean lecithin (2 g l^{-1}) and N-Rh-PE (0.01 g l^{-1}) it was used. It can be observed a reduction of 35% of rhodamine emission in polyamide and 71% in cotton.

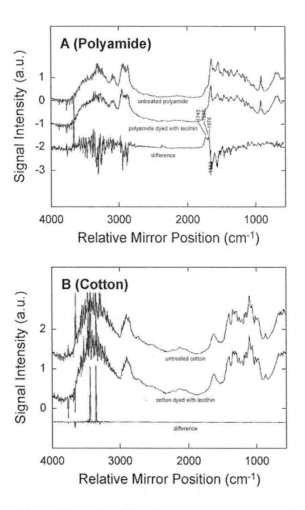

Figure 1. FTIR spectra of textile fibers: A – polyamide; B- cotton. *Figure modified from reference [11].*

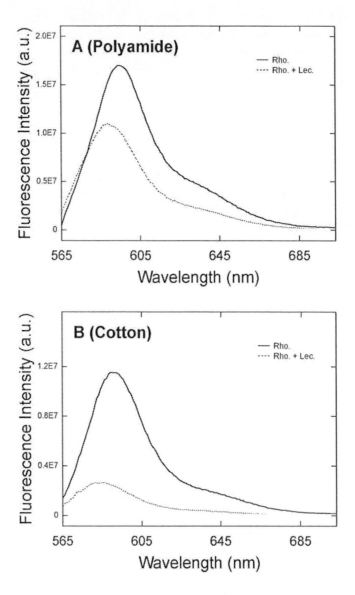

Figure 2. Fluorescence spectra of N-Rh-PE of textile fibres: A – polyamide; B- cotton. *Figure modified from reference [11].*

As in soybean lecithin PC and PE content is approximately the same, it would seems that PC has a stronger interaction with cotton than N-Rh-PE and binds less efficiently with polyamide sites than N-Rh-PE. In both fibers the incorporation of both lecithin and N-Rh-PE induces a small blue shift in the rhodamine emission. This is a result of a different and less polar environment of the fluorescence probe. The possibility of some N-Rh-PE molecules being imbibed in a local "film" of lecithin present in the fibers could contribute to the observed blue shift (lecithin polar group has a polarity similar to ethanol).

In order to clarify which lecithin components are incorporated in the fiber a reflectance spectrum (specular and diffuse) of the fibers untreated and dyed with soybean lecithin, PC and PE it was performed (Figures 3A and 3B).

The phospholipids usually absorbed in the region 220-300 nm. In polyamide we conclude that the main lecithin component that is incorporated in these fibers is PC. PE is incorporated only slightly and probably on the positive binding sites due to its anionic characteristics. In cotton the variations in the reflectance spectra are more complicated. Cotton acts as a mirror in the spectral region of 200-210 nm.

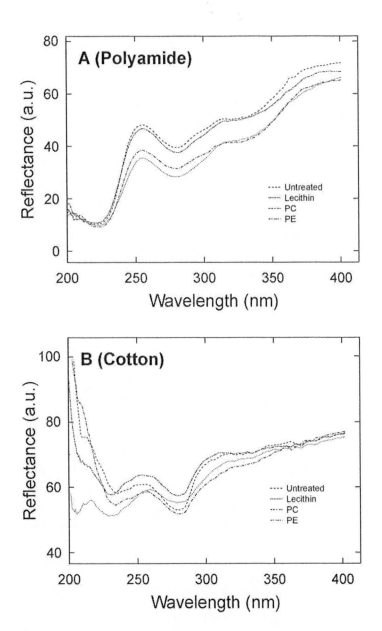

Figure 3. Reflectance spectra of textile fibres: A – polyamide; B- cotton. *Figure modified from reference [11].*

It can be seen that PE has no effect in this region whereas PC decreases the mirror effect and when lecithin is present it is practically lost. This is mainly a surface effect and thus we can conclude that some other lecithin component interacts strongly with cotton surface, probably the phosphatidylinositol [30], which has a head group similar to D-glucose, monomer of the cellulose polymer, present in the structure of the cotton. The region of phospholipid absorbance is not so indicative which is a confirmation of the difficulty in assigning phospholipid characterization in the FTIR experiment. Nevertheless we can see a little absorption due to lecithin and PC.

In order to understand what kind of interaction has the lecithin with the fibers, Scanning Electron Microscopy was used to analyze the surface and the interior of the two different fibers, untreated and treated with lecithin.

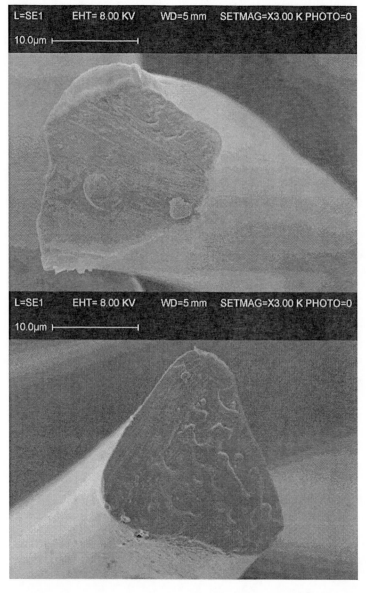

Figure 4. Cross section optical views of polyamide (x 3000): A – untreated; B- dyed with lecithin. *Figure modified from reference [11].*

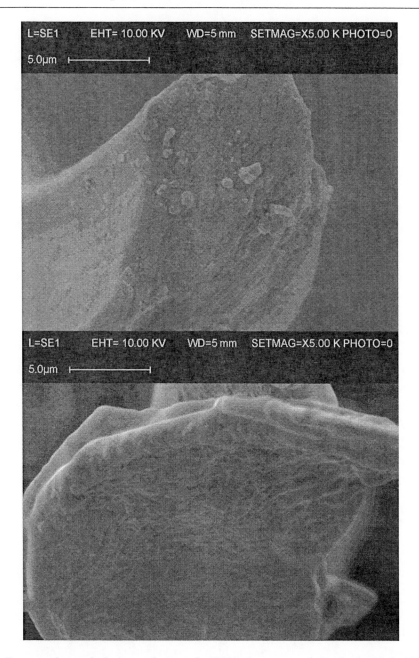

Figure 5. Cross section optical views of cotton (x 5000): A – untreated; B- dyed with lecithin. *Figure modified from reference [11].*

Figure 4 shows the cross section of polyamide untreated (A) and dyed with lecithin (B).

Figure 5 shows the cross section of cotton untreated (A) and dyed with lecithin (B). The three-dimensional images clearly show surface features, such as the presence of surface or cross section modifications. This confirms the reflectance results and shows that the interaction of the lecithin with the cotton is more at the surface through a coating layer. The interaction with the polyamide is more in the interior, because we can observe changes in the morphology of the cross section of the fiber, which are not so evident in cotton.

4. RELEASE OF A MICROENCAPSULATED ACID DYE IN POLYAMIDE DYEING USING MIXED CATIONIC LIPOSOMES

4.1. Telon® Blue RR in Homogeneous Media

The retarding effect of liposomes on the dye release was analyzed through changes in the absorption and fluorescence spectra of the acid dye in different environments, in homogeneous media with different polarity and encapsulated.

In order to understand the dye behavior in environments of different polarity, solutions of Telon® Blue RR in different solvents were performed. Telon Blue RR has a very low solubility in non-polar media. UV-Visible absorption and fluorescence emission spectra were recorded in ethanol and acetate buffer pH = 5.5 (Figure 6).

Absorption spectra of the dye are similar in ethanol and aqueous media (Figure 6A), the latter presenting a very small red shift (2 nm). From the absorption spectra obtained at several dye concentrations, molar absorption coefficient values (ε) in ethanol and acetate buffer (pH = 5.5) were determined through the Lambert-Beer law, $\varepsilon = 8.75 \times 10^3 \, M^{-1} \, cm^{-1}$ at 634 nm for ethanol and $\varepsilon = 1.06 \times 10^4 \, M^{-1} \, cm^{-1}$ at 636 nm in acetate buffer.

The fluorescence emission of the dye, in ethanol and acetate buffer, exhibits distinct spectral features (Figure 6B). In aqueous media, the emission is large and structureless (with a maximum near 715 nm), while in ethanol a more structured spectrum with two bands appears (with maxima at ~680 nm and ~708 nm). For the same concentration, the dye is substantially more fluorescent in ethanol than in buffer solution. This different behaviour is essential to assess the dye environment when encapsulated in liposomes and the changes along the dyeing process of polyamide.

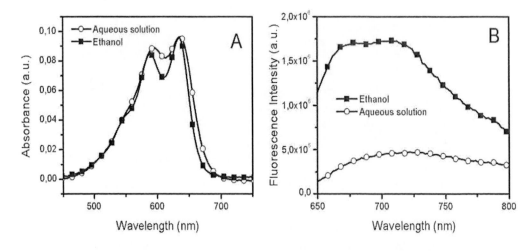

Figure 6. Absorption (left) and fluorescence emission (right) spectra of Telon® Blue RR dye (1.0 × 10⁻⁵ M) in aqueous acetate buffer (pH = 5.5) and in absolute ethanol. *Figure modified from reference [32].*

4.2. Telon® Blue RR Encapsulated in Lecithin Liposomes

In order to study the retarding effect of the acid dye Telon® Blue RR (C.I. Acid Blue 62) release on polyamide fibers dyeing, the dye was encapsulated in mixed cationic liposomes of dioctadecyldimethylammonium bromide (DODAB)/soybean lecithin (containing a 10% molar fraction of DODAB) and its release was compared with pure soybean lecithin liposomes or synthetic auxiliaries.

The fluorescence emission of Telon®Blue RR encapsulated in lecithin liposomes was studied at different temperatures (Figure 7). At room temperature, the fluorescence emission spectra of the dye exhibits notable differences relative to the emission in pure water (Figure 6B), presenting a more structured band and a higher fluorescence quantum yield. This behavior shows that the dye feels a less hydrated environment when encapsulated in lecithin liposomes.

An expected decrease of fluorescence intensity with increasing temperature is observed (~50% reduction between 25 and 70°C) due to the increase of non-radiative deactivation pathways. However, a change in the emission spectral shape is observed, the spectra at higher temperatures being more similar to the one of free dye in buffer solution (spectral shape of free dye does not vary in this temperature range - *data not shown*). In fact, at lower temperatures, the fluorescence spectrum presents two bands (at ~685 nm and ~715 nm), and the spectral shape is similar to the one observed in ethanol.

This behavior indicates that, at lower temperatures, the dye is in a less hydrated environment in lecithin liposomes, which can correspond to a location in the liposome membrane, probably near the polar head groups.

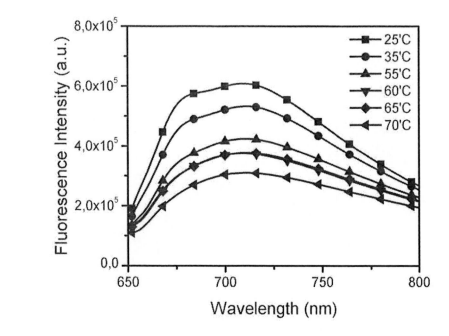

Figure 7. Fluorescence spectra of Telon® Blue RR (2.2×10^{-5} M) encapsulated in soybean lecithin liposomes (1.4 mM), with increasing temperature ($\lambda_{exc} = 640$ nm). *Figure modified from reference [32].*

With increasing temperature, the dye relocates to a more hydrated environment (Figure 7), as inferred from the emission spectral shape and position. Above 55°C, the emission spectrum is less structured with only one band and the maximum emission wavelength reaches the value in pure aqueous buffer ($\lambda_{max} \sim 716$ nm). This behavior shows that, at higher temperatures, the dye is released from the liposome membrane to the aqueous solution.

4.3. Telon® Blue RR Encapsulated in Lecithin: DODAB Liposomes

With the intent of improving the dyeing efficiency with acid dyes, a mixed liposome formulation with commercial soybean lecithin and a cationic synthetic lipid (DODAB) was optimized. The molar ratio 9:1 lecithin: DODAB revealed promising in preliminary polyamide dyeing assays. Therefore, the fluorescence emission of Telon® Blue RR in mixed lecithin/DODAB liposomes (9:1) was studied at several temperatures (Figure 8). As observed for lecithin liposomes, a 47% decrease in emission is detected in the range 25 to 70°C. Until the melting temperature of DODAB (~ 45°C) [23,24], the fluorescence spectrum is clearly structured with two bands (more structured than the ones observed in lecithin at the same temperatures, e.g. 25 and 35°C).

All spectra are narrower and more intense in lecithin/DODAB liposomes than in pure lecithin liposomes (Figures 7 and 8). Considering that the concentration of dye is the same, this behaviour shows that the dye is globally in a less hydrated environment in the mixed liposomes than in lecithin ones.

Figure 9 shows a schematic representation of the interaction of the dye with the liposome components. This behavior leads us to expect a higher retarding effect in dyeing with the mixed cationic liposomes, promoted by the electrostatic attraction between the positive charge of the cationic lipid and the anionic dye molecule.

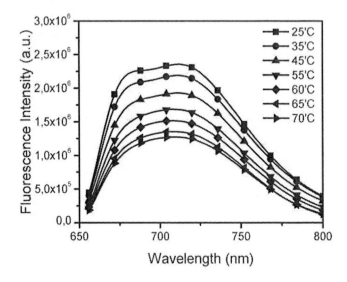

Figure 8. Fluorescence spectra of Telon® Blue RR (4.5×10^{-5} M) encapsulated in mixed soybean lecithin/DODAB (9:1) liposomes (1.29 mM in lecithin), with increasing temperature (λ_{exc}=640 nm). *Figure modified from reference [32].*

Figure 9. Proposed mechanism for the interaction of Telon® Blue RR acid dye (B, in black) with liposomes; left side: soybean lecithin liposomes; right side: DODAB:lecithin 1:9 (mol/mol) liposomes. Soybean lecithin components (in white): C: phosphatidylcholine, E: phosphatidylethanolamine, I: phosphatidylinositol, A: phosphatidic acid, O: other components; D: DODAB molecules (in gray). *Figure modified from reference [32].*

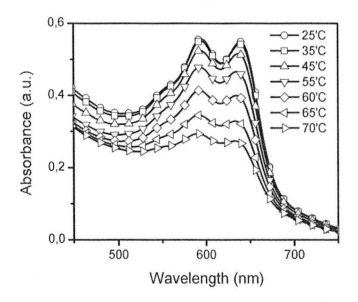

Figure 10. Absorption spectra of Telon® Blue RR (3×10^{-5} M) encapsulated in soybean lecithin liposomes (1.4 mM) in the presence of polyamide, with increasing temperature. *Figure modified from reference [32].*

4.4. Telon® Blue RR Encapsulated in Lecithin Liposomes in the Presence of Polyamide

From UV/visible absorption measurements, it can be observed that the concentration of dye in solution decreases with increasing temperature (diminution of *ca.* 50% between 25 and 70ºC), as the dye is progressively being incorporated into the fiber (Figure 10). The effect is very small at low temperatures (≤ 35°C). The rising of the spectra at lower wavelengths is due to the characteristic light scattering effect caused by the presence of large structures. Previous work showed that the mean hydrodynamic radius (R_H) of soybean lecithin liposomes was near 800 nm [2].

A decrease in fluorescence intensity with increasing temperature is also observed (Figure 11), but in a higher extent (*ca.* 78%) than in the absence of polyamide (Figure 7)

The changes in spectral shape are similar to those previously observed in the absence of polyamide suggesting the relocation of the dye in a more hydrated medium at higher temperatures. This shows that, besides the effects previously observed (50% reduction in emission), there is an additional decrease in the dye fluorescence in the presence of polyamide. This behavior is certainly due to the incorporation of Telon® Blue RR into the polyamide fiber that promotes further release of dye from the liposomes. The decrease in fluorescence emission is especially notable between 65 and 70°C, showing that lecithin liposomes release the dye mainly at higher temperatures, which is confirmed by the exhaustion curves (discussed below).

4.5. Telon® Blue RR Encapsulated in Lecithin/DODAB Liposomes in the Presence of Polyamide

The absorption spectra of Telon® Blue RR encapsulated in lecithin/DODAB (9:1) liposomes in the presence of polyamide are shown on Figure 12.

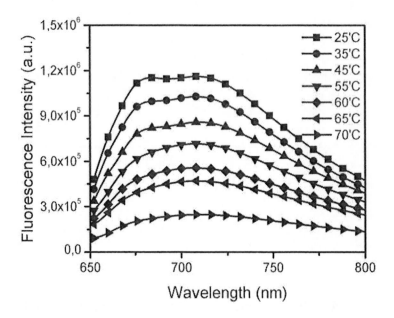

Figure 11. Fluorescence spectra of Telon® Blue RR (3×10^{-5} M) encapsulated in soybean lecithin liposomes (1.4 mM) in the presence of polyamide, with increasing temperature ($\lambda_{exc} = 640$ nm). *Figure modified from reference [32].*

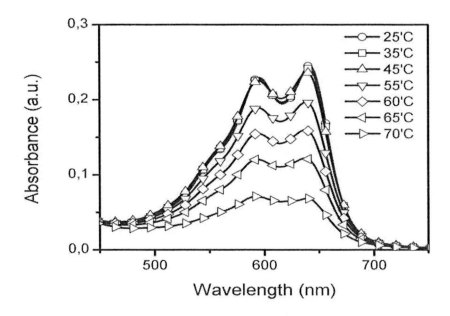

Figure 12. Absorption spectra of Telon® Blue RR (3 × 10⁻⁵ M) encapsulated in mixed lecithin/DODAB (9:1) liposomes (1.29 mM in lecithin), in the presence of polyamide, with increasing temperature. *Figure modified from reference [32].*

As observed for lecithin liposomes, the dye is progressively incorporated into polyamide but in a higher extent than for lecithin liposomes (in this case, a diminution in absorbance of 72% in the range 25-70°C is detected). It is observed that changes in absorbance are negligible at temperatures below 45°C, while a significant and progressive decrease is detected at temperatures ≥ 55°C. This behaviour shows that, not only the consumption of dye is larger when it is encapsulated in lecithin/DODAB liposomes, but also the retarding effect of these liposomes is more effective, when compared with neat lecithin liposomes.

Another distinct feature is the much lower effect of light scattering in the absorption spectra, indicating that these mixed cationic liposomes are smaller than the lecithin ones. In fact, neat DODAB vesicles are smaller (R_H ≈ 544 nm) [31] than the neat soybean lecithin liposomes (R_H ≈ 800 nm) [2].

Figure 13 shows the effect of the temperature in the fluorescence of the dye in the presence of polyamide in solution. A decrease in fluorescence intensity of the dye with increasing temperature is observed in a higher extent (*ca.* 75%) than in absence of polyamide (Figure 3), due to the progressive incorporation of the dye into the fiber.

The behavior is roughly similar to the one observed with lecithin liposomes, but some important differences are detected. The diminution in fluorescence is almost insignificant between 25 and 35°C, showing that dye release practically does not occur at these temperatures. The fluorescence spectrum remains slightly structured at 55°C, indicating that, in average, dye molecules that remain out of the fiber are in a less hydrated environment than in lecithin liposomes at the same temperature.

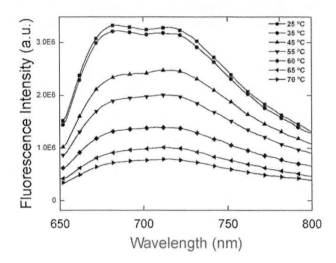

Figure 13. Fluorescence spectra of Telon® Blue RR (3×10^{-5} M) encapsulated in mixed lecithin/DODAB liposomes (1.29 mM in lecithin), in the presence of polyamide, with increasing temperature (λ_{exc} = 640 nm). *Figure modified from reference [32].*

Therefore, for dyeing experiments with these cationic liposomes, we expect a higher retarding effect at lower temperatures, but a higher exhaustion level at higher temperatures, as confirmed by the exhaustion curves obtained in dyeing assays.

4.5.1. Exhaustion Curves

Figure 14 compares the exhaustion curves for Telon® Blue RR free in solution, in the presence of auxiliaries, and when encapsulated in liposomes (lecithin and lecithin/DODAB).

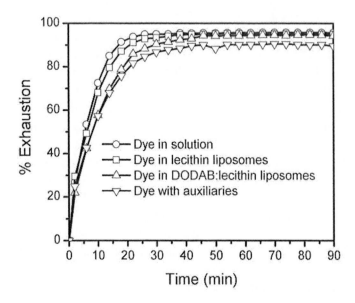

Figure 14. Exhaustion curves for the dyeing of polyamide with Telon® Blue RR in solution, either alone, with auxiliaries Sandogene CN/Sandogene NH (1% each), or when encapsulated in lecithin or lecithin/DODAB liposomes. *Figure modified from reference [32].*

It can be observed that the commercial auxiliaries have a higher retarding effect, but the exhaustion is not complete at the end of the dyeing process, 90% as compared to 95% obtained with lecithin/DODAB. There is a significant difference when comparing the higher quantity of free dye left in solution than with lecithin/DODAB (5%), with implications in both, the efficiency of dyeing and in removing the dye from the effluent.

Liposomes have in fact a dye retention effect, lecithin/DODAB being more effective than the pure lecithin ones. Considering the final level of exhaustion, both types of liposomes have a similar performance, near to that obtained with the free dye.

5. CONCLUSION

In conclusion, we can say that lecithin has more affinity for polyamide than cotton. The interactions between polyamide and lipids occur especially in the interior of the fiber while in cotton those interactions are located at the surface, as we can observe in SEM images. In polyamide the lecithin component responsible for those interactions is essentially phosphatidylcholine as we can see in reflectance spectra, and it seems that phosphatidylinositol, with a chemical structure similar to cellulose, interact more strongly with cotton.

The retarding effect promoted by mixed cationic liposomes showed to be more effective than that of pure lecithin liposomes. Comparing with commercial auxiliaries, the retarding effect of the lecithin/DODAB liposomes in dyeing experiments was similar, but a higher final exhaustion level was achieved. This confirms the potential of the cationic lipid DODAB when used in mixed liposome formulations for dyeing applications.

ACKNOWLEDGEMENTS

This work was funded by Project ECONATUR, Program SI I&DT - QREN, Agência de Inovação - Portugal, and by Foundation for the Science and Technology (FCT) through the financial support to Centro de Física (CFUM) of University of Minho.

REFERENCES

[1]   Gomes, J.I.N.R., & Baptista A.L.F. (1998). Microencapsulation of acid dyes and application to the dyeing of wool and polyamide fibers: an ecological alternative to retarding agents, *Proceedings of the 7th International Conference on Organic Dyes and Pigments*, Colorchem' 98, Check Republic; 11.

[2]   Gomes, J.I.N.R., & Baptista A.L.F. (2001). Microencapsulation of Acid Dyes in Mixed Lecithin/Surfactant liposomic structures. *Textile Research Journal,* 71(2): 153-156.

[3]   Martí, M., Coderch L., De La Maza A. & Parra J.L. (2007). Liposomes of phosphatidylcholine: A biological natural surfactant as a dispersing agent. *Coloration Technology* 123(4): 237–41.

[4]   Kim, I., Kono, & K., Takagishi, T. (1996). Textile Research Journal, 66 (12): 763-770.

[5]   Barani, H., & Montazer M. (2008). A Review on Applications of Liposomes in Textile Processing, *Journal of Liposome Research,* 18(3): 249-262.

[6]   Malam, Y., Loizidou, M., & Seifalian, M.A. (2009). Liposomes and nanoparticles: nanosized vehicles for drug delivery in cancer. *Trends Pharmacology Science*, 30(11): 592-599.

[7]   Bergers, J.J., Ten Hagen, T.L.M., Van Etten, E.W.M., & Bakker-Woudenberg, I.A.J.M. (1995). Liposomes as delivery systems in the prevention and treatment of infectious diseases. *Pharmacy World and Science*, 17 (1): 1-11.

[8]   Wang, G. (2005). *Liposomes as drug delivery vehicles.* In: *Drug Delivery: Principles and Applications.* Wang B, Siahaan T, Soltero R, Ed., John Wiley and Sons, Inc., 411-434.

[9]   New, R.C.C. (1990). *Liposomes - A practical approach*, Rickwood D, Hames BD, Ed., IRL Press, Oxford.

[10]   Jones, M.N., & Chapman, D. (1995). *Micelles, monolayers and biomembranes*, Wiley-Liss, Inc, New York.

[11]   Baptista, A.L.F., Coutinho, P.J.G., Real Oliveira, M.E.C.D., & Gomes J.I.N.R. (2004). Lipid interaction with textile fibers in dyeing conditions, *Progress in Colloid Polymers Science,* 123: 88-93.

[12]   Baptista, A.L.F., Coutinho, P.J.G., Real Oliveira, M.E.C.D., & Gomes J.I.N.R. (2003). Effect of Temperature and Surfactant on the Control Release of Microencapsulated Dye in Lecithin Liposomes I, *Journal of Liposomes Researches,* 13(2): 111–121.

[13]   Baptista, A.L.F., Coutinho, P.J.G., Real Oliveira, M.E.C.D., & Gomes, J.I.N.R. (2003). Effect of pH on the Control Release of Microencapsulated Dye in Lecithin Liposomes II, *J Liposomes Res*, 13 (2):23–130.

[14]   El-Zawahry, M.M., El-Shami, S, & Hassan El-Mallah, M. (2007). Optimizing a wool dyeing process with reactive dye by liposome microencapsulation, *Dyes and Pigments*, 74: 684-691.

[15]   Marti, M., De La Maza, A., Parra, J.L., & Coderch L, Serra S. (2004). New generation of liposomic products with high migration properties. *Textile Research Journal*, 74(11):961–966.

[16]   Montazer, M., Validi, M.,& Toliyat, T. (2006). Influence of temperature on stability of multilamellar liposomes in wool dyeing. *Journal Liposomes Research,* 16:81-89.

[17]   Lasic, D.D. (1993). *Liposomes. From Physics to Applications*, Elsevier: Amsterdam

[18]   Rosoff, M. (1996). *Vesicles*, Marcel Dekker: New York.

[19]   Felgner, P.L. (1997). Nonviral strategies for gene therapy. *Sci. Am.* 276:102–106.

[20]   Felgner, P.L., & Ringold GM. (1989). Cationic liposome-mediated transfection, *Nature* 337: 387–388.

[21]   Merianos, J.J. (1991). *Quaternary Ammonium Antimicrobial Compounds, in: Disinfection, sterilization, and preservation*, S. S. Block, Ed. Lea & Febiger, Philadelphia, 225-255.

[22]   Frier, M. (1971). *Derivatives of 4-amino-quinaldinium and 8-hydroxyquinoline, in: Inhibition and destruction of the microbial cell*, Hugo WB, ed. Academic Press, London, 107-120.

[23]   Jonsson, B., Lindman, B, Holmberg, & K., Kromberg, B. (1998). *Surfactants and Polymers in Aqueous Solution*; John Wiley & Sons: New York.

[24] Feitosa, E., & Brown, W. (1997). Fragment and Vesicle Structures in Sonicated Dispersions of Dioctadecyldimethylammonium Bromide, *Langmuir*, 13:4810-4816.

[25] Feitosa. E., Barreleiro, P.C.A., & Olofsson G. (2000). Phase transition in dioctadecyldimethylammonium bromide and chloride vesicles prepared by different methods. *Chem. Phys. Lipids*, 105: 201–213.

[26] Feitosa, E., Karlsson, G., & Edwards, K. (2006). Unilamellar vesicles obtained by simply mixing dioctadecyldimethylammonium chloride and bromide with water, *Chem. Phys. Lipids*, 140: 66-74.

[27] Baptista, A.L.F., Coutinho, P.J.G., Real Oliveira, M.E.C.D., & Gomes, J.I.N.R. (2000). *J Liposomes Res*, 10 (4): 419-429.

[28] Valeur, B. (2001). *Molecular Fluorescence – Principles and Applications*, Wiley-VCH, Chap.3, 34-70.

[29] Gohl, E.P.G., & Vilenky, L.D. (1983). *Textile Science*, Longman, Cheshire, UK.

[30] New, R.R.C. (1989). *Liposomes,* Oxford, IRL Press.

[31] Alves, F.R., Zaniquelli, M.E.D. Loh, W., Castanheira, E.M.S., Real Oliveira M.E.C.D., & Feitosa, E. (2007). Vesicle-micelle transition in aqueous mixtures of the cationic dioctadecyldimethylammonium and octadecyltrimethylammonium bromide surfactants, *J. Colloid Interf. Sci.*, 316: 132-139.

[32] Sousa, I.S.C., Castanheira, E.M.S., Gomes, J.I.N.R., & Real Oliveira, M.E.C.D. (2010). Study of the release of a microencapsulated acid dye in polyamide dyeing using mixed cationic liposomes, *J Liposomes Res*, 1–7, DOI: 10.3109/08982104.2010.492478.

INDEX

N

O

P

Q

R